Collins Advanced Modular Sciences

Stars, Spectra and Surgery

Dave Kelly and Alan Pickwick

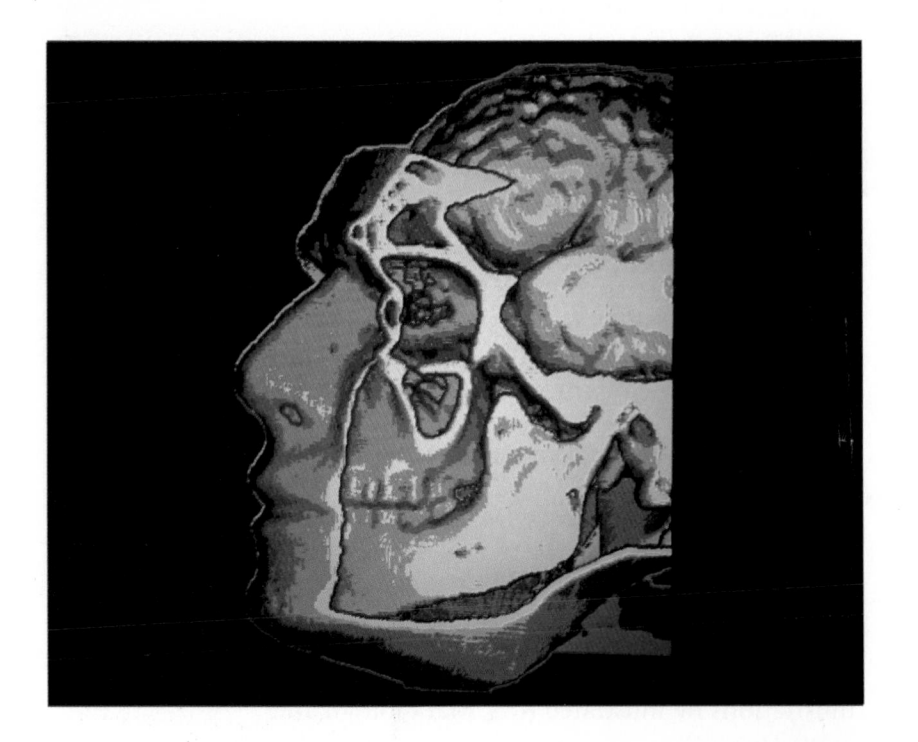

Series Editor: Mike Coles

Collins Educational
An Imprint of HarperCollinsPublishers

Published by Collins Educational
An *imprint* of HarperCollins*Publishers*
77–85 Fulham Palace Road
Hammersmith
London
W6 8JB

First published 1998

ISBN 0 00 322408 2

Series design by Ewing Paddock at PearTree Design

Layout and composition by Derek Lee

Edited by Mike Nugent and Mark Jordan

Picture research by Caroline Thompson

Illustrations by Illustrated Arts, Mark Jordan and
 Alan Trewartha

Production by Anna Pauletti

Printed and bound by Scotprint Ltd, Musselburgh

Contents

Acknowledgements

Every effort has been made to contact the holders of copyright material, but if any have been inadvertently overlooked the publishers will be pleased to make the necessary arrangements at the first opportunity.

The publishers would like to thank the following for permission to reproduce photographs
(T = Top, B = Bottom, C = Centre, L= Left, R = Right):
Bryan & Cherry Alexander 133;
Allsport/M Cooper 109T, 162R;
D Thompson/Ancient Art & Architecture 47R;
D Malin/Anglo-Australian Observatory 30CR, 47TL;
J Allan Cash Ltd 114L, 140;
Center for High Angular Resolution Astronomy (CHARA), Georgia State University 21B;
CNRS/OHP 50B;
Bruce Coleman Ltd/A J Purcell 93R, G McCarthy 95, J Rydell 101, K Taylor 123, J Cancalosi 127;
Professor Rod Davies 22R;
Gemini 8-M Telescopes Project 11, 13, 18;
Getty Images 26, 97, 103T, 105, 118R;
Ann Ronan/Image Select 163;
Mark Jordan 104, 142T, 143, 158R;
Dave Kelly 89;
Walt Disney (courtesy Kobal) 78;
Andrew Lambert 41B;
Mr Christopher Liu/Sussex Eye Hospital 82;
NASA 62, 70BL;
NHPA/M Leach 96;
NRAO/AUIV 31TL;
Obertreis/Bildenberg/Network Photographers 118L;
M Hutson/Redferns 98;
D Redfern/Redferns 102;
Rex Features Ltd 91, 99, 107, 110, 122L, 125, 137, 141, 162L;
Science Photo Library 6TL & TR, 21C, 24, 28CR & BL, 30BL, 31TR, 38, 41T, 42, 50C, 52, 54, 55, 61, 63, 67, 70TL,CR&BR, 74, 80, 83, 92, 94, 103B, 109C, 114C, 117, 126, 129, 139, 142B, 148, 149, 151, 152, 153, 154, 158L, 161, 165, 168, 169, 170, 171, 172, 173, 174;
Science Museum/Science & Society Picture Library 6C, 12;
Dr N Shashar/Dr T W Cronin 93L;
SHOUT Photo Library 32, 115;
Gamma Press/FSP 131;
EAS/NASA/Starland Picture Library 73;
J Jones/Sygma 122R, 128;
C & S Thompson 43, 86;
UKAEA 146;
Professor Sir Arnold Wolfendale 40;

All other images in Chapters 1 to 7 supplied by Alan Pickwick.

Cover photograph supplied by Science Photo Library.

To the student

This book aims to make your study of advanced science successful and interesting. The authors have made sure that the ideas you need to understand are covered in a clear and straightforward way. The book is designed to be a study of scientific ideas as well as a reference text when needed. Science is constantly evolving and, wherever possible, modern issues and problems have been used to make your study interesting and to encourage you to continue studying science after your current course is complete.

Working on your own

Studying on your own is often difficult and sometimes textbooks give you the impression that you have to be an expert in the subject before you can read the book. I hope you find that this book is not like that. The authors have carefully built up ideas, so that when you are working on your own there is less chance of you becoming lost in the text and frustrated with the subject.

Don't try to achieve too much in one reading session. Science is complex and some demanding ideas need to be supported with a lot of facts. Trying to take in too much at one time can make you lose sight of the most important ideas – all you see is a mass of information. Use the learning objectives to select one idea to study in a particular session.

Chapter design

Each chapter starts by showing how the science you will learn is applied somewhere in the world. Next come learning objectives which tell you exactly what you should learn as you read the chapter. These are written in a way which spells out what you will be able to do with your new knowledge, rather like a checklist – they could be very helpful when you revise your work. At certain points in the chapters you will find key ideas listed. These are checks for you to use, to make sure that you have grasped these ideas. Words written in **bold type** appear in the glossary at the end of the book. If you don't know the meaning of one of these words check it out immediately – don't persevere, hoping all will become clear.

The questions in the text are there for you to check you have understood what is being explained. These are all short – longer questions are included in a support pack which goes with this book. The questions are straightforward in style – there are no trick questions. Don't be tempted to pass over these questions, they will give you new insights into the work which you may not have seen. Answers to questions are given in the back of the book.

Good luck with your studies. I hope you find the book an interesting read.

Mike Coles, Series Editor
University of London Institute of Education, June 1998

The story of the telescope

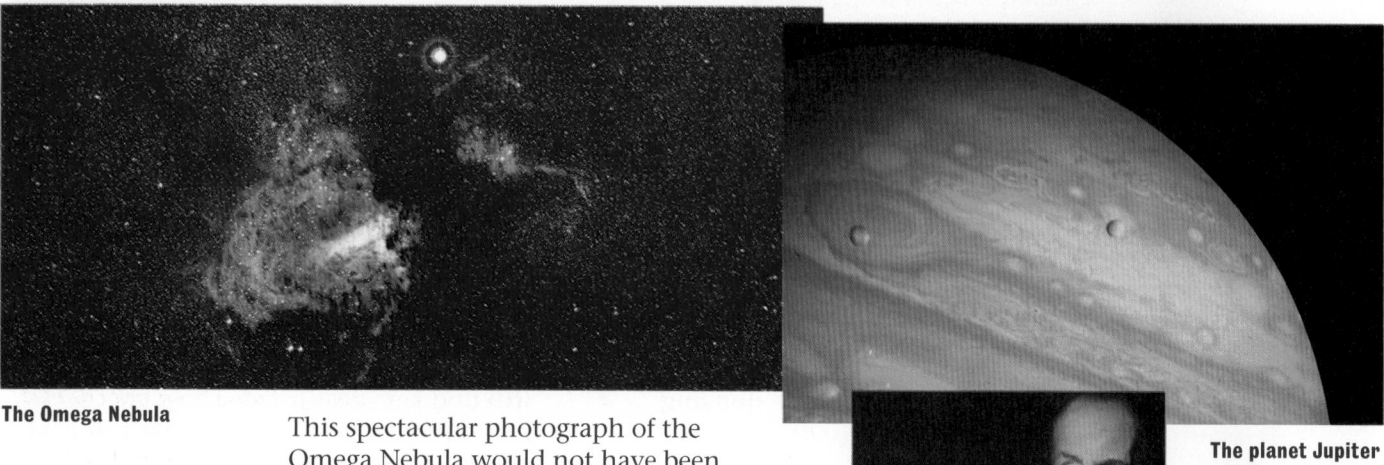

The Omega Nebula

This spectacular photograph of the Omega Nebula would not have been possible without the invention of the telescope. This nebula is too faint to be seen with the unaided eye, but large telescopes equipped with state-of-the-art technology can reveal the fine detail in sharp images like this. Modern astronomy would be impossible without such instruments.

Before the seventeenth century, all observations of stars were made with the naked eye. The Italian Galileo Galilei was the first astronomer to use a telescope (in 1609) and burst apart the ancient models of the 'heavens' as unchanging and perfect. Modern astronomy had begun. Within a year Galileo had seen the moons of Jupiter, the rings of Saturn and individual stars in the Milky Way – all of which had been unknown until then.

The planet Jupiter and two of its large moons – the moons were first seen by Galileo in 1610

Galileo Galilei (1564–1642)

Galileo's telescope – built around two lenses – revolutionised our understanding of the Universe. This chapter shows how light behaves when it passes through a lens, and how lenses can be combined to create telescopes.

1.1 Learning objectives

After working through this chapter, you should be able to:

- **understand** how a lens forms an image;

- **predict** the position of the image formed by a lens;

- **understand** the differences between real and virtual images;

- **draw** ray diagrams for refracting and reflecting telescopes;

- **predict** the positions and focal lengths of the lenses in a telescope;

- **calculate** the angular magnification produced by a telescope;

- **explain** the advantages and disadvantages of lens and mirror telescopes;

- **understand** chromatic and spherical aberration;

- **explain** why modern CCD detectors are important to astronomers.

1.2 Simple lenses

Finding images using ray diagrams

Galileo's 1609 telescope contained just two lenses. How did such a simple arrangement allow Galileo to produce such significant results? In order to be able to understand how the lenses in his telescope formed such a clear image, we need to be able to answer questions such as:

- how does a lens form an image?
- where will that image be?
- what size will the image be?

We can use scale drawings, called **ray diagrams**, to find out how a lens forms an image. These drawings use two rays that always behave in simple, predictable ways (Fig. 1):

- a ray that passes through the centre of the lens carries on in its original straight line;

- a ray that approaches the lens parallel to the optical axis leaves the lens heading for the focal point.

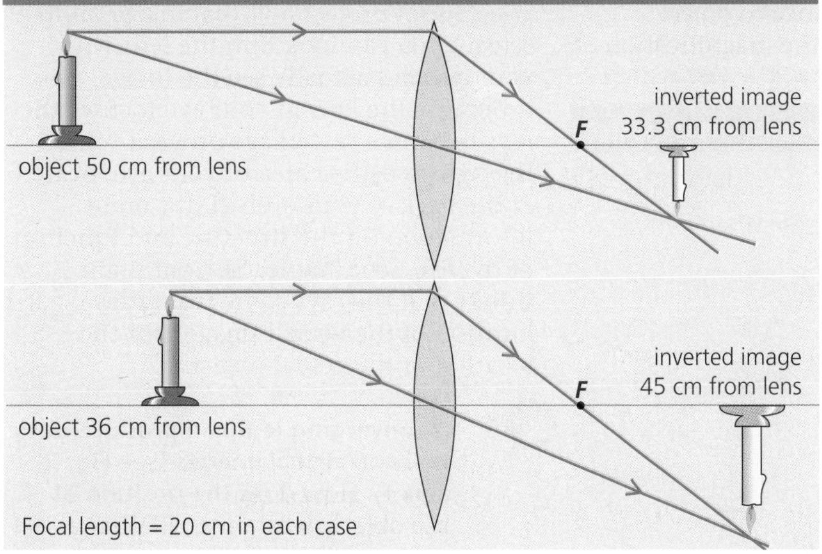

These two rays are traced from the top of the object and are drawn onwards until they cross. The top of the image forms at this crossing point. In order to simplify the ray diagram, the base of the object is placed on the optical axis and the object is assumed to be at right angles to the optical axis. This means that the base of the image will also be on the optical axis and the image will be at right angles to the optical axis.

The **optical axis** is the line that passes through the centre of the lens at right angles to the lens. The **focal point**, also known as the principal focus, of a lens is the point on the optical axis where rays parallel to the optical axis converge to or diverge from. The **focal length** of a lens is the distance along the optical axis from the focal point to the centre of the lens.

Lenses come in two basic types: **converging** and **diverging**. These two types of lens cause light rays to deviate in different ways. A converging lens can produce a real, inverted image (Fig. 2). The image is called a **real image** because the rays really cross on the far side of the lens. You can see a real image on a screen that is placed where the rays cross. In the first example the image is smaller than the object, but in the second example the image is larger.

In order to draw a ray diagram, the steps 1–6 should be followed:

1 draw in the horizontal axis – this is the optical axis;
2 draw in the lens – make sure that it is at right angles to the optical axis;
3 mark the position of the focal point;
4 draw in the object, with its base on the optical axis;
5 draw in the two rays of light from the top of the object;
6 draw in the top of the image at the point where the two rays of light cross.

The ray direction changes at each surface of the lens, but by convention it is shown changing at the lens centre.

Fig. 1 Ray diagram for a lens

ray parallel to optical axis heads towards focal point

focal point
F

optical axis

object

rays that pass through the centre of the lens carry on in a straight line

lens

image at the crossing point of the two rays

Fig. 2 A converging lens – real images

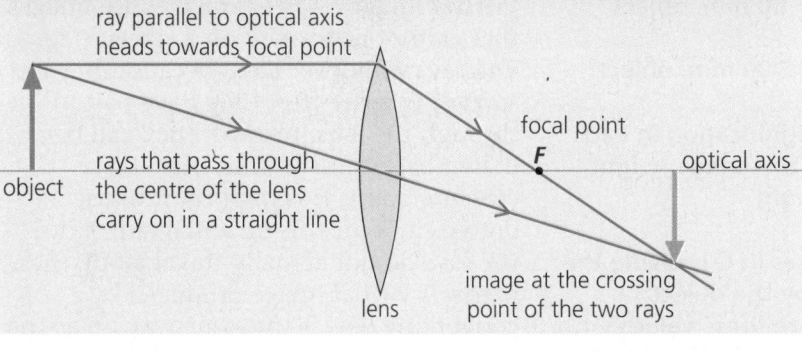

object 50 cm from lens

inverted image 33.3 cm from lens
F

object 36 cm from lens

inverted image 45 cm from lens
F

Focal length = 20 cm in each case

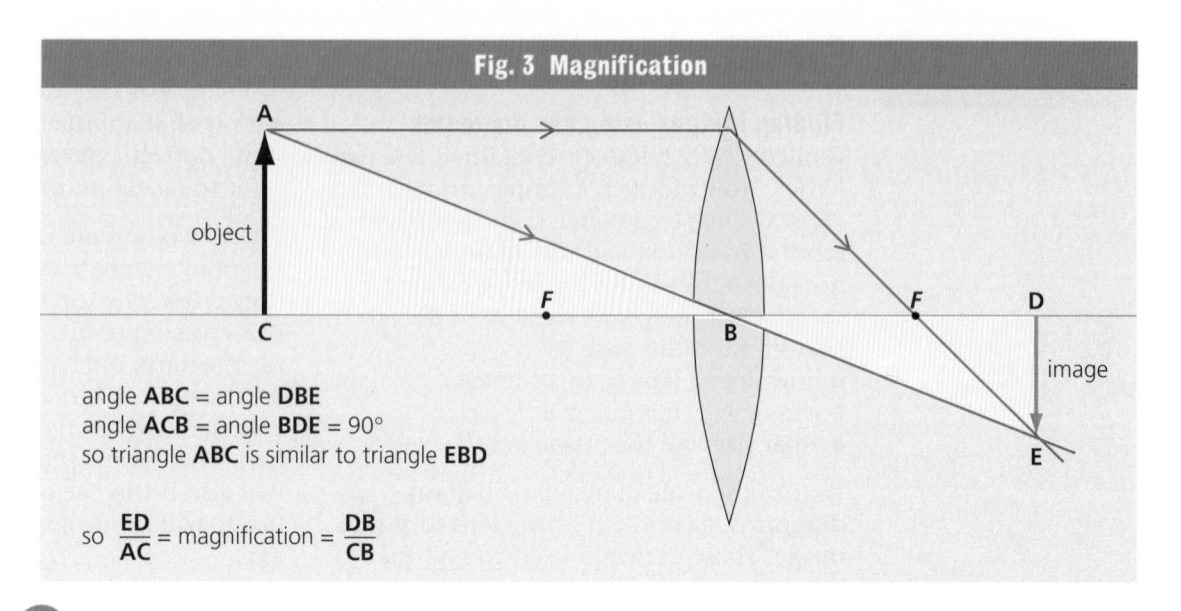

Fig. 3 Magnification

angle **ABC** = angle **DBE**
angle **ACB** = angle **BDE** = 90°
so triangle **ABC** is similar to triangle **EBD**

so $\dfrac{ED}{AC}$ = magnification = $\dfrac{DB}{CB}$

1 For a converging lens of focal length 40 mm, draw scale diagrams using the following data:
  a object distance = 60 mm, object height = 40 mm;
  b object distance = 80 mm, object height = 30 mm;
  c object distance = 100 mm, object height = 50 mm.
  Calculate the magnification in each case by dividing the image height by the object height.

2 For the three cases in Q1, divide the image distance by the object distance. Compare these values with the magnifications calculated in Q1.

The ratio of image distance to object distance is the same as the magnification of the image compared to the object. The two methods give the same value because of the similar triangles on the left-hand and right-hand sides of the ray diagrams (Fig. 3).

Converging lenses can also produce **virtual images**. Virtual images are images that cannot be formed on a screen (Fig. 4). The rays will never cross because they are spreading apart after they have passed through the lens. Instead, they can be drawn backwards to find the virtual crossing point. It is important to use dotted lines for this on a diagram, since the rays do not actually travel along these paths. A virtual image produced by a converging lens is the same way up as the object and is larger than the object. A magnifying glass works this way. Although you cannot project a virtual image on to a screen, you can look into the lens with your eye and actually see the image. This is because the lens in your eye focuses the rays to form a real image on your retina, the light-sensitive area of your eye located at the back of your eyeball (for more information on the structure and function of the eye, see Chapter 8). Your brain thinks that the rays come from the location of the virtual image, not the location of the actual object.

3 A converging lens can produce both real and virtual images (see Figs 2 and 4). How does the position of the object determine whether a real or virtual image will be formed?

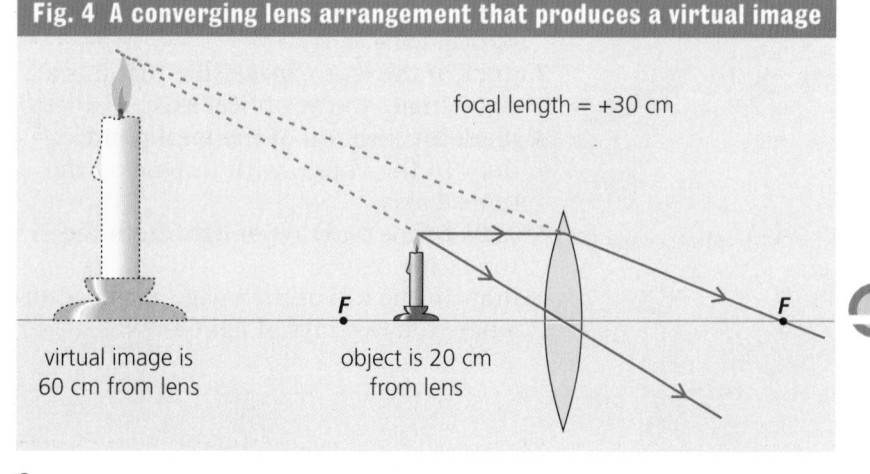

Fig. 4 A converging lens arrangement that produces a virtual image

focal length = +30 cm

virtual image is 60 cm from lens

object is 20 cm from lens

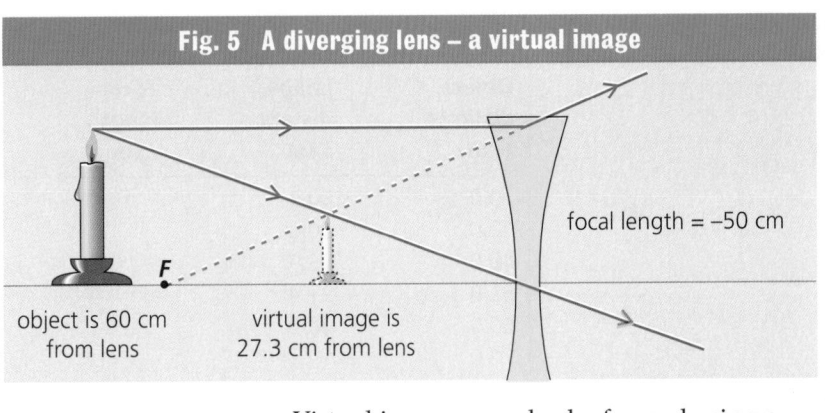

Fig. 5 A diverging lens – a virtual image

focal length = –50 cm

F

object is 60 cm from lens

virtual image is 27.3 cm from lens

Virtual images can also be formed using a diverging lens (Fig. 5). A diverging lens will never form a real image from a real object because the rays can never cross. The focal point of a diverging lens is the point where rays parallel to the optical axis appear to diverge from, so that the ray that runs parallel to the optical axis diverges as if it had come from the focal point on the left-hand side of the lens. By drawing its path backwards, a virtual crossing point is found. The resulting image is always smaller than the object and is always virtual. Short sight is corrected with a diverging lens. If you wear glasses to correct short sight, then the world you see is one big virtual image.

Use of the lens formula

Mathematical models are useful because they can predict results without the need to do experiments. Using the lens formula, you can calculate the position of an image relative to a lens without having to make a scale drawing.

The formula links three distances:
- the distance of the object from the lens (u),
- the distance of the image from the lens (v) and
- the focal length (f).

$$\frac{1}{u} + \frac{1}{v} = \frac{1}{f}$$

If you prefer, you can remember this formula as:

$$\frac{1}{\text{object distance}} + \frac{1}{\text{image distance}} = \frac{1}{\text{focal length}}$$

The formula has some rules for the signs of the distances:
- real object and image distances are positive;
- virtual object and image distances are negative;
- converging lenses have positive focal lengths;
- diverging lenses have negative focal lengths;
- if a calculation gives a negative image distance, then the image is virtual.

Table 1 contains calculations to predict the image positions for the scale drawings in Figs 2, 4 and 5.

 4   Complete the spaces in Table 1.

Table 1 Using the lens formula					
Object distance / cm	Focal length / cm	Substitute in formula	Rearrange terms	Image distance / cm	Is the image real or virtual?
50	20	$\dfrac{1}{50} + \dfrac{1}{v} = \dfrac{1}{20}$	$\dfrac{1}{v} = \dfrac{1}{20} - \dfrac{1}{50}$	+33.3	real
36	20	$\dfrac{1}{36} + \dfrac{1}{v} = \dfrac{1}{20}$	$\dfrac{1}{v} = \dfrac{1}{20} - \dfrac{1}{36}$		
20	30	$\dfrac{1}{20} + \dfrac{1}{v} = \dfrac{1}{30}$			
60	–50 (diverging lens)				

9

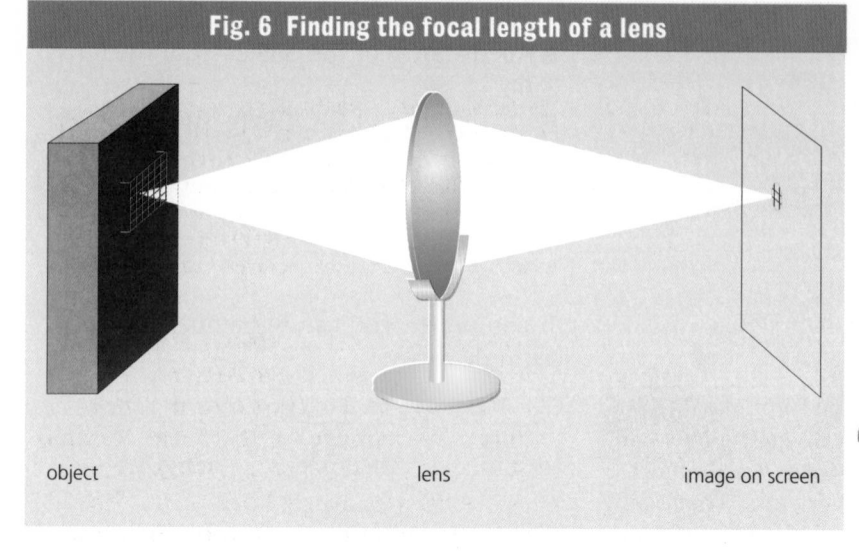

Fig. 6 Finding the focal length of a lens

object   lens   image on screen

Table 2 Experimental results		
Object distance / cm	Image distance / cm	Focal length / cm
20.0	60.2	
30.0	30.0	
40.0	23.9	
50.0	21.4	
60.0	20.0	
70.0	19.2	

Measurement of the focal length of a converging lens

The most accurate way to measure the focal length of a lens is to use it to focus a bright object on to a white screen (Fig. 6):

- record the object and image distances;
- collect several more pairs of results by moving the object and then refocusing the image by moving the screen;
- use the lens formula to calculate the focal length in each case and then find the average value for higher accuracy.

Alternatively, plot a graph of $1/v$ against $1/u$ and draw the best straight line. Both the points where the line crosses the axes of the graph will have the value $1/f$. Table 2 contains some results from such an experiment.

 **5** Using the values in Table 2, calculate the focal length of the lens that was used.

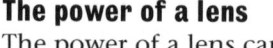 **6** Suggest reasons why you would expect a small spread of values in the focal lengths you have calculated.

The power of a lens

The power of a lens can be expressed as:

$$\frac{1}{\text{focal length of lens in metres}}$$

This gives the power of the lens in dioptres. As a converging lens has a positive focal length, its power will have a positive value. A diverging lens will have a negative power.

7 When focused on a distant object, the combined power of the lens and cornea of a human eye is 55 dioptres. Use this fact to calculate the depth of a human eyeball.

Key ideas

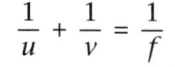

- A beam of parallel light converges to or diverges from the focal point (principal focus) of a lens.
- A converging lens can produce both real and virtual images.
- A diverging lens produces virtual images from real objects.

- Magnification = $\dfrac{\text{image length}}{\text{object length}}$
- The lens formula links object distance (u), image distance (v) and focal length (f):
$$\frac{1}{u} + \frac{1}{v} = \frac{1}{f}$$

1.3 Telescopes

Dr Matt Mountain – director of the Gemini Project

The Gemini telescope on Mauna Kea, Hawaii, under construction in 1997; the telescopes will use the most advanced technologies available, including charge coupled device (CCD) detectors, which will be explained later. By choosing to locate the telescopes in Hawaii and Chile astronomers will have excellent observing conditions for both the Northern and Southern skies.

Dr Matt Mountain is the director of the Gemini Project.

'We are building two optical telescopes with 8 metre diameter mirrors, one in Chile and one in Hawaii. This is a joint venture between the UK, the United States, Canada, Chile, Argentina and Brazil. The Gemini telescopes are descendants of the telescopes invented by Galileo Galilei and Isaac Newton. The discovery by Galileo that four bright moons were orbiting Jupiter made it much easier for the rest of the world to accept that the planets orbited the Sun. I feel sure that the Gemini telescopes will lead to many fascinating discoveries in the 21st century.'

There are two main types of telescope:
- **refracting telescopes**, which use lenses, developed from Galileo's telescope;
- **reflecting telescopes**, which use mirrors, developed from Sir Isaac Newton's telescope of 1668. The Gemini telescopes are reflecting telescopes.

Astronomical two-lens telescope – the refracting telescope

To understand how the telescope magnifies, you need to know how your eye/brain system judges the size of any object. It judges size by sensing the size of the image on your retina. You perceive an object as small if it covers only a small area of your retina. To magnify a distant object, like the Moon or a planet, a telescope must form an enlarged image so that an increased area of your retina is covered by the image. The size of the image on your retina is proportional to the angle between rays from the top and bottom of the object (Fig. 7). An enlarged image will lead to an increase in this angle.

The simple two-lens telescope increases the angle between the rays that reach your eye and also inverts the image (Fig. 8). To ease the strain of looking through the telescope, the rays leave the telescope in a parallel 'bundle' so that the final image is formed at infinity. Your eye then does not have to refocus between looking directly at the distant object and looking through the

Fig. 7 The size of a distant object

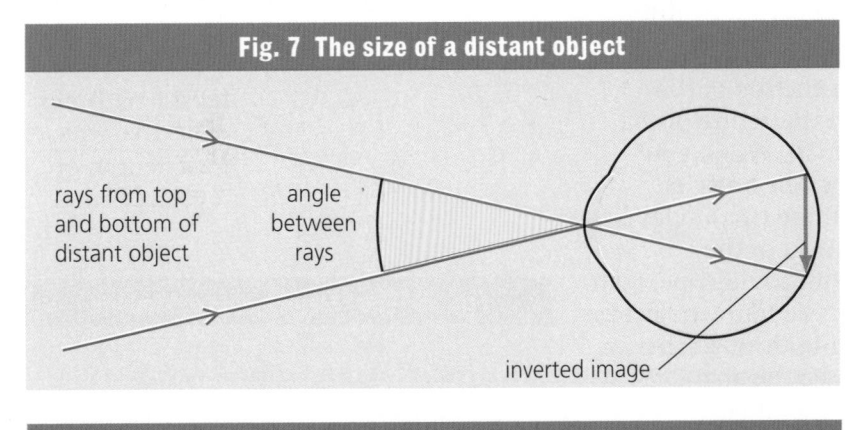

rays from top and bottom of distant object

angle between rays

inverted image

Fig. 8 Lens diagram for a refracting telescope

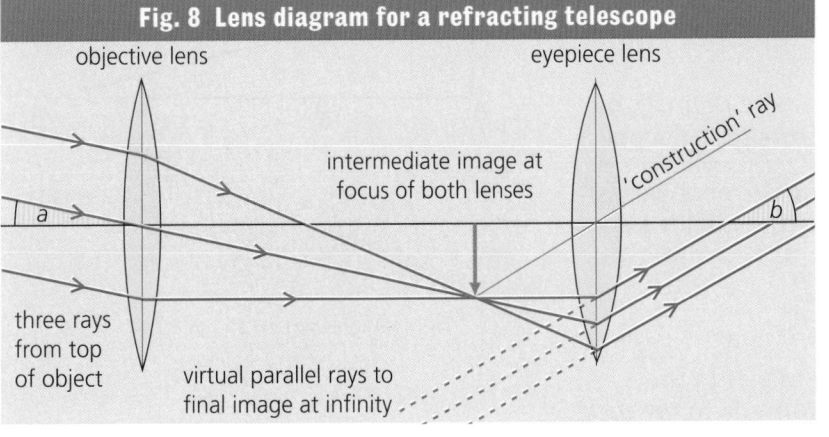

objective lens

eyepiece lens

intermediate image at focus of both lenses

'construction' ray

a

b

three rays from top of object

virtual parallel rays to final image at infinity

Fig. 9 Angular magnification

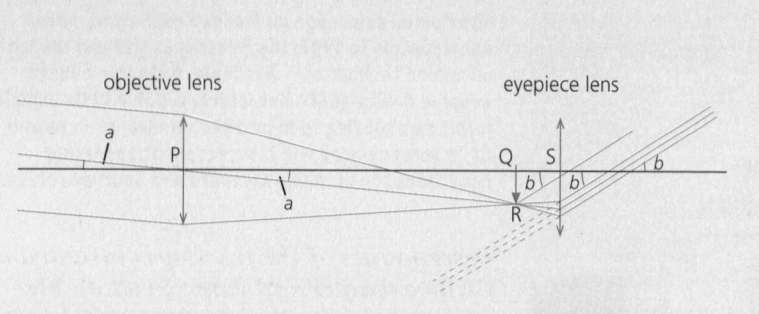

objective lens

eyepiece lens

a = angular size of object as seen by the unaided eye
b = angular size of image as seen through telescope

From the opposite angle theorem, angle **QPR** is equal to a.

Parallel rays from the object form an intermediate image at the focus of the objective lens. This intermediate image then acts as an image for the eyepiece lens. The eyepiece lens is positioned so that the intermediate image is at its focus. This means that the final image is formed at infinity.

The ray **RS** is constructed parallel to the exit rays so the angle **QSR** is b.

lengths of the lenses; the focal length of the objective lens is PQ and the focal length of the eyepiece lens is QS. Triangle PQR shares a side (QR) with triangle QRS. In PQR the angle opposite QR is a because of the opposite angles theorem. In triangle QRS the angle opposite QR is b because the construction ray RS is parallel to the exit rays. Taking tangents of angles a and b:

$$\tan a = \frac{QR}{PQ}$$

and

$$\tan b = \frac{QR}{QS}$$

In an astronomical telescope both these angles will be quite small, so the tangents can be approximated to the angles expressed in radians (Fig. 10). Hence the angular magnification is given by:

$$\text{angular magnification} = \frac{\text{angle } b}{\text{angle } a}$$

$$= \frac{QR/QS}{QR/PQ}$$

$$= \frac{PQ}{QS}$$

$$= \frac{\text{focal length of objective lens}}{\text{focal length of eyepiece lens}}$$

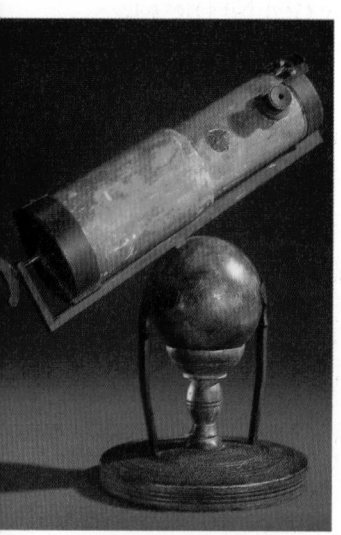

Newton's reflecting telescope, invented in 1668

telescope. This setting is called 'normal adjustment'.

What you see when looking at a distant object such as the Moon is a disc. The angle between light rays from the top of the Moon's image and from the centre of the Moon's image will be small. When you look through a telescope, the angle is increased. The ratio of these two angles is the **angular magnification** of the telescope (Fig. 9). Without a telescope, your eye will see the angular size of the object as the small angle a. Looking through the telescope your eye will see the angular size as the larger angle b. The angular magnification of this telescope is the ratio of angle b to angle a.

$$\text{angular magnification} = \frac{\text{angular size of image as seen through telescope}}{\text{angular size of object as seen by the unaided eye}}$$

$$= \frac{\text{angle } b}{\text{angle } a}$$

It is possible to link the angles in the angular magnification formula to the focal

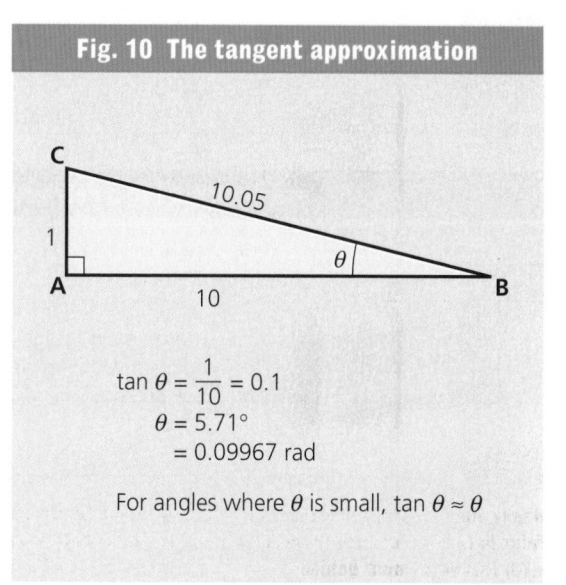

Fig. 10 The tangent approximation

$$\tan \theta = \frac{1}{10} = 0.1$$
$$\theta = 5.71°$$
$$= 0.09967 \text{ rad}$$

For angles where θ is small, $\tan \theta \approx \theta$

Fig. 11 Focal point of a curved mirror

curved mirror
(silvered front)

two rays
from centre
of object

focus

Fig. 12 Viewing arrangements for reflecting telescopes

(a) Newtonian arrangement

primary mirror
(silvered front)

two rays
from centre
of object

prime
focus

Newtonian mirror
(flat surface)

eyepiece

(b) Cassegrain arrangement

primary mirror
(silvered front)

two rays
from centre
of object

prime
focus

Cassegrain mirror
(convex surface)

eyepiece

Heavy and complex optical equipment is needed to make images and spectra using the faint light from distant stars. It is much easier to balance and manoeuvre the telescope with this equipment behind the primary mirror and on its central axis; this is the multi-point supporting structure for the mirror of the Gemini Telescope.

Astronomical reflecting telescopes

The latest generation of astronomical telescopes, including the Gemini Project instruments, use curved mirrors; in the case of the Gemini telescope the mirror has a diameter of about 8 metres. That piece of precision glass would be too large to fit into a normal classroom. Despite its size, the mirror is smooth to an accuracy of 25 nm. The main reason for having large-diameter telescopes is to collect more light and so allow fainter objects to be detected in a shorter time. This also increases the clarity of the image by reducing diffraction (see Chapter 2).

Reflecting telescopes use a curved mirror to bring parallel light to a focus (Fig. 11). When used in astronomy, mirrors are coated on their front surfaces with either silver or aluminium. This avoids the distortions that the light would suffer if it had to travel through glass to the back surface.

There are at least three ways in which the image can be viewed (Fig. 12):
(a) at the side of the tube (the Newtonian arrangement);
(b) behind the primary mirror (the Cassegrain arrangement);
(c) at the prime focus in the centre of the telescope tube.

The Newtonian arrangement is popular in amateur telescopes as it is simple to construct and allows the eyepiece to be in a convenient viewing position. The Cassegrain arrangement allows complex and heavy detectors to be attached to the base of large telescopes with comparative ease. The prime focus arrangement is popular for direct imaging as the light only makes contact with one optical component, the primary mirror.

In the Cassegrain telescope the rays of light are reflected by the primary mirror on to a convex secondary mirror (see Fig. 12). The rays then come to a focus behind the primary mirror. This is the arrangement chosen for the Gemini telescopes.

13

Key ideas

- Refracting astronomical telescopes consist of two converging lenses.

- magnification = $\dfrac{\text{angular size as seen through telescope}}{\text{angular size of object as seen by the unaided eye}}$

- magnification = $\dfrac{\text{focal length of objective lens}}{\text{focal length of eyepiece lens}} = \dfrac{f_o}{f_e}$

- Reflecting telescopes in the Cassegrain arrangement consist of two mirrors, one concave and the other convex.

1.4 Relative merits of reflecting and refracting telescopes

Large mirrors versus large lenses

All large telescopes in use today are reflecting telescopes, except for a few wide-field survey instruments that combine lenses and mirrors. This is for the following reasons:

- it is difficult to make blemish-free glass plates large enough for metre diameter telescopes;
- large lenses can only be supported at the edge and would tend to sag under their own weight;
- lenses produce false colours in images in the same way as prisms split up light into the colours of the spectrum.

Mirrors have the following advantages:
- large mirrors use their front surface for reflection, so removing any distortion due to the glass;
- large mirrors can be supported from behind at many points to stop them sagging;

- large mirrors can be made just a few centimetres thick because they can be supported at many points – this makes them much lighter than comparable lenses;
- thin mirrors cool down quickly at night – this is very important as convection currents from the surface of the mirror will distort the images.

One advantage of the refracting telescope concerns blocking of light. The reflecting telescope ray diagrams (see Fig. 12) show that the secondary mirrors block some of the light. Refracting telescopes have no such light loss and so dominate the small telescope market. However, for large telescopes, such as the Gemini instruments, even a one metre diameter secondary mirror would only block 1/64 of the light (this is the ratio of the area of the secondary mirror to the area of the main mirror).

Chromatic aberration and spherical aberration

Two other problems associated with refracting telescopes are **chromatic aberration** and **spherical aberration**.

The **refractive index** of glass for blue light is slightly greater than the refractive index of glass for red light. This means that the blue light comes to a focus slightly closer to the lens than the red light. This is called chromatic aberration. To illustrate this point, a simple model lens can be made by holding together two thin prisms, base to base (Fig. 13).

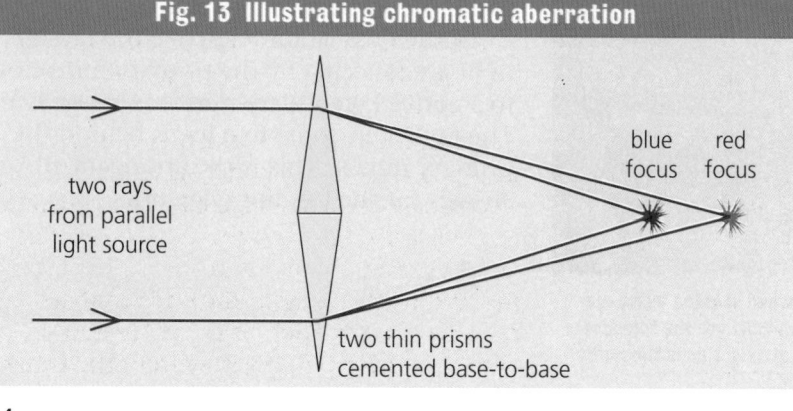

Fig. 13 Illustrating chromatic aberration

two rays from parallel light source

blue focus   red focus

two thin prisms cemented base-to-base

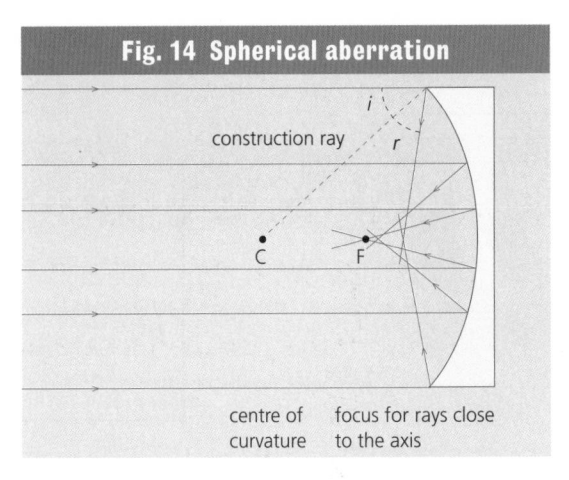

Fig. 14 Spherical aberration

construction ray

C   F

centre of   focus for rays close
curvature   to the axis

Spherical aberration. Study the light and dark areas in the lower part of the tea.

Chromatic aberration leads to falsely coloured images and to a poor focus. The problem is much reduced by placing two lenses of slightly different glass in contact with each other. The differences of refractive index and focal length can be chosen to cancel the aberration at two particular wavelengths and to minimise it at others. Such a lens combination is called an achromatic doublet. Reflecting telescopes do not suffer from chromatic aberration as they use mirrors, not glass lenses.

Spherical aberration occurs in lenses and mirrors (Fig. 14). Rays that strike close to the centre of the lens or mirror are focused to one point. However, rays that strike towards the edge of the lens or mirror are focused to different points. The diagram is built up using equal angles of incidence and reflection, as shown with the construction ray.

Telescope mirrors are the shape of a parabola in cross-section. This removes the problem of spherical aberration. Unfortunately, objects off the optical axis produce images that suffer from **coma** – they look egg or comma shaped.

Lenses may be corrected for spherical aberration by having their surfaces ground to complex shapes that are often determined experimentally by ray tracing. A good camera lens might be made up of six separate lenses in one metal body in an attempt to correct spherical aberration.

Key ideas

- Reflecting telescopes are usually used for large astronomical telescopes.

- Refracting telescopes are usually used for small-scale amateur astronomy.

- Refracting telescopes can suffer from chromatic aberration.

- Both reflecting and refracting telescopes can suffer from spherical aberration.

1.5 Electronic detectors – charge coupled devices

Charge coupled devices (CCDs) have more or less taken over from photographic film in optical astronomy. They are large silicon wafers divided into an array of tiny light-sensitive regions called **pixels**. A modern CCD is typically 40 mm square and is made up of 4096×4096 pixels, each of which is about 10 μm square. Each CCD costs about £10 000, which may seem to be a considerable expense, but not when put against the £55 million of the new Gemini telescope. The CCD's efficiency gains over conventional photographic film are so great that its use is essential.

As light falls on to the pixels, electrons are liberated from atoms of silicon near the surface of the pixel. These free electrons are trapped in the body of the CCD by the positive charge of the electrodes (Fig. 15).

After a few minutes of exposure on a large telescope, many thousands of electrons will have collected in each pixel. At this point the exposure is stopped. The packets of electrons are 'read out' by moving them along to the ends of their respective rows. Each of the three control wires is made more positive than the other

Fig. 15 The structure of a CCD

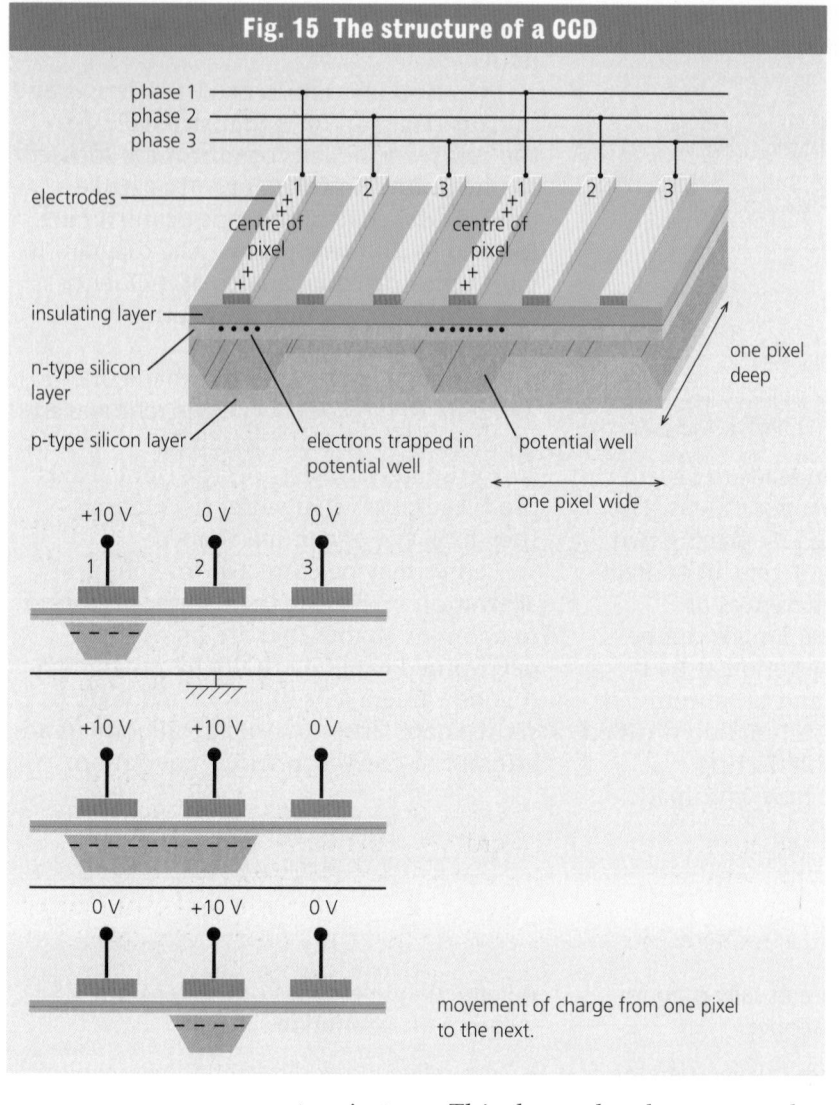

Fig. 16 Quantum efficiency of a CCD

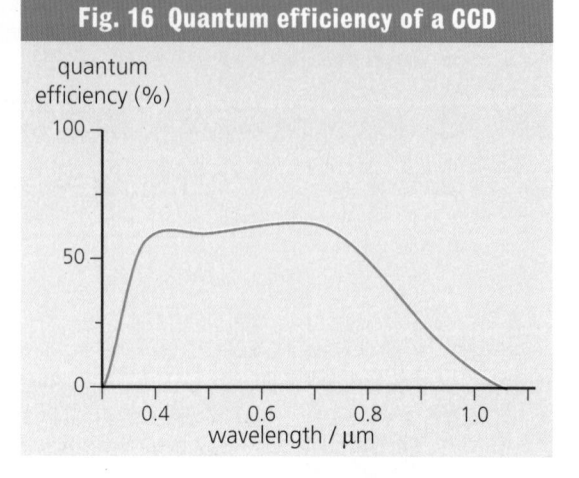

collected per observing session. Alternatively the greater sensitivity can be used to see fainter objects by tracking them for long periods. The way in which a good CCD responds to different wavelengths of light is shown in Fig. 16. It is able to respond uniformly to the full range of visible light and has some response to the infrared part of the spectrum.

CCDs have a large **dynamic range**. This is the ability to record very faint as well as very bright objects on the same image. CCDs can record objects that are so faint that they produce just a few electrons in each pixel as well as objects that produce up to 100 000 electrons in each pixel. A photographic film can only record over a dynamic range where the brightest object is a few hundred times brighter than the faintest, but a CCD can cope with a dynamic range where the brightest object is tens of thousands of times brighter than the faintest. This means that on the same exposure, detail can be seen in the faint spiral arms of a galaxy as well as in its bright nucleus.

The final advantage of a CCD is that the charge collected is directly proportional to the brightness of the source. This is called **linearity of response**.

CCDs are often cooled to −100 °C to reduce random emission of electrons. At this temperature, a small electric current as low as 5 electrons per hour can be formed by these random effects in each pixel. This tiny electric current is called the dark current.

These devices have revolutionised astronomy by speeding up the collection and handling of data.

two in turn. This draws the electrons to the more positive electrode each time and so moves the charges from left to right in the diagram. The sequence is repeated until all the charges have been moved to the end of each row. When they reach the ends of the rows the groups of electrons are detected using a specially sensitive amplifier. The data is then sent to a computer system that displays the image.

The **quantum efficiency** of a detector is defined as the percentage of the incoming photons that go to produce the image rather than being lost. For the CCD the quantum efficiency is perhaps greater than 70% (Fig. 16). This quantum efficiency can be compared to the value for photographic film, which is between 1% and 4%. This allows images to be obtained more rapidly, so increasing the number of images

Key ideas

- Charge coupled devices (CCD) are used as detectors in most modern telescopes.

- The quantum efficiency of a CCD is greater than 70%.

- CCDs have a large dynamic range and a linear response.

1.6 The story continues ...

All that Galileo saw in 1610 when looking at the rings of Saturn was two bright patches, one on either side of the planet. His telescope was powerful enough to see the rings, but the image was of very poor quality. He interpreted what he saw as a triple planet. Christiaan Huygens (1629–1695), a Dutch astronomer, developed an improved method of grinding and polishing lenses. He made observations of Saturn, and was able to note that Saturn was 'surrounded by a thin ring not adhering to the planet at any point'. Following further developments in the quality of telescopes, the French astronomer Jean Dominique Cassini (1625–1712) discovered that what had seemed to be a single ring was actually split in two.

Continual improvements in the telescopes and detectors used by astronomers have led to increased understanding of the Universe. The parallel strands of technological improvement and scientific progress continue today with, among others, the Hubble Space Telescope and the Gemini telescopes. The 8 m primary mirrors of the Gemini telescopes will gather considerably more light than the older 4 m telescopes they will supersede. The scientific programmes planned for the Gemini telescopes are, according to the Gemini education Web site, 'concerned with observing and understanding the origins and evolution of stars and planetary systems, of galaxies, and of the Universe itself'.

Receiving signals from outer space

As well as the optical telescopes introduced in Chapter 1, astronomers also use radio telescopes. These are like large satellite TV dishes and can detect the radio waves emitted by atoms and molecules in far reaches of space where stars are being born. The atmosphere hardly affects metre and centimetre wavelength radio waves, so conventional radio telescopes can be located at ground level. The shorter millimetre waves are quite strongly absorbed by carbon dioxide and water in the atmosphere and so telescopes designed to receive them are put on mountain tops.

The atmosphere completely absorbs X-rays, so all X-ray observations are made from satellites. One of the most interesting X-ray sources is probably the best candidate we have for a black hole. It seems to be a normal star orbiting a very small and dense object that is pulling gas from the star and heating it very strongly, so making the X-rays.

Dr Matt Mountain, project director for the 8 m Gemini telescopes, knows that there are two main limitations to visual observing from the surface of the Earth.

'The first problem is that a mirror can only collect part of the wavefront from the source. This means that the image can never be pinpoint sharp. Larger mirrors do a better job but the problem is always there – it is called diffraction. The second problem is that the waves have to travel through the atmosphere. If the air was perfectly still it would be less of a problem but as it is in constant motion it causes the images of the stars to dance about – this is called scintillation. You can reduce this effect of the atmosphere by choosing a high location with smooth air currents but the diffraction of the waves is a limit of nature.'

This chapter explores the diffraction of waves, introduces radio astronomy and then discusses the effect that the Earth's atmosphere has on both optical and radio astronomy.

2.1 Learning objectives

After working through this chapter, you should be able to:

- **explain** how light waves react when they pass through a narrow gap;

- **calculate** the fineness of detail you will see through a particular telescope;

- **explain** how a radio telescope works;

- **discuss** the similarities and differences between optical and radio telescopes;

- **explain** the need for large radio telescopes in terms of diffraction;

- **understand** the difficulties of observing stars through the Earth's atmosphere, due to scintillation and molecular absorption;

- **understand** the success of ground-based radio astronomy;

- **describe** observations that are only possible from above the Earth's atmosphere;

- **explain** why radio waves can reach us from the centre of our Galaxy even though light waves are absorbed.

2.2 Diffraction

Without realising it, you experience the effects of diffraction every day. If you hear somebody talking round the corner of a building, the sound waves have reached your ears by diffraction. If you throw a stone into a pond, the ripples are not stopped by small obstructions but curve round them by diffraction. In telescopes the light waves are obstructed by the edges of the mirrors and lenses and so spread out just a little. This diffraction makes the images slightly fuzzy and so limits the fine detail you can see on astronomical photographs.

Diffraction at a single slit – Fraunhofer diffraction

Diffraction is easy to see using water waves in a ripple tank. If you place two barriers in the water to form a narrow gap, the waves will spread out from the gap (Fig. 1). If the width of the gap is large compared to the wavelength, the effect will be small. To see the effect clearly you need to set the width of the gap to be similar to the wavelength of the ripples. The spreading out of the waves is called diffraction.

The wavelength of light is much smaller than that of the ripples in the tank, but the same effect exists. When a beam of light passes through a gap then diffraction of the light waves occurs.

The image that can be formed on a screen has a central bright region. On either side of this is a succession of dark and light bands that get fainter with distance from the centre of the image. The locations of the dark bands are given by the formula:

$$\lambda = \frac{d \sin \theta}{n}$$

where λ is the wavelength in metres, d is the slit width in metres, θ is the angle to the first minimum and n is the 'order' of the minimum. The first order is at $n = 1$, the second order is at $n = 2$ and so on.

The most important regions to note are the first dark bands on either side of the centre. These are called the first minima of the diffraction pattern. They are areas of darkness where no energy is directed. Their positions define the edges of the central maximum. It is the size of the central maximum that determines how much detail you can see in an image. This is because a typical star is never 'seen'; all we see or photograph is the diffraction pattern. If two stars are close enough together their patterns overlap and they are indistinguishable. The same applies to small features that are close together on a planet, so the detail is not seen clearly.

For the first minima, the formula becomes:

$$\lambda = \frac{d \sin \theta}{1}$$

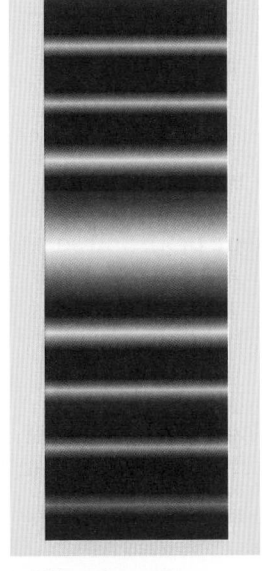

A Diffraction pattern from a single slit.

Q1 The wavelength of red light is about 0.7 μm and the wavelength of blue light is about 0.4 μm. Which colour will produce the wider diffraction pattern?

Diffraction caused by a circular aperture

When light passes through a circular pinhole, it too will form a diffraction pattern. Since the hole is circular, the pattern will have circular features. If you look at a distant light through a pinhole, you will see that the light is spread out into a circular spot. This is called an **Airy disc**, after its discoverer, and it is an

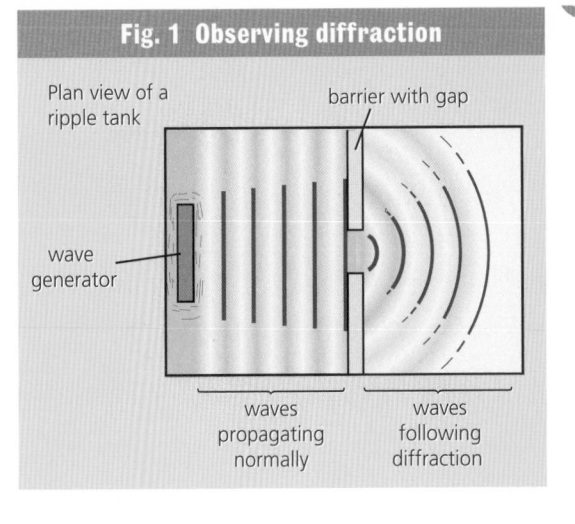

Fig. 1 Observing diffraction

Plan view of a ripple tank

barrier with gap

wave generator

waves propagating normally

waves following diffraction

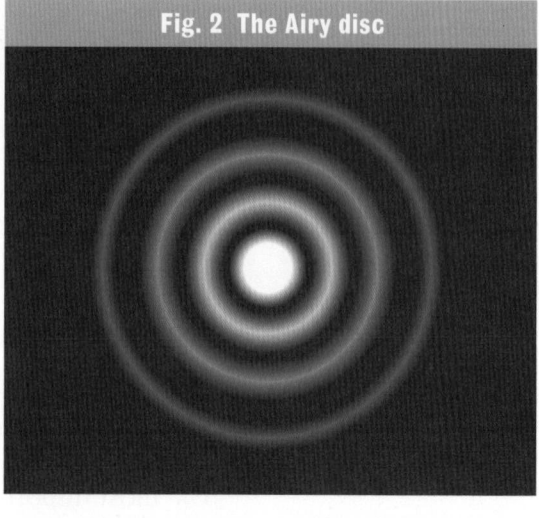

Fig. 2 The Airy disc

important limitation in any optical system (Fig. 2).

Now diffraction is a problem when viewing distant objects. Although the distant object may be large, the vast distances involved mean that the object appears extremely small (Fig. 3).

It does not matter how good the lenses and mirrors in your telescope are, the final image of a star will never be smaller than the Airy disc. The Airy disc could stop you from seeing a planet orbiting a nearby star or the fine details of a distant galaxy. The method used to obtain the maximum detail from a telescope is to make the diameter of the objective lens (in a refracting telescope) or primary mirror (in a reflecting telescope) as large as possible to minimise the diffraction effects. Consider the equation:

$$\lambda = \frac{d \sin \theta}{n}$$

when $n = 1$. For small values of θ, measured in radians, the approximation $\sin \theta \approx \theta$ can be used (Fig. 4). The equation then becomes:

$$\lambda \approx d\theta$$

Rearranging leads to:

$$\theta \approx \frac{\lambda}{d}$$

As d is the diameter of the lens or mirror, the greater the value of d, the smaller the value of θ (for a fixed value of λ), and so the smaller the Airy disc and the finer the detail or the smaller the object that can be seen by the telescope. If two stars are very close together their Airy disc patterns will overlap (Fig. 5) and you cannot tell them apart. Lord Rayleigh suggested the criterion that you should just be able to see two stars

Fig. 3 A large object at a vast distance

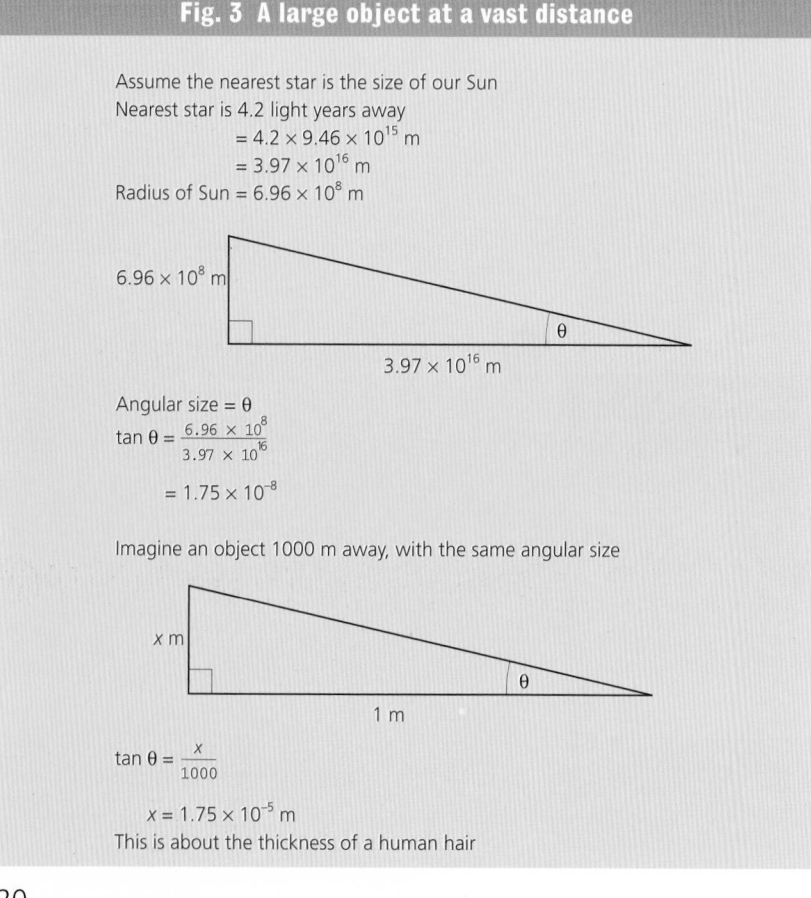

Assume the nearest star is the size of our Sun
Nearest star is 4.2 light years away
$$= 4.2 \times 9.46 \times 10^{15} \text{ m}$$
$$= 3.97 \times 10^{16} \text{ m}$$
Radius of Sun $= 6.96 \times 10^{8}$ m

Angular size $= \theta$
$$\tan \theta = \frac{6.96 \times 10^{8}}{3.97 \times 10^{16}}$$
$$= 1.75 \times 10^{-8}$$

Imagine an object 1000 m away, with the same angular size

$$\tan \theta = \frac{x}{1000}$$

$$x = 1.75 \times 10^{-5} \text{ m}$$
This is about the thickness of a human hair

Fig. 4 Showing that sin $\theta \approx \theta$

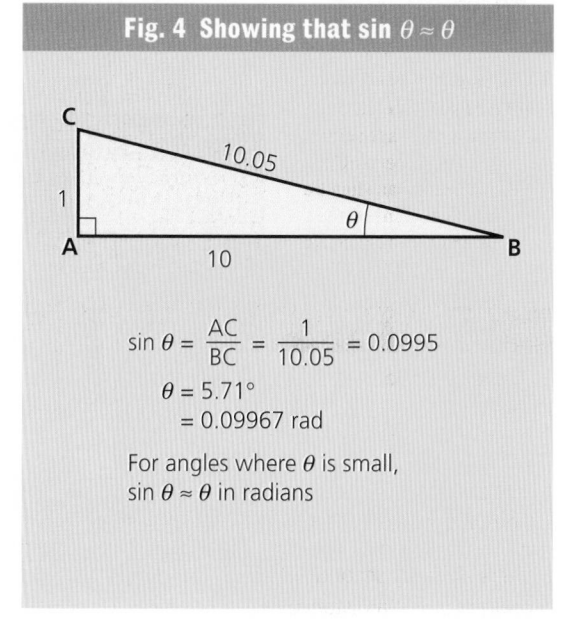

$$\sin \theta = \frac{AC}{BC} = \frac{1}{10.05} = 0.0995$$

$$\theta = 5.71°$$
$$= 0.09967 \text{ rad}$$

For angles where θ is small,
$\sin \theta \approx \theta$ in radians

distinctly if they are separated by the angle θ given by the formula

$$\theta = \frac{\lambda}{d}$$

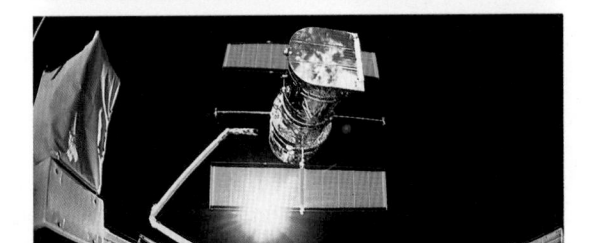
Fig. 5 The overlap of Airy disc patterns

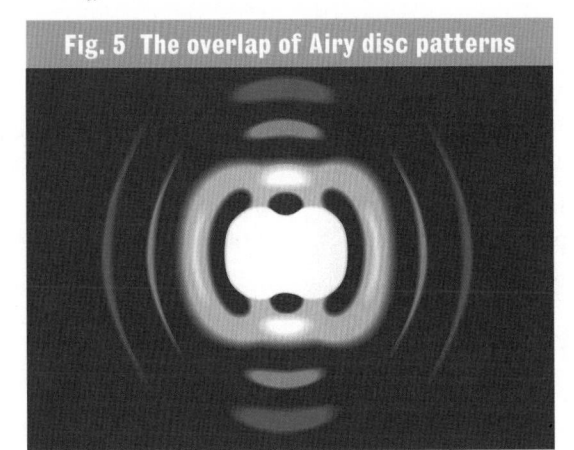
The Hubble Space Telescope

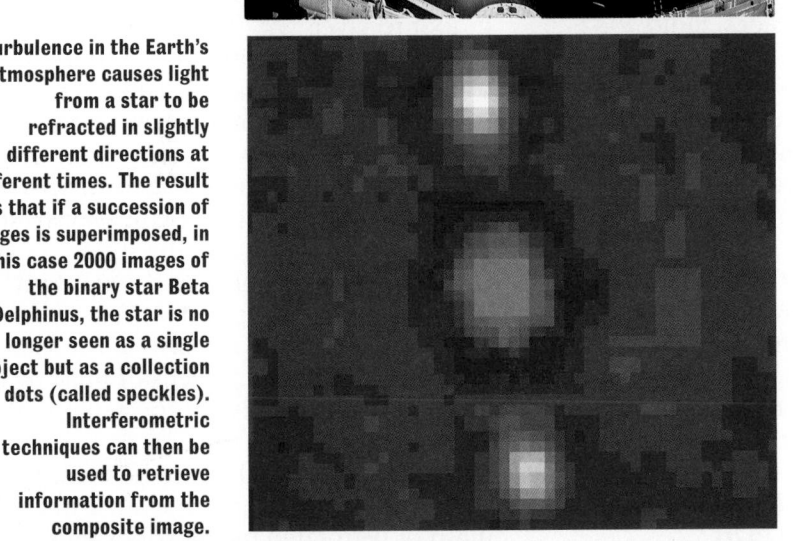

Turbulence in the Earth's atmosphere causes light from a star to be refracted in slightly different directions at different times. The result is that if a succession of images is superimposed, in this case 2000 images of the binary star Beta Delphinus, the star is no longer seen as a single object but as a collection of dots (called speckles). Interferometric techniques can then be used to retrieve information from the composite image.

Table 1 contains values for the resolving power of various instruments.

2 Stand a pound coin on edge so you can see its face and then walk away from it. How far away can you go before you can't see it? What angle is this in seconds of arc? Check that your answer is roughly in agreement with the resolution of the eye given in Table 1.

Diffraction and seeing limits

Unfortunately, Earthbound optical telescopes can never reach their theoretical performance. The images are blurred by variations in the refractive index of the air caused by convection currents. This is called **scintillation** or twinkling and these telescopes are said to be 'seeing limited'. The image is larger than the theoretical Airy disc. The Hubble Space Telescope is able to produce such sharp images because it is above the Earth's atmosphere.

Even at the best mountain-top observatories the 'atmospheric seeing' limits resolution to about one second of arc. From the data in Table 1 it would seem only worth building optical telescopes with a maximum diameter of about 0.2 m. However, resolution is not the only consideration. Although no finer detail is observed with greater diameters, the telescopes do act as better 'light-buckets'. This means more observations can be made per night. The amount of light entering the telescope is proportional to the area of the telescope. A larger telescope requires shorter exposures to 'catch' the same amount of light, compared to a smaller telescope.

Table 1 Resolving power			
Detector type	Size	Theoretical resolution in space / seconds of arc	Ground-based resolution / seconds of arc
eye	3 mm pupil	34	≈60
Hubble Space Telescope	2.4 m diameter	0.043	1
Gemini optical telescope	8 m diameter	0.013	1

There are sixty seconds of arc in a minute and sixty minutes of arc in a degree. One second of arc is the angle subtended at your eye by a pound coin at a distance of about five kilometres!!

Key ideas

- Diffraction by a single slit is governed by the equation:

$$\lambda = \frac{d \sin \theta}{n}$$

- A circular aperture produces a diffraction pattern called an Airy disc.

- Diffraction limits the detail that can be observed by a telescope.

- The resolving power of a telescope is controlled by the equation:

$$\theta \approx \cdot \frac{\lambda}{d}$$

- Finer detail can be seen by increasing the diameter of a telescope.

- Images from optical telescopes on Earth are blurred by scintillation.

2.3 Radio astronomy

Up to this point we have been concentrating on the techniques that apply to visible light. Until the 1930s, astronomers worked almost exclusively with visible light. As radio engineering improved, the combination of sensitive radio receivers and large radio aerials led to some interesting discoveries. Observations showed that some of the background radio signals came from beyond the Earth's atmosphere.

In the following decades, radio astronomy improved. Using the same principles as for light waves, radio waves can be focused and detected. It is not practicable to make lenses for radio waves; instead, radio waves are reflected from curved mirrors just like light waves.

Jodrell Bank Observatory

Single dish radio telescopes

Prof. Rod Davies is an astronomer at Jodrell Bank in Cheshire.
'The large radio telescopes here allow us to receive signals from galaxies that are so far away that the Sun had not formed when the radio signals set out on their journey to us.'

RADIO QUIET ZONE

DO NOT USE
MOBILE PHONES
OR OTHER
RADIO TRANSMITTERS
ON THIS SITE

Prof. Rod Davies of Jodrell Bank

There is very little difference between a radio telescope and a satellite TV dish on the side of your house. They both have curved metal surfaces that are made of either solid sheets or a fine mesh. The curved surface focuses a faint radio signal from a distant object on to an aerial. Immediately behind the aerial is a low-noise, high-gain amplifier that boosts the signal and sends it down a cable to the indoor receiver.

A wavefront arriving from a nearby source is curved. However, radio astronomy is involved with radio waves from far distant sources and so the wavefront can be considered to be straight (Fig. 6). The wave is a **plane wave**. When a plane wavefront arrives from space, it hits the surface of the dish. The shape of the dish is important. It must ensure that all parts of the wavefront arrive at the focus of the dish at the same time. All parts of the wavefront must be in phase when they arrive at the aerial so they add together.

Reflectors do not have to be made of solid material; they can be made from wire mesh or perforated metal. For example, satellite TV dishes contain perforations that are quite small. These dishes focus signals of about 30 mm wavelength. The holes are about 1.5 mm across which makes them about one-twentieth of a wavelength in diameter. At this size the loss is 0.1 % of the signal and is hardly measurable.

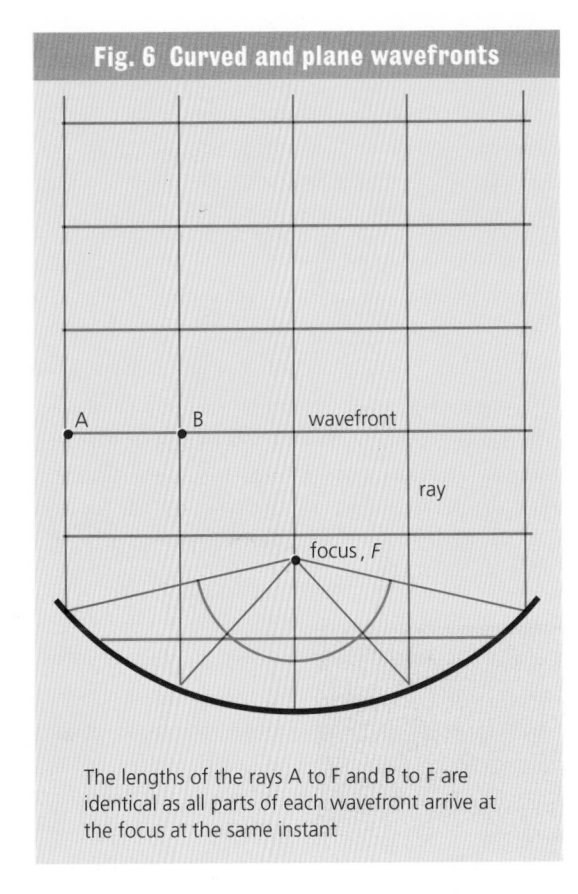

Fig. 6 Curved and plane wavefronts

A   B   wavefront

ray

focus, F

The lengths of the rays A to F and B to F are identical as all parts of each wavefront arrive at the focus at the same instant

Tracking

A satellite TV dish points at a geostationary satellite and so does not have to move. However, our radio astronomer must set his telescope to follow a radio source around the sky. The telescope is driven by motors so that it tracks the source as the Earth turns.

When the radio waves have been brought to a focus by the dish, the signal is received by the aerial. It is then amplified. To send the signal to the control room, its frequency must be reduced or much of it would be lost in the long cables (Fig. 7). In the control room of the Lovell Telescope at Jodrell Bank there are special radio receivers that analyse the signal for the weak tell-tale signs of distant radio sources.

The astronomer can select the required band of frequencies. The signal is then detected and fed to a recording device. In the early days of radio astronomy chart recorders were used, but now a computer records the data. The signals can be analysed to reveal chemical elements present in the distant source and to measure its velocity.

Making images

A single radio telescope can only make maps by scanning across successive strips of the sky. Many early radio maps of the sky were built up in this way. On its own, the telescope just produces a signal containing information about all the radio sources in its line of sight and frequency range. In simple systems it just produces a wavy line on a paper chart.

Collecting area

The power of the signal focused on to the aerial is proportional to the collecting area of the telescope.

3 Calculate the ratio of the collecting area of the Lovell Telescope (76 m diameter) to the area of a satellite TV dish (1 m diameter).

4 Domestic satellite TV dishes can be purchased with either 600 mm or 800 mm diameters. How much more power can be received from the larger dish?

Radio telescopes are not much troubled by the atmosphere and can approach their theoretical performance limit. They are said to be 'diffraction limited'. Table 2 shows that their theoretical and ground-based resolutions are the same.

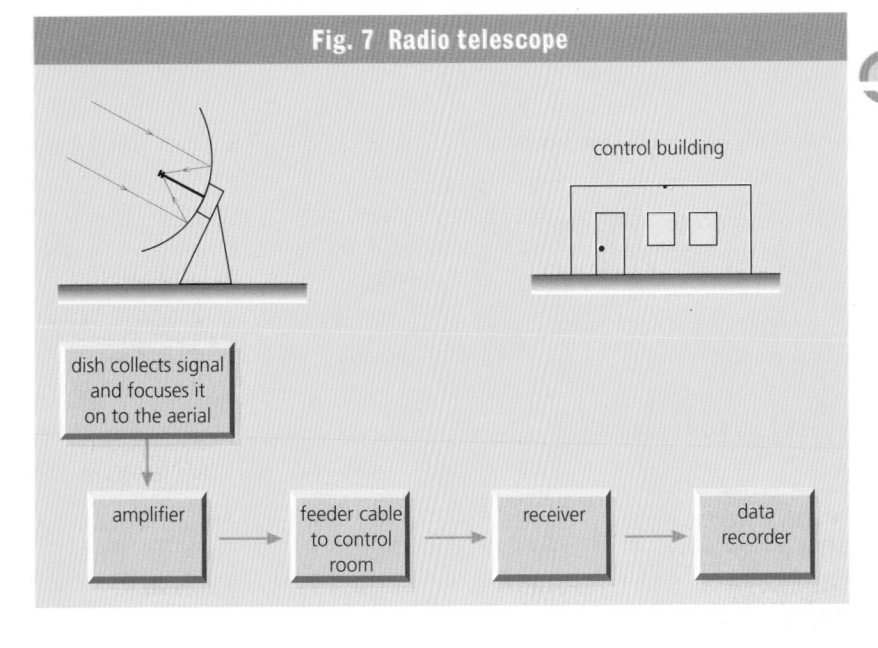

Fig. 7 Radio telescope

control building

dish collects signal and focuses it on to the aerial

amplifier → feeder cable to control room → receiver → data recorder

Table 2 Resolving power of radio telescopes			
Detector type	Size	Theoretical resolution in space / seconds of arc	Ground-based resolution / seconds of arc
Lovell Radio Telescope at 73 cm wavelength	76 m diameter	2000	2000
MERLIN Radio Array at 18 cm wavelength	134 km spacing	0.27	0.27

The diameters of radio telescopes are always much greater than those of optical telescopes. The designers of both types of telescope strive to achieve the best possible resolution. However, radio telescopes are at a severe disadvantage.

The Very Large Array, the world's largest radio telescope array, located in New Mexico, USA, is an interferometer system. It consists of 27 radio dishes, each 25 m in diameter, which can be positioned along three tracks up to 21 km in length.

Radio waves have wavelengths that are thousands of times longer than those of light waves. To achieve a resolution similar to an optical telescope, a radio telescope would need to be thousands of metres in diameter. This is mechanically impossible. The solution adopted in radio astronomy is to use a pair of telescopes, separated by a great distance. This arrangement is called an **interferometer** because the signals from the telescopes are added together. This process of adding waves is called **superposition** and it produces an interference pattern. Fine detail can be revealed in the radio sources after the patterns have been processed by powerful computer systems. The MERLIN array based at Jodrell Bank works in this way. In the Very Large Array (VLA) in New Mexico, 27 radio telescopes are linked to form an interferometer.

Key ideas

- Radio waves can be received, focused by a curved mirror, detected and amplified to produce radio maps of the sky.

- The power of a radio signal is proportional to the collecting area of the radio telescope.

- Radio telescopes can be used in pairs, as an interferometer, to increase the resolution of the telescope.

2.4 The optical window

Molecular absorption in the atmosphere

Until relatively recently all telescopes have had to be located on the surface of the

Earth. This means that the light arriving at the telescope has to pass through the Earth's atmosphere. In the 1950s, rockets that travelled above the Earth's atmosphere for short periods of time were used to make observations in the ultraviolet region of the electromagnetic spectrum. Since then many orbiting observatories, which are above the Earth's atmosphere, have been launched.

In the infrared, visible and ultraviolet portions of the electromagnetic spectrum, the main problems for the passage of light are caused by ozone, molecular oxygen, carbon dioxide and water vapour (Fig. 8). Dust can also absorb and scatter the light on its way to the telescope.

The various molecules in our atmosphere are responsible for absorbing energy at different wavelengths. This shows the problems of making observations from the surface of the Earth.

In the ultraviolet region, **ozone** is the main absorber. Ozone is formed in the upper atmosphere by the action of sunlight on molecular oxygen. It is such an effective screen that it is only possible to do serious ultraviolet observations from high-flying aircraft, balloons or satellites. This is good news for life on Earth since the ozone layer protects us from the ultraviolet light emitted by the Sun.

There is now an international agreement to stop the production of compounds that damage the ozone layer. In particular, the CFCs (chloro-fluoro-carbon compounds) are very stable which is why they have been widely used in refrigerators. When they escape they can eventually reach the top of the atmosphere where the sunlight breaks them up. The free chlorine atoms catalyse the change of ozone to molecular oxygen. They are not consumed in the process and can continue to reduce the proportion of ozone for many years before they eventually react with an atom other than oxygen and are taken out of the picture. Even though CFC production has almost stopped, it will be decades before its effects fade away.

In the infrared region, the frequencies of the incoming waves are similar to the natural frequencies of vibration of the various molecules. The waves set off resonant vibrations in the molecules, turning the energy of the waves into low grade heat.

In the near infrared region, molecular oxygen is the problem but does not prevent satisfactory observations from high mountain observatories (at altitudes of above 4500 m). In the far infrared region, the many resonances of water vapour and carbon dioxide molecules are encountered and there are only narrow regions of good transmission.

Carbon dioxide and water vapour stop astronomers observing in the infrared because they absorb very strongly at particular wavelengths. It is this very reason that keeps the Earth as warm as it is, but if we increase the levels of carbon dioxide excessively by burning fossil fuels, we might well increase the global temperature. This could change weather patterns and raise sea levels.

Scattering in the atmosphere

Scattering of light in the atmosphere is responsible for the colour of clouds, the colour of the sky during the day and the colour of the sky at sunset.

Scattering of light by molecules or other particles in the atmosphere needs to be considered in three separate conditions:
- the particles are much larger than the wavelength of light;
- the particles are about the same size as the wavelength of light;
- the particles are much smaller than the wavelength of light.

You may have wondered why clouds – made up of water droplets – appear white.

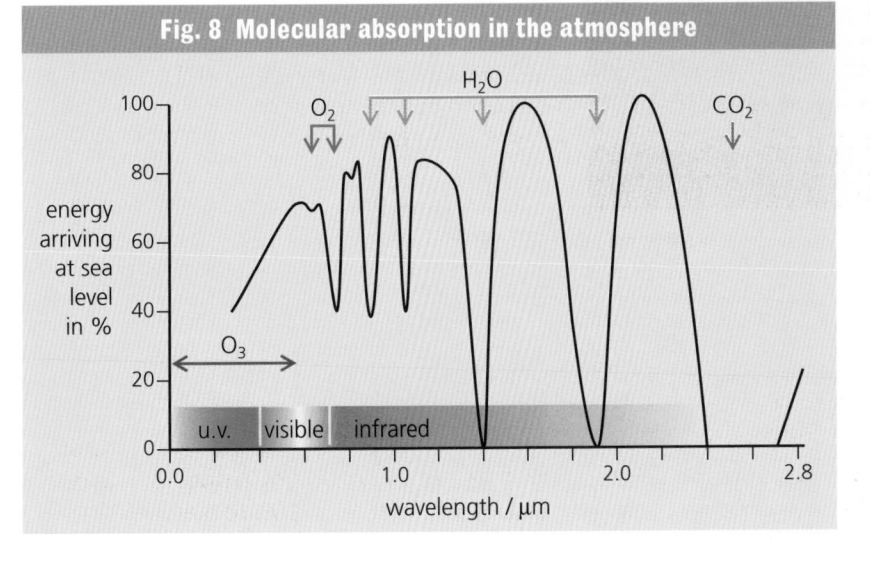

Fig. 8 Molecular absorption in the atmosphere

energy arriving at sea level in %

O_2 H_2O CO_2 O_3

u.v.   visible   infrared

wavelength / μm

Water droplets in clouds are about 10 μm in size. The wavelength of blue light is about 450 nm (0.45 μm) and the wavelength of red light is about 700 nm (0.7 μm). The water droplets are quite large compared to the wavelengths of visible light. Droplets of this size act like tiny mirrors and so light is reflected, and not changed in colour.

When the particles that the light is passing through are approximately the same size (0.1–1 μm) as the wavelength (λ) of the light, the effectiveness of the scattering is proportional to $1/\lambda$. Hence blue light (smaller λ) is scattered more than red (larger λ).

When the particles are much smaller than the wavelength of the light, the effectiveness of the scattering is proportional to $1/\lambda^4$. This is a more pronounced effect and is known as **Rayleigh scattering** (Fig. 9).

Have you ever wondered why the sky is blue? Oxygen and nitrogen molecules in the atmosphere are about 0.2 nm in size (the oxygen-oxygen bond length is 0.12 nm). They cause Rayleigh scattering that has a much stronger scattering effect on blue light than on red. Comparing the wavelengths of blue and red light:

$$\frac{\text{Wavelength of blue light}}{\text{Wavelength of red light}} = \frac{0.4 \text{ μm}}{0.7 \text{ μm}} = 0.57$$

Using the Rayleigh scattering formula, this ratio of 0.57 is raised to the fourth power and then inverted, so the ratio of scattering of blue to red light is:

$$\frac{1}{0.57^4} = 9 \text{ times}$$

so the sky looks blue!

Some of the most vivid sunsets are caused by dust in the atmosphere. When a volcano erupts, it throws enormous quantities of very fine ash into the upper atmosphere. The ash is so fine that it takes months to settle out. In the meantime it scatters the blue light very strongly, leading to dramatic red sunsets and sunrises, when it is the transmitted light and not the scattered light that is viewed. The Gemini telescopes are situated on high mountains to reduce the problems of scattering and absorption.

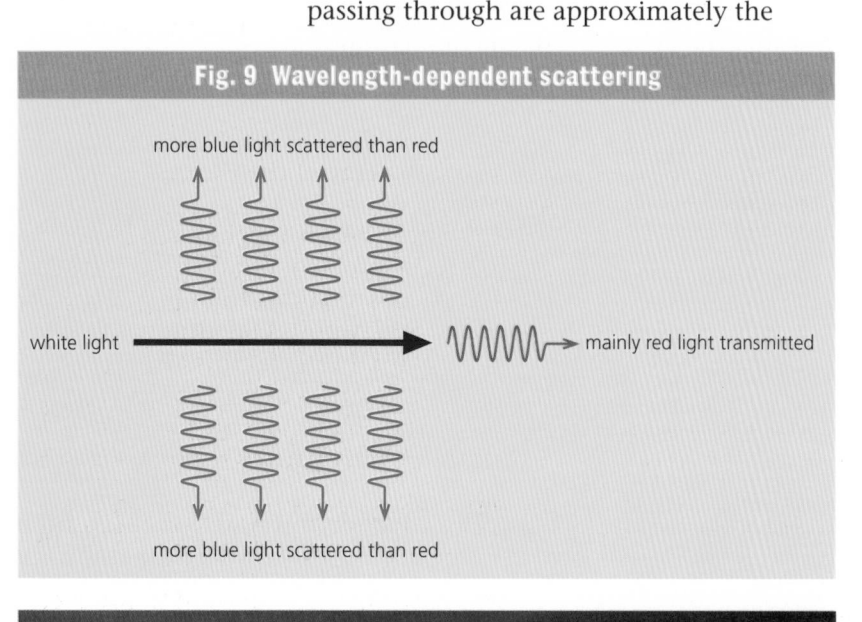

Fig. 9 Wavelength-dependent scattering

more blue light scattered than red

white light → mainly red light transmitted

more blue light scattered than red

The red sky at sunset is due to scattering of the blue light by molecules of oxygen and nitrogen

2.5 The radio window

Radio waves from the Solar System and beyond can be received over a wide range of frequencies: from 30 MHz to 600 GHz.

At the low frequency end there are two factors that make reception difficult. The sky background radiation is quite high, masking the signal in noise and below 30 MHz the ionosphere, part of the upper atmosphere, strongly absorbs the signal. Above 10 GHz absorption by water vapour in the atmosphere is a problem.

At all frequencies, man-made interference is a serious problem. Overall, radio astronomy does have one great advantage over optical astronomy: it can carry on in the daylight.

Artificial interference

Radio telephones and radio pagers in the 100 to 1000 MHz range and radars in the 400 to 10 000 MHz range pose major threats to radio astronomy. Global navigation satellites and direct broadcasting satellites are also a potential problem as they necessarily contain powerful transmitters and they orbit above the telescopes.

Q5 **What pieces of electrical equipment in your home are most likely to make radio interference? Use a portable radio tuned to a quiet part of the long waveband to do your checks.**

Air traffic control radar scanners emit very powerful radio pulses to create moving maps of the aircraft flying near to major airports. The dishes do not transmit in the frequency bands reserved for radio astronomy, but, unfortunately, the signals are so strong that they can disturb the very sensitive radio receivers needed for astronomy and so spoil observations.

Just like optical astronomers, radio astronomers have had to move away from the centres of population. For microwave observations they have moved to the tops of mountains to avoid the water vapour. Within a few years, the growing use of satellite broadcasting and telephone systems is likely to make some radio astronomy projects impossible. It has been seriously suggested that the far side of the Moon might be the best site for the next generation of radio telescopes.

This radar dish, at Manchester airport, will cause problems for radio astronomers

Key ideas

- Molecular absorptions limit the observations that can be made from the Earth.

- Ozone in the upper atmosphere absorbs ultraviolet radiation.

- Molecular oxygen absorbs in the near infrared; water vapour and carbon dioxide absorb in the far infrared.

- Dust and mist in the atmosphere scatter light.

- Low-frequency radio waves are absorbed by the ionosphere.

- High-frequency radio waves are absorbed by water vapour in the atmosphere.

- Artificial interference, by radio telephones, radar and navigation and broadcasting satellites, interfere with radio astronomy.

2.6 Telescopes in space

Radio telescopes

It is just becoming possible to create large radio telescopes in Earth orbit. The first orbiting radio telescope of this type is the Japanese HALCA satellite. It has a 10 metre diameter dish that can receive signals in the three microwave bands of 1.6, 5 and 22 GHz.

Orbiting telescopes will be used in conjunction with Earth-based dishes to form interferometers. The large distances between the dishes will allow very fine detail to be mapped in the radio sources. This is because the greater the separation of the dishes, the finer the diffraction pattern of the system. In effect it will be possible to create a dish system the size of the Earth. The resolution will be 100 micro arc seconds, which is ten times better than present ground-based systems. With this resolution, it is hoped to be able to track the movement of material ejected from the nuclei of active galaxies.

Q 6 What size object could be seen on the Moon using a telescope of 100 micro arc second resolution?

Infrared telescopes

Scintillation is much less of a problem with the longer infrared wavelengths. At a wavelength of 10 μm, a 2 m diameter infrared telescope is diffraction limited.

The HALCA orbiting radio telescope

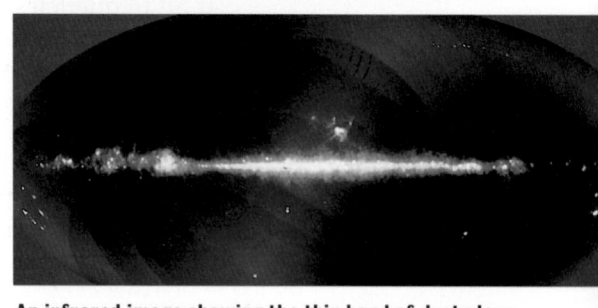

An infrared image showing the thin band of dust along the Milky Way that radiates strongly at the detected wavelengths of 60 and 100 μm; the faint blue S-shaped feature is the dust in our Solar System radiating strongly at 12 μm

IRAS, the Infra Red Astronomy Satellite, found 250 000 infrared sources during its productive survey in 1983. To put this number into perspective, up to the time of the survey, the whole of the astronomy community had only catalogued 500 000 sources of any type. The detectors in IRAS operated at wavelengths of 12, 25, 60 and

IRAS, the Infra Red Astronomy Satellite

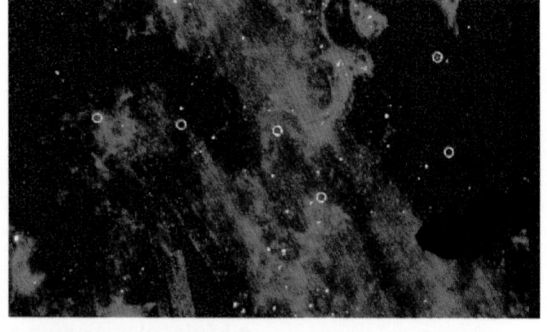

The sky looks very different in the infrared: this is an image of the sky near the constellation of the Plough – the stars are bright in the visible part of the spectrum but in this infrared image their positions have been circled as they are hard to see because of the intense infrared radiation from the gas and dust in that region of the sky.

100 μm. In late 1995, ISO, the Infrared Space Observatory was launched and is busy building on the work of IRAS.

Astronomers want infrared surveys for two main reasons. Such surveys will show up cool objects such as dust clouds in our solar system and planet-forming rings of dust orbiting nearby stars. Surveys will also allow objects that are hidden by dust at optical wavelengths to be seen. These objects include newly forming stars in dense gas and dust clouds, the centre of our Galaxy, red giants that are surrounded by clouds of dust they have thrown off, dusty galaxies where star formation is likely to be under way, and the infrared emissions of radio-quiet and radio-loud **quasars**.

The 10 000 galaxies found in the survey will still be the subject of research far into the twenty-first century. The success of IRAS has led to an explosion of interest in the infrared wavebands. The UK, with its telescope (UKIRT) high up on Mauna Kea, has been in the forefront of the ground-based work.

Ultraviolet telescopes

IUE, the International Ultraviolet Explorer, has a detector that operates in the 120 to 320 nm wavelength range. These wavelengths are totally absorbed by the Earth's atmosphere so the detector had to be put in a satellite. This telescope has discovered water molecules in the tails of comets and has measured the energy profile of exploding stars.

X-ray telescopes

ROSAT, the Röentgen Satellite, is working at X-ray wavelengths, covering a range of 1 to 12 nm. It is able to detect emissions from clouds of very hot gas. Some of these gas clouds have been detected moving between adjacent galaxies.

Particularly interesting research has been undertaken on X-ray emitting **pulsars**. The pulses indicate that very violent collisions are occurring in the gas that surrounds a spinning **neutron star**.

When a large star comes to the end of its life the remaining material collapses to become a sphere a few kilometres across consisting entirely of neutrons. If there is enough mass it may collapse further into a **black hole**.

The gravity is very strong near these objects and material falling into them suffers violent collisions. The resulting energy is released, mainly as X-rays. These sources are interesting because they are often **binary star** systems. Material for the collisions comes from the second star in the system.

Gamma ray telescopes

The Compton Gamma Ray Observatory detects rays with wavelengths between 10^{-12} and 10^{-17} m. This corresponds to an energy range from 3×10^4 to 3×10^{10} electron volts, which is at the very top end of the electromagnetic spectrum.

The most perplexing observations are those of gamma ray bursts. These occur at random at a rate of about one per day. They come from all directions in the sky and because the Compton Gamma Ray Observatory can only give approximate directions, the sources have not yet been identified.

Optical telescopes in space

The main advantage of placing a telescope in orbit is that there is no atmosphere to distort the image or to absorb the radiation. In addition, telescopes do not have their shape distorted by gravity.

On the surface of the Earth, the scintillation caused by the atmosphere limits the resolution of optical telescopes to about 1 second of arc. In space, optical telescopes can function up to their diffraction and surface accuracy limits.

Key ideas

- Telescopes can be placed in space to overcome problems caused by molecular absorption in the Earth's atmosphere and artificial interference.

- Orbiting radio telescopes can be linked with Earth-based radio telescopes to form very large interferometers.

- Orbiting infrared telescopes have observed dust clouds in our Solar System and round other stars.

- Orbiting ultraviolet telescopes have observed water in the tails of comets.

- Orbiting X-ray telescopes have observed gas clouds in adjacent galaxies.

- Orbiting optical telescopes are not affected by scintillation and so are diffraction limited.

2.7 Radio emission from the Milky Way

Fig. 10 Viewing the centre of the Galaxy is like being in a swimming pool

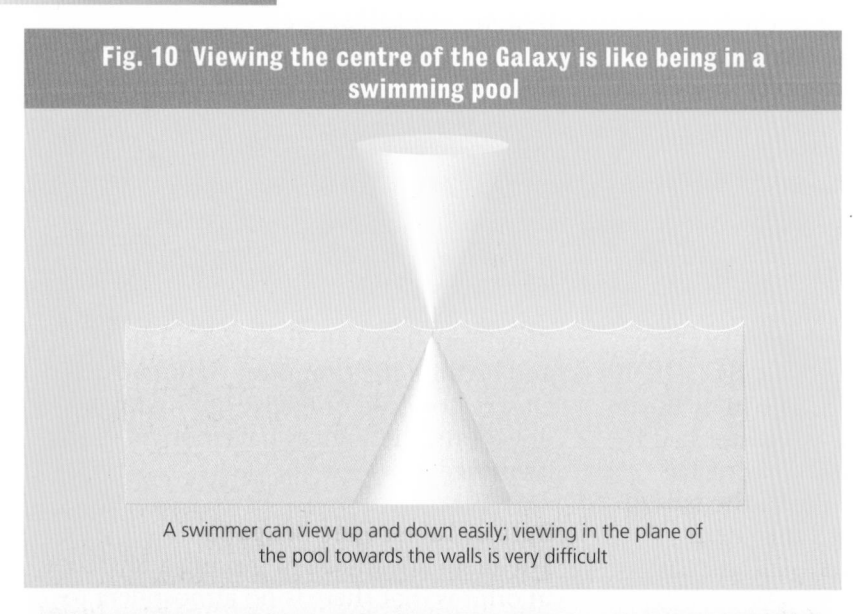

A swimmer can view up and down easily; viewing in the plane of the pool towards the walls is very difficult

The centre of the Milky Way

Our Galaxy is full of gas and dust that absorbs visible light. If you look in the direction of the galactic plane it is only possible to see nearby stars through the absorbing clouds. It is absolutely impossible to see as far as the galactic centre in visible light (Fig. 10).

Radio astronomy comes into its own in the plane of the Galaxy because of the longer wavelength of the emissions. In an earlier section we saw that scattering is not so bad if the wavelength is much greater

Fortunately the disc of our Galaxy is quite thin so we are able see out to many distant galaxies: this photograph, of NGC 891, is what you might see if you could move outside our Galaxy and look back – very narrow dust lanes, a somewhat broader distribution of stars and, as with most spiral galaxies, a central bulge

The dense clouds of dust obscure many stars in the lower part of the photograph, creating the illusion of the horse's head in the Horsehead Nebula

Radio image of the centre
of our Galaxy, taken by
the Very Large Array

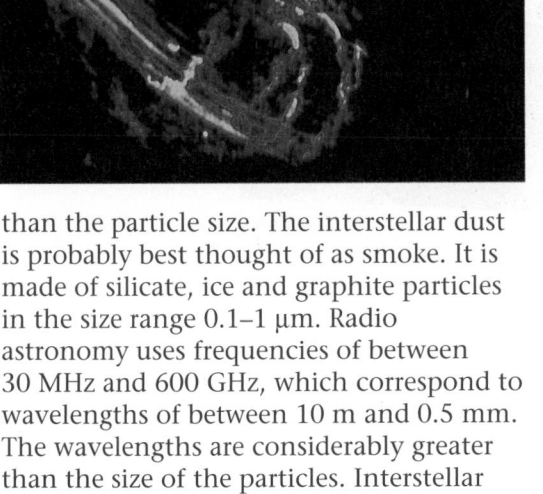

The Andromeda galaxy

than the particle size. The interstellar dust is probably best thought of as smoke. It is made of silicate, ice and graphite particles in the size range 0.1–1 μm. Radio astronomy uses frequencies of between 30 MHz and 600 GHz, which correspond to wavelengths of between 10 m and 0.5 mm. The wavelengths are considerably greater than the size of the particles. Interstellar dust is also very diffuse, with as few as 100 particles in each cubic kilometre. This means that each particle is tens of metres from its neighbours. As a result we can easily see through the dust to the centre of our Galaxy using radio waves.

Careful observations over the last 50 years have convinced astronomers that our Solar System is a very small part of a large spiral galaxy. We are about two-thirds of the way from the centre to the edge of our Galaxy, in one of the spiral arms. Our Galaxy is quite like our near neighbour Andromeda, which itself has two small companions.

With all these observations you might ask if astronomers have seen any trace of life out there! There are some interesting clues. The infrared images of nearby dust clouds show stars with discs of dust in orbit round them. Perhaps planets could be forming in these dust rings.

The microwave astronomers have detected radiation from some very complicated molecules. The signatures of ammonia, ethanol and water have been seen. Some very complicated carbon-based molecules have recently been detected.

All this points to the possibility of life being able to form in other parts of the Universe. The jury is still out on this question. It will be many years before we have telescopes good enough to detect planets orbiting even the nearest stars. Meanwhile some groups are using radio telescopes to listen for signals from intelligent life but nothing has been heard so far.

Key ideas

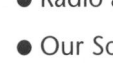

- Gas and dust prevent clear observation of the centre of our Galaxy using visible light.
- Radio astronomy can be used to observe the centre of our Galaxy.
- Our Solar System is in one spiral arm of a spiral galaxy, about two-thirds of the way from the centre.

The Doppler effect

A modern radar gun can measure the speed of a car when it is well over 100 metres away. The speeding driver has no chance to slow down before I have an accurate reading. Excessive speed increases the chance of accidents, and injuries are much more likely to be serious. Even at 40 mph it is almost certain that a pedestrian hit by a car will be killed. We must do all we can to encourage safer driving habits.

One fact of everyday life for car drivers is the radar speed trap. The police officer aims a radar gun that sends out a beam of radio waves. The waves are reflected from the car and the receiver in the gun measures their wavelength. The change in the original wavelength of the waves is directly related to the speed of the car. This is a practical use of the Doppler effect.

The Doppler effect is also used by astronomers, in order to extract information from the faint light of distant stars and galaxies. Astronomers collect as much light as possible with their telescopes and then direct the light on to a diffraction grating. This splits the light into a spectrum and, using the Doppler effect, the astronomer can calculate the speed of the object.

3.1 Learning objectives

After working through this chapter, you should be able to:

- **use** the Doppler effect to calculate the speed of a galaxy from the red shift of its light;

- **calculate** the orbital period and speed of binary stars using the Doppler effect.

3.2 The Doppler formula

Imagine you are standing on the shore of a lake (Fig. 1). The water is very calm and a rowing boat is coming in very slowly to land. Each time the oars dip into the water, ripples spread out from them. In your direction, the boat is trying to overtake the ripples but they spread out more quickly than the boat is moving forward. However, this means that the distance between the ripples is less in your direction than in all others on the surface of the water. The wavelength has been shortened by the motion of the boat. This is an example of the Doppler effect.

You will often hear the Doppler effect in sound waves. When an ambulance passes by, the pitch of the siren suddenly drops. This is because the wavelength is shortened as the ambulance approaches and then lengthens as it moves away.

The Doppler effect formula for light is made simple by the fact that the speed of light is not affected by the motion of the source or the observer. This fact is a fundamental property of nature and is the foundation of the special theory of relativity.

Also, most calculations that you will

Fig. 1 Illustrating the Doppler effect

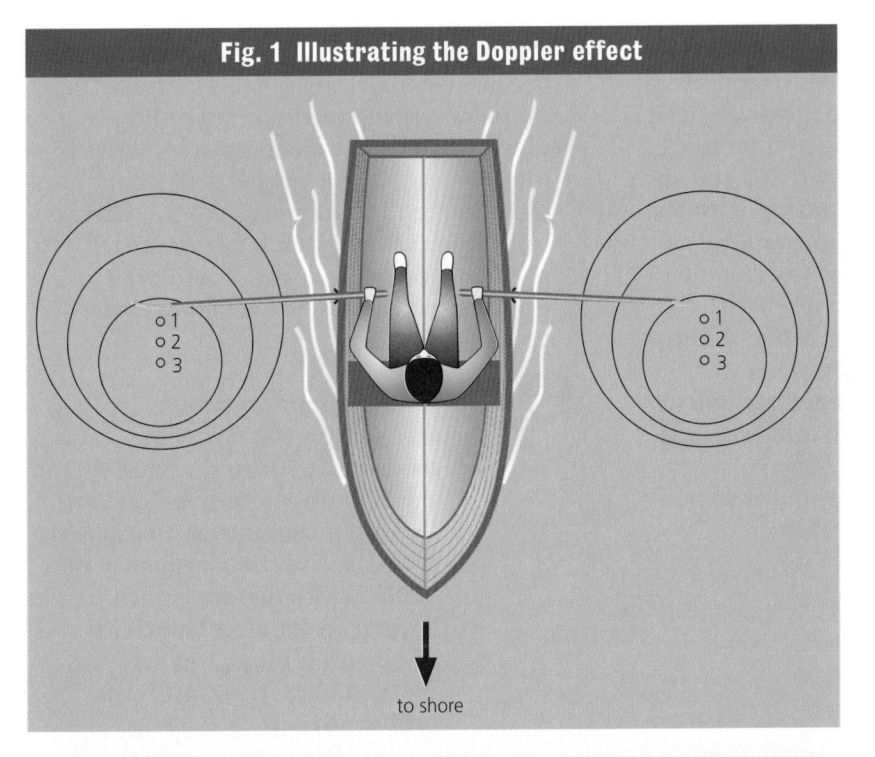

to shore

Fig. 2 The Doppler formula

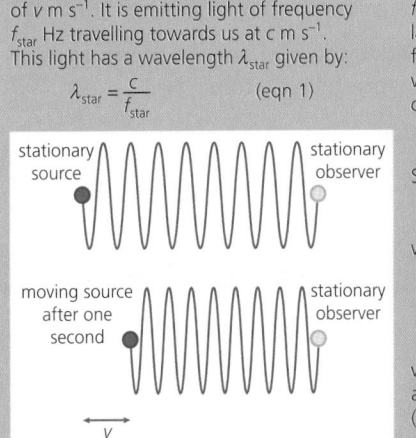

Think of a star approaching Earth at a speed of v m s^{-1}. It is emitting light of frequency f_{star} Hz travelling towards us at c m s^{-1}. This light has a wavelength λ_{star} given by:

$$\lambda_{star} = \frac{c}{f_{star}} \qquad \text{(eqn 1)}$$

stationary source — stationary observer

moving source after one second — stationary observer

v

c

Consider one second's emission: the star emits f waves, but because the star is moving, the last wave is a distance $c - v$ metres behind the first wave. This means a telescope on Earth would pick up f_{star} waves in this distance of $c - v$ metres, so that they have a wavelength:

$$\lambda_{telescope} = \frac{c - v}{f_{star}} \qquad \text{(eqn 2)}$$

Substituting for f_{star} using (eqn 1) gives:

$$\lambda_{telescope} = \frac{c - v}{c / \lambda_{star}} \qquad \text{(eqn 3)}$$

which (you should check) simplifies to:

$$\lambda_{telescope} = \lambda_{star} \frac{c - v}{c} = \lambda_{star} - \lambda_{star} \frac{v}{c}$$

$$\lambda_{telescope} - \lambda_{star} = \Delta\lambda = -\lambda_{star} \frac{v}{c} \qquad \text{(eqn 4)}$$

where $\Delta\lambda$ is the difference between emitted and observed wavelengths. In astronomy, this (eqn 4) is written as the **Doppler formula**:

$$\frac{\Delta\lambda}{\lambda_{star}} = -\frac{v}{c}$$

| − = blue shift |
| + = red shift |

---

meet will involve relative velocities that are much smaller than the speed of light. The more complete formula that comes from the theory of relativity is discussed later.

The theory of the Doppler effect

Consider a star emitting electromagnetic waves at a certain frequency and wavelength. The observed frequency and observed wavelength of the waves are affected by the relative motion of the star and the observer (Fig. 2). If the star and the observer approach one another, the wavelength appears shortened and if they recede from one another the wavelength appears lengthened. Theory predicts that the change in wavelength will be:

$$\frac{\text{Change in wavelength}}{\text{Original wavelength}} = \frac{\text{Relative velocity}}{\text{Speed of light}}$$

$$\frac{\Delta\lambda}{\lambda} = -\frac{v}{c}$$

where $\Delta\lambda$ is the change in wavelength in m, λ is the wavelength emitted by the star in m, v is the relative velocity between the star and the observer in m s^{-1} and c is the speed of light in m s^{-1}.

The formula holds provided the relative velocity is much smaller than the speed of light. This is normally the case, except for the more distant quasars. See Section 3.3 for how to deal with large relative velocities.

Notice the minus sign in the formula. The relative velocity v is taken as positive when the source and observer are approaching each other. The change in wavelength $\Delta\lambda$ will *then be negative, indicating a decrease in wavelength.* This is known as a **blue shift**, because the wavelength of a spectral line appears shorter, i.e., it moves towards the blue end of the spectrum (Fig. 3).

Fig. 3 Wavelengths of visible light

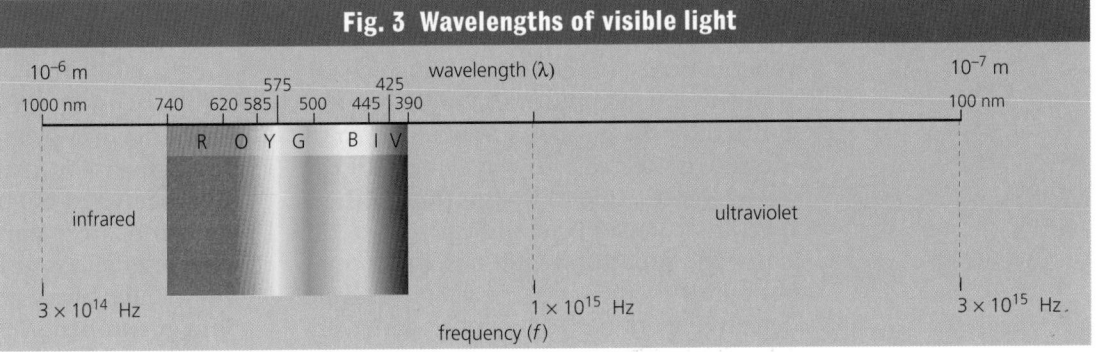

When the source and observer are moving apart, the relative velocity is taken as negative. The change in wavelength is then positive, indicating an increased wavelength. This is known as a **red shift**. The radiation involved may not appear red or blue following a Doppler shift; the terms just give the direction of the change in wavelength of the observed light.

If you find it hard to remember this sign convention, all you need to remember is that approaching objects shorten the wavelength and receding objects lengthen it.

The Doppler formula may also be expressed in terms of *frequency*:

$$\frac{\text{Change in frequency}}{\text{Original frequency}} = \frac{\text{Relative velocity}}{\text{Speed of light}}$$

$$\frac{\Delta f}{f} = \frac{v}{c}$$

The minus sign has gone from the formula because approaching objects increase the frequency of the waves and receding objects reduce it. Calculations to do with infrared, visible, ultraviolet and X-ray radiation tend to use wavelength, whereas calculations to do with radio waves tend to use frequency. This is just a result of the way the subject has developed over the years.

Q1
a A star is emitting light of wavelength 600 nm. If the star is receding at 50 km s⁻¹, calculate the wavelength as observed on Earth.
b The radio transmitter on a space probe was set to a frequency of 4000.00 MHz before launch. Several weeks after launch its frequency is measured as 3999.84 MHz. How fast is the probe moving?

Key ideas

- Relative motion between an object emitting electromagnetic radiation and an observer leads to an alteration in the observed frequency of the electromagnetic radiation.

- The red shift is given by:

$$\frac{\Delta \lambda}{\lambda} = -\frac{v}{c} \quad \text{when } v \ll c$$

Table 1 A summary of Doppler shift effects			
Relative motion	Relative velocity	Frequency	Wavelength
towards observer	positive	higher	shorter	blue shift
away from observer	negative	lower	longer	red shift

3.3 Red shift of galaxies

When a police officer uses a radar speed gun, the wavelength of the radio waves emitted by the gun are known, and so the increase or decrease in wavelength of the reflected rays, due to the motion of the speeding car, can be easily calculated. This is not the situation when observing the light emitted by a moving galaxy. A little detective work has to be done to identify

the elements that emitted or absorbed the light. By using our knowledge of the elements in nearby stars and the fact that the Universe is mainly composed of hydrogen and helium we can identify the emissions from particular atoms. Their characteristic wavelengths can be measured in the laboratory and then compared to the longer wavelengths seen in the light of the receding galaxy. The increase in wavelength can then be used to calculate the velocity of the galaxy.

When distant galaxies are observed, all the wavelengths of their **emission** and/or **absorption lines** are found to be longer than the corresponding lines observed in stationary sources. This is a red shift. As the wavelengths are increased, so the galaxies must be moving away from us – evidence for the expansion of the Universe (see Chapter 7, page 73).

We have to be careful about the galaxies within our local group. The local galaxies are bound together by gravitational forces that are sufficiently strong to pull some of them towards us. For example, the Andromeda galaxy M31 is approaching at 400 km s^{-1} and might eventually cartwheel through our galaxy.

The red shift is given the symbol z and is defined as:

$$\frac{\Delta\lambda}{\lambda} = z; \; z \geq 0$$

By taking spectra of the most distant and faint objects, it has recently been proved possible to identify galaxies with red shifts as great as 4.5. So far, no object has been found with a greater red shift and many nearer galaxies have much smaller red shifts. For example, the light that originated in a quasar has been observed. The red shift of the quasar was calculated to be 4.733; this was measured by observing the change in wavelength of the Lyman alpha line of the hydrogen spectrum. This line is emitted in the ultraviolet at 121.6 nm but in this example has been Doppler shifted to the red end of the visible spectrum at 700 nm. This is nearly a six fold increase in wavelength. An object receding rapidly can cause a spectral line normally in the ultraviolet part of the spectrum to be shifted into the visible range.

2a Use the Doppler formula to calculate the recession speed of this quasar.

b Is your answer sensible?

The Doppler shift formula is an approximation that only works for relative velocities up to about one-tenth of the speed of light. At a red shift of 0.2 an error of 12% in the calculated velocity is introduced.

A better approximation can be made using the special relativity version of the formula:

$$\text{red shift} = \frac{\Delta\lambda}{\lambda} = \frac{1 + \dfrac{v}{c}}{\sqrt{1 - \dfrac{v^2}{c^2}}} - 1$$

3 Assuming a relative velocity (v) of 2.82×10^8 m s^{-1} (i.e. 94% of the speed of light), work out the red shift using the special relativity version of the Doppler shift formula.

The special relativity version of the Doppler shift formula is part of a better theory of the expansion of the Universe. However, the full depth of the problem can only be explored through the general theory of relativity, which is beyond the scope of this book.

Key ideas

- Approaching objects look bluer and receding objects look redder than they are in fact.

- The observed red shifts from distant galaxies support the theory of an expanding universe.

- For objects moving at speeds of over one-tenth of the speed of light, a special relativity version of the red shift formula needs to be used.

3.4 Applications of the Doppler shift

Rotation

When you view any astronomical system that is rotating, one half of the system will appear to be approaching you and the other half moving away (receding). The system in question can be a star, a planet, a binary star system or set of planetary rings.

In a **binary star** system, two stars are held together by gravity and orbit their common centre of mass. The maximum velocities will be recorded when one star is directly approaching and the other is receding from the observer (Fig. 4).

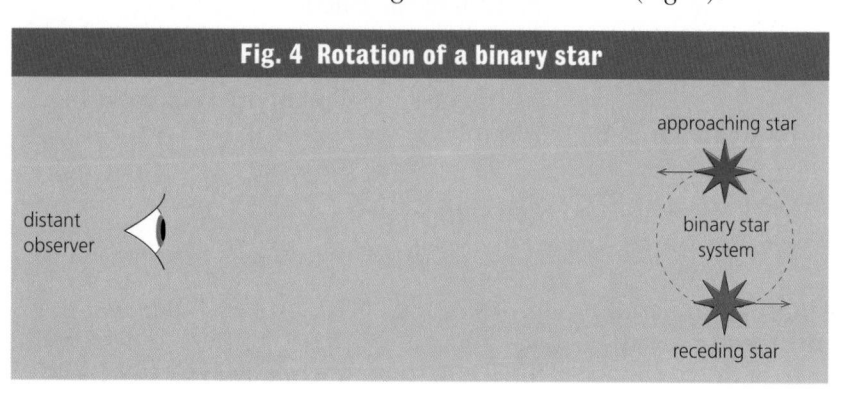

Fig. 4 Rotation of a binary star

approaching star

binary star system

receding star

distant observer

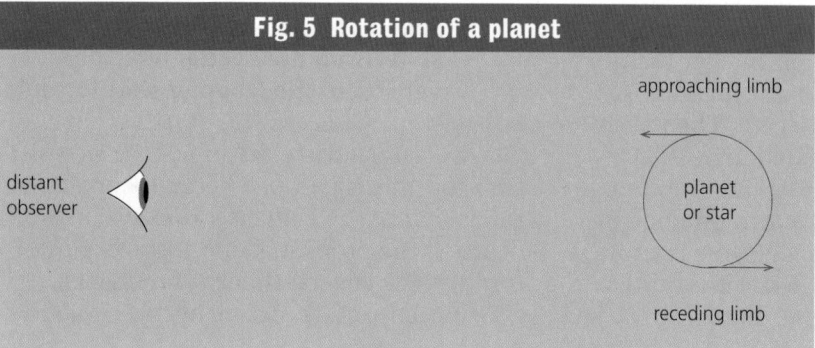

Fig. 5 Rotation of a planet

approaching limb

planet or star

receding limb

distant observer

In a rotating planet or star, the maximum Doppler shifts will correspond to the approaching and receding limbs (Fig. 5). However, the whole system may also be moving towards or away from the observer. The true relative velocity may be measured from the centre of the object, where there is no component of the rotation in the direction of the observer. Alternatively, the mean value of the velocities can be used.

The Doppler shift observed in this way will enable the tangential velocity (v) of the

star or planet to be calculated. Starting with the mechanics formulae:

$$v = r\omega \quad \text{and} \quad \omega = \frac{2\pi}{T}$$

Rearranging:

$$v = \frac{2\pi r}{T}$$

where v is the tangential velocity in m s^{-1}, r is the radius of the star in m, and T is the time for one revolution in s, i.e., the period. For example, for a star of radius 1.5×10^9 m, rotating once every 10 days,

$$v = \frac{2\pi \times 1.5 \times 10^9 \text{ m}}{10 \text{ days} \times 24 \text{ hours} \times 60 \text{ min} \times 60 \text{ sec}}$$

$$= 1.09 \times 10^4 \text{ m s}^{-1}$$

The Sun is the only star for which separate observation can be made for the approaching and receding limbs (Fig. 6). For the Sun, the approach speed of the limb is about 2000 m s^{-1}. This gives a shift of about 7 parts in a million, which would require a high resolution spectrum in order to observe it.

For all stars except the Sun it is impossible to focus on each limb independently. For a particular line in the spectrum, the result that you see is a broadened profile whose blue and red edges represent the approaching and receding limbs of the star. Wavelength measurements can be taken as before to find the velocity of the limbs (Fig. 7).

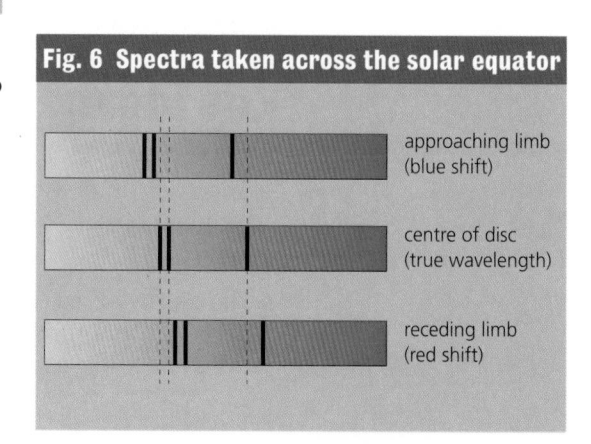

Fig. 6 Spectra taken across the solar equator

approaching limb (blue shift)

centre of disc (true wavelength)

receding limb (red shift)

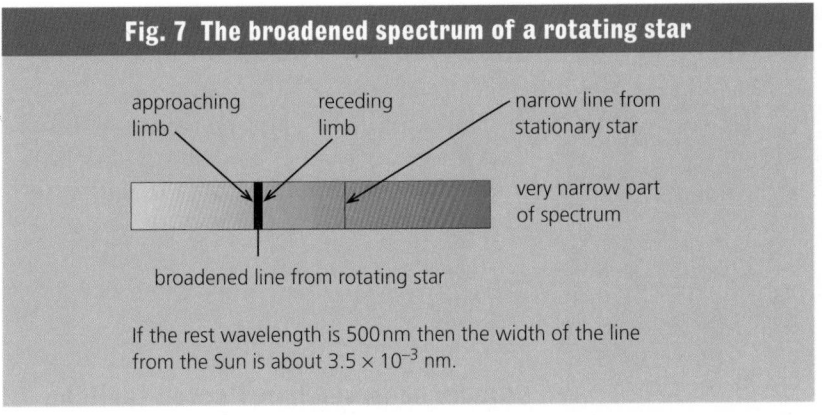
Fig. 9 Eclipsing binary stars

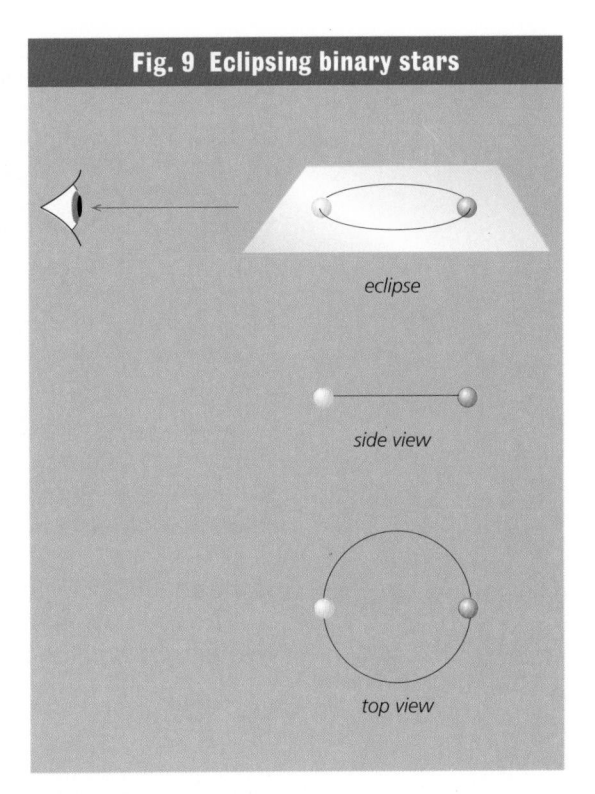

eclipse

side view

top view

Spectroscopic binary systems

Binary star systems are often distant from the Earth and their components relatively close together. This means that they cannot be resolved as two separate objects, even with the best telescopes. Their binary nature is only revealed when light gathered by a telescope is directed on to the slit of a spectroscope. The resulting spectrum allows the Doppler shifts to be measured. This is why these objects are called **spectroscopic binaries**.

Some spectroscopic binary systems show two distinct sets of spectral lines, one set from each star. As the stars orbit each other, the lines move from longer to shorter wavelength and back again (Fig. 8). By observing a complete cycle we can measure the period, i.e., time for one complete revolution of the system. From the Doppler shifts we can calculate the velocities of the stars.

Once the period and velocities have been found, they can be combined to obtain the distance between the stars.

Further theory shows that the ratio of the orbital radii is equal to the ratio of the masses of the two stars. This is a powerful measuring technique when you consider that the stars are too far away to be seen individually.

So far we have overlooked the problem that if you cannot see the individual stars that make up the binary system, you cannot find the inclination of their orbit to our line of sight. This difficulty vanishes if the stars are **eclipsing binaries** (Fig. 9). In this case their orbital plane must be edge-on to the observer for the eclipse to be visible. All calculations dealt with here will be confined to the simple case of the edge-on orbit.

Theory of binary star orbits

The orbital theory for two stars of equal mass is quite simple. The force of gravity must provide the centripetal force for the circular orbits. For two stars of equal mass, distance R m apart, their centre of mass is half way between them and they will each orbit this point. The centripetal force (F) required to maintain an orbit is given by:

$$F = mr\omega^2$$

where m is the mass of the star in kg, and $\dot\omega$

Fig. 8 Spectra from a binary star system

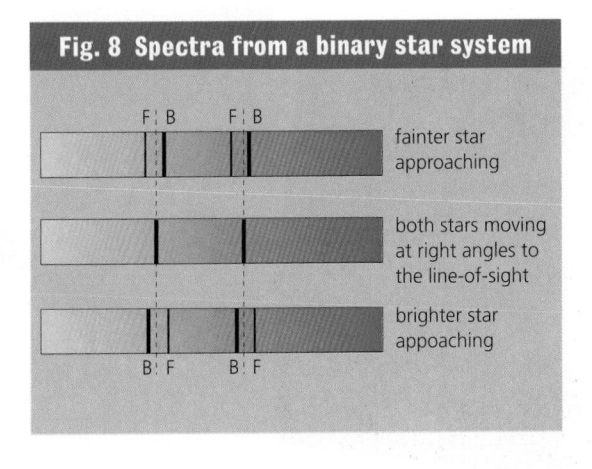

fainter star approaching

both stars moving at right angles to the line-of-sight

brighter star approaching

Fig. 10 Binary star orbits

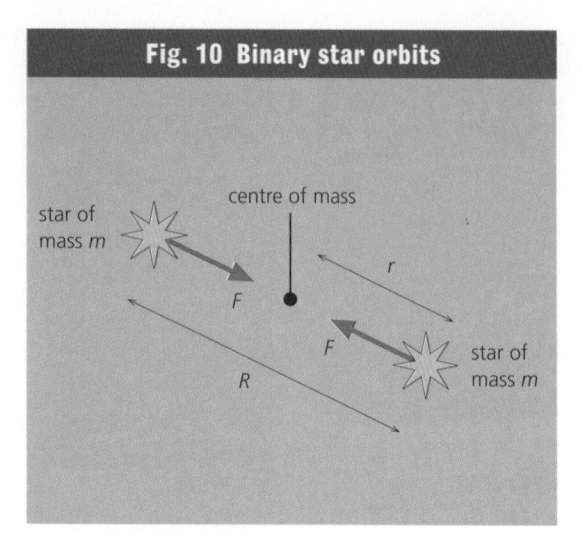

is the angular velocity in radian s^{-1} (Fig. 10).

The gravitational attraction (F) between two masses is given by:

$$F = \frac{Gmm}{R^2}$$

where G is the gravitational constant in N m^2 kg^{-2}, m is the mass of each star in kg and R is the distance between the stars in m.

For a stable orbit these forces must be equal to each other, hence:

$$\frac{mR\omega^2}{2} = \frac{Gmm}{R^2}$$

and by definition

$$\omega = \frac{2\pi}{T}$$

where T is the period of each orbit in s.

Substituting and rearranging:

$$m = \frac{2\pi^2 R^3}{GT^2}$$

If you know the radius of the orbit and its period, you can calculate the mass of the stars.

The formula can also be rearranged so that the two variables are the velocity and the period, which can be obtained directly from observations of the spectra:

$$m = \frac{2v^3 T}{\pi G}$$

Objects observed in reflected sunlight

An important point to remember about the Doppler effect is that it will occur even when the light is reflected by a moving object. If a planet is moving relative to the incoming sunlight, this creates one Doppler shift. The planet then re-emits the light whilst moving relative to the observer, so creating a second Doppler shift. Normal sunlight contains many absorption lines that are created just above the Sun's surface. The observer sees these absorption lines in the reflected sunlight from the planet. The lines have suffered **two** Doppler shifts.

Hence:

$$\frac{\Delta\lambda}{\lambda} = \frac{2v}{c}$$

if the Sun, Earth and planet are in a straight line.

This theory can be used in studies of the rotation of planets and their rings and to calculate the velocities of asteroids.

A good example of this is the spectrum emitted by Saturn and its rings (Fig. 11).

The lines shown are the Fraunhofer lines from the Sun, *doubly* Doppler shifted by the

Saturn and its rings; measuring the Doppler shifts of light from the planet and its rings enables their rotation to be studied

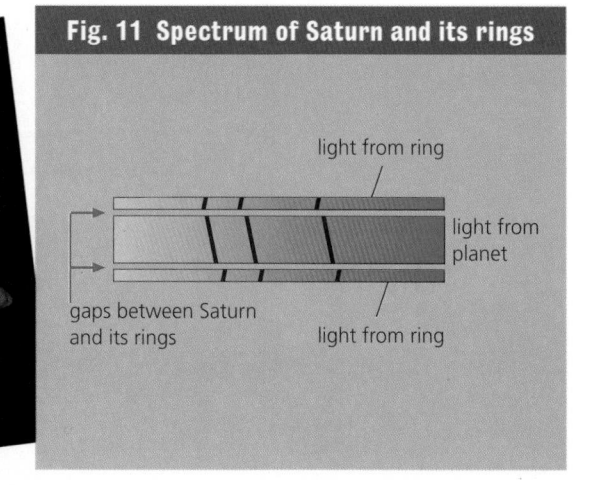

Fig. 11 Spectrum of Saturn and its rings

light from ring

light from planet

gaps between Saturn and its rings

light from ring

motion of the rings and planet. The slant of the planetary lines is due to the increase in the component of velocity of the surface of Saturn in our direction. As we look at parts of the equator further from the centre of the disc so the Doppler shift increases.

The rings of Saturn are freely orbiting particles and so their velocity decreases with distance from the planet. This causes the Doppler shift to decrease with distance from Saturn and the lines to slope the opposite way to those of the disc.

Eclipsing binary systems

The star, Algol, is easily visible with the naked eye. It comprises a bright star and a faint star orbiting around their common centre of mass. Once every 68 hours the fainter star covers the brighter one and the magnitude falls by 1.2 units. The other eclipse, when the bright star covers the faint star, is difficult to see. This effect, which is clearly visible to the naked eye, is only observable because the Earth happens to lie in the plane of the orbits of the two stars.

When an eclipse occurs there is no component of orbital velocity in our direction (the bright star's velocity is perpendicular to our line of sight when it crosses it). In this position, the Doppler shift of spectral lines from both stars is zero. It will also be zero half an orbit later (Fig. 12).

These Doppler shifts can be used to calculate the angular velocity, period and distance between the two stars of Algol (Fig. 13).

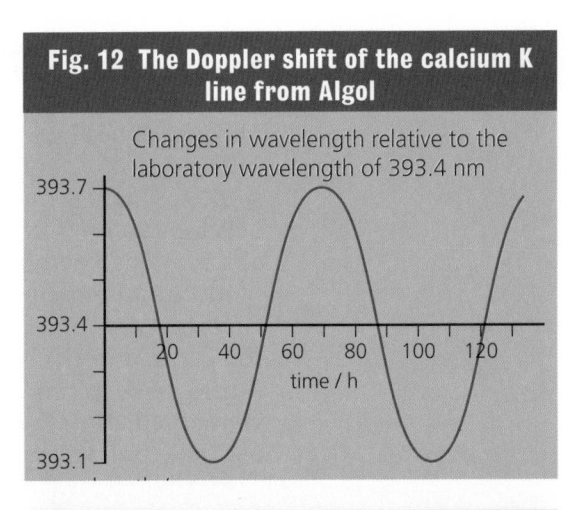

Fig. 12 The Doppler shift of the calcium K line from Algol

Changes in wavelength relative to the laboratory wavelength of 393.4 nm

time / h

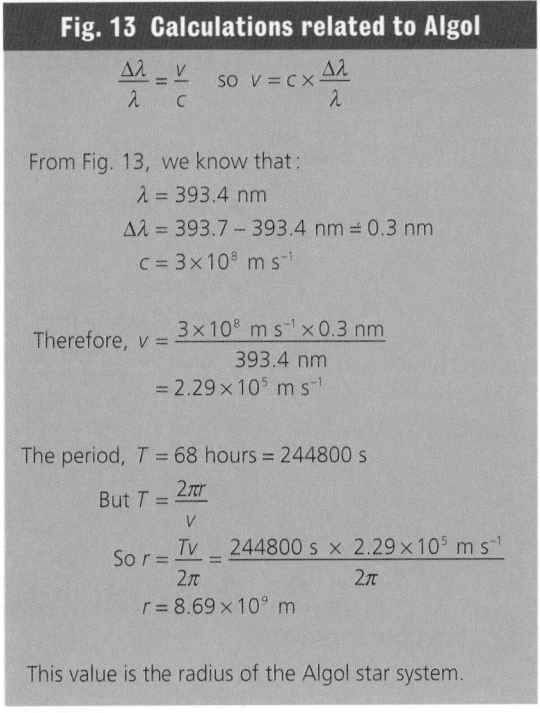

Fig. 13 Calculations related to Algol

$$\frac{\Delta\lambda}{\lambda} = \frac{v}{c} \quad \text{so} \quad v = c \times \frac{\Delta\lambda}{\lambda}$$

From Fig. 13, we know that:
$$\lambda = 393.4 \text{ nm}$$
$$\Delta\lambda = 393.7 - 393.4 \text{ nm} = 0.3 \text{ nm}$$
$$c = 3 \times 10^8 \text{ m s}^{-1}$$

Therefore, $v = \dfrac{3 \times 10^8 \text{ m s}^{-1} \times 0.3 \text{ nm}}{393.4 \text{ nm}}$
$$= 2.29 \times 10^5 \text{ m s}^{-1}$$

The period, $T = 68$ hours $= 244800$ s

But $T = \dfrac{2\pi r}{v}$

So $r = \dfrac{Tv}{2\pi} = \dfrac{244800 \text{ s} \times 2.29 \times 10^5 \text{ m s}^{-1}}{2\pi}$
$$r = 8.69 \times 10^9 \text{ m}$$

This value is the radius of the Algol star system.

Key ideas

- Binary stars can be studied by observing the Doppler shifts of the approaching and receding stars.

- Some binary stars are only revealed spectroscopically.

4 Radiation

Theories about how the Universe began are numerous. Most civilisations have 'creation stories'. Theories of cosmology have developed alongside the advances in observational astronomy. The development of more and more powerful telescopes has enabled astronomers to look further from the Earth, effectively looking further and further back in time. The COBE satellite viewed radiation that was 15 billion years old. The discoveries from COBE were greeted with great excitement, but some people counselled caution: 'It's either the discovery of the decade or pure codswallop. We really do need confirmation before people get too excited' (so said the then Astronomer Royal, Professor Arnold Wolfendale).

Professor Sir Arnold Wolfendale

4.1 Learning objectives

After working through this chapter, you should be able to:

- **describe** the spectrum of light emitted by a star;

- **estimate** the temperature of a star from its continuous spectrum (blackbody spectrum);

- **predict** how the colour of a star changes with its temperature;

- **estimate** the power output of a star from its temperature and radius;

- **calculate** the theoretical temperature of the Earth by considering the balance of energy flows;

- **explain** why astronomers support the hot big bang theory of the Universe.

4.2 Planck radiation curves

The COBE satellite was launched in 1990 to make precise measurements of the microwave radiation that seems to fill space and to come from all directions. The plan was to confirm the theory that this radiation was the remains of energy emitted when the Universe was small and hot, soon after the big bang. The radiation 'cooled down' as the Universe expanded and Earth-based measurements had already suggested that it would have a temperature of 2.7 K – close to absolute zero.

Measurements through the atmosphere were very difficult and so it was necessary to take the readings from space. COBE's results were so precise that they triumphantly supported the hot big bang theory. The temperature of the radiation was found to be 2.726 K.

The exciting results from COBE were that the temperature varied slightly from one part of the sky to another, suggesting that the matter in the early Universe was not uniformly distributed but was arranged in wispy clouds. It was very important for cosmologists to find slight variations on the cosmic microwave background. The faint ripples show that at the time the radiation separated from the matter of the Universe, about 300 000 years after the big bang, the matter was sufficiently lumpy for gravity to pull it together and form the galaxies we see today. If the matter had been very smooth then the galaxies would have taken so long to form that the

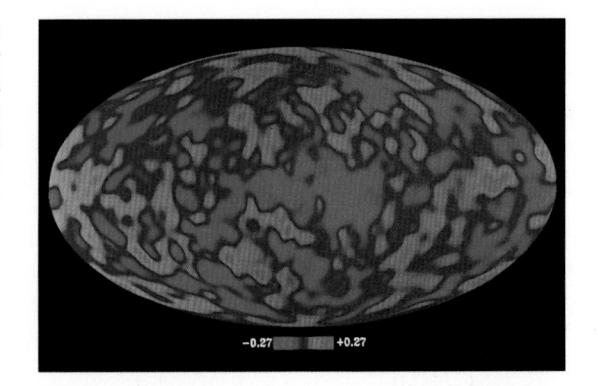

−0.27 +0.27

Fig. 1 Emission and absorption in a blackbody

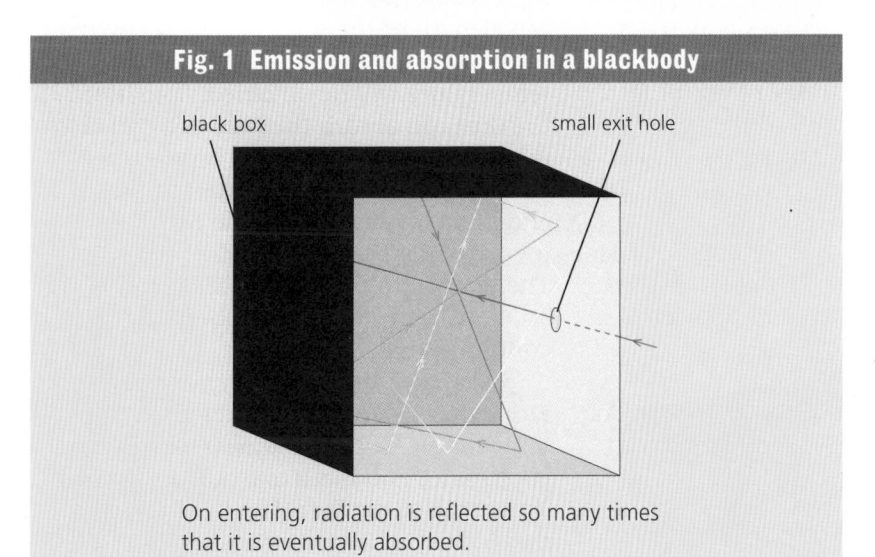

black box   small exit hole

On entering, radiation is reflected so many times that it is eventually absorbed.

Fig. 2 Planck radiation curves

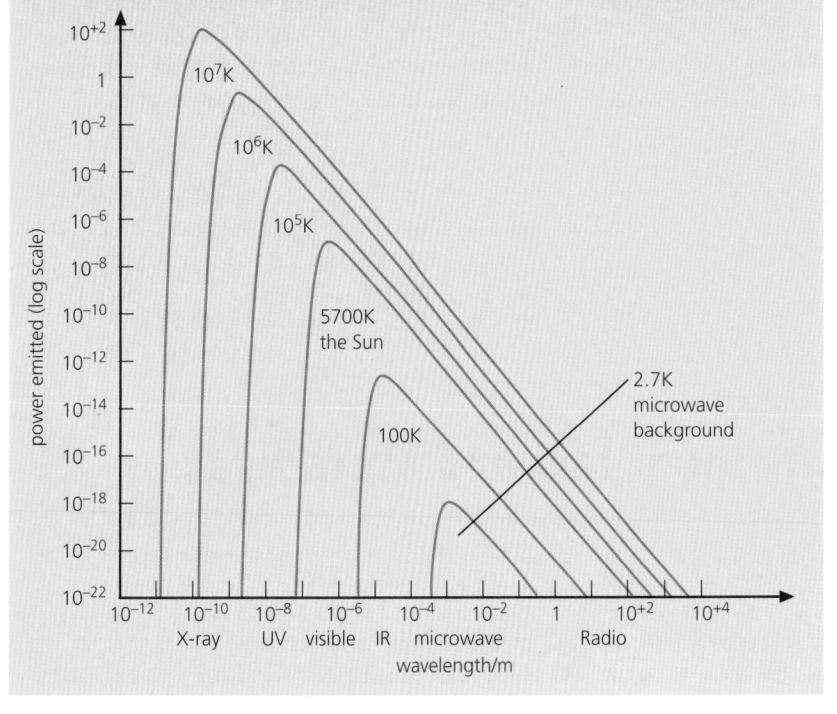

power emitted (log scale)

10^7K
10^6K
10^5K
5700K the Sun
100K
2.7K microwave background

10^{+2}
1
10^{-2}
10^{-4}
10^{-6}
10^{-8}
10^{-10}
10^{-12}
10^{-14}
10^{-16}
10^{-18}
10^{-20}
10^{-22}

10^{-12} 10^{-10} 10^{-8} 10^{-6} 10^{-4} 10^{-2} 1 10^{+2} 10^{+4}

X-ray   UV   visible IR microwave   Radio

wavelength/m

Universe would not be in such a developed state as it is now. You might now ask how radiation can have a temperature.

Most thermometers need direct contact with the object whose temperature they are measuring. However, it is possible to link the range of electromagnetic radiation emitted by an object to the temperature of that object. Consider the filament of an ordinary light bulb. When switched off it is cold and grey. When switched on, the filament glows white hot and emits electromagnetic radiation over a wide range of wavelengths. Temperatures between these extremes can be observed on the rings of an electric cooker. When a ring is switched on, its colour changes from black through red to orange. Other examples are the yellow light from a run-down electric torch and the blue light from a camera flash gun (a very hot plasma).

In what follows we assume that hot objects are perfect emitters of radiation. This means that the intensity of the radiation (the energy it carries) at a particular wavelength depends only on the temperature of the object. Such objects emit a continuous spectrum of radiation whose intensity varies smoothly with wavelength (Figs 1 and 2). The pattern of emission is called blackbody radiation. A blackbody in equilibrium at a given temperature absorbs all radiation and emits it all again in the same pattern of wavelengths (otherwise it would warm up or cool down and so not be in equilibrium with its surroundings). It may seem strange to call a glowing object a blackbody but the

The wavelength of the radiation emitted by the rings on this electric cooker is linked to the temperature of the ring; the black ring is much cooler than the ring that is glowing red.

41

name refers to the distribution of the wavelengths it emits. Most solid objects are a fair approximation to a blackbody, but gases in particular also emit and absorb spectral lines. This makes the calculations more difficult.

The graphs in Fig. 2 show the theoretical output of perfect emitters at various temperatures. The theory was produced by the German physicist Max Planck in 1900 and these emission curves are often called **Planck radiation curves**.

The Planck radiation curves may seem rather abstract, but you will have experience of them each day of your life. Whether you switch on the ring of a cooker, a gas fire, an electric kettle or just stand in the sunlight, these curves describe the effects you see and feel.

Each curve shows how the output power of a blackbody varies with wavelength. The family of curves shows how the power depends on temperature. At very high temperatures the peak of the emission is well into the X-ray part of the spectrum. At very low temperatures the only significant emission is in the microwave region, and it is this region that has been explored by the COBE satellite.

The rings on an electric cooker can emit radiation from the invisible infrared to the visible orange. This corresponds to temperatures ranging from 300 K to about 1000 K. The surface of the Sun, at a temperature of 5700 K, appears white. The peak of its curve falls directly in the visible region so that the Sun gives out roughly equal amounts of all the visible colours. In fact it is slightly yellow, as it is not quite hot enough to be white.

Q 1 Study the curve for 10^6 K. What colour would such a star appear?

Temperature measurements of stars

The Earth's atmosphere and interstellar dust clouds are always a problem to astronomers when observing spectra, as they absorb different parts of the spectrum. Fortunately the broad shape of the curve can be reconstructed from observations over a range of wavelengths. There is a great deal of gas and dust in our Galaxy, so nearly all measurements of stars suffer some absorption of the light. As long as the light is absorbed fairly evenly, the wavelength of the star's emission curve peak will not be changed and the true temperature will be obtained. Sometimes the dust can absorb the blue light much more strongly than the red light. In this case the peak would be shifted to the red end of the spectrum and the temperature measured for the star would be too low. The temperature estimates are reasonably accurate even though the observing conditions may be difficult.

Spica exhibits a good example of a radiation curve. It has a surface temperature of 20 000 K, is blue-white in appearance and has a mass of perhaps 20 times that of the Sun. The high pressure and density at its centre makes it burn its hydrogen fuel much faster than the Sun, so it will have a much shorter lifetime.

Another example is Antares, a supergiant at a temperature of 3000 K. It is orange in appearance, has a mass of perhaps 10 times that of the Sun, and has evolved off the main sequence and expanded its outer layers. Its radius is at least as large as the distance between the Sun and the Earth. It is burning hydrogen and helium in its very hot core. Its large surface area means that the low surface temperature is sufficient for it to radiate away the energy being produced.

Spica

Antares

4.3 Wien's displacement law and Stefan's law

Wien's displacement law

If you examine the Planck curves (see Fig 2) you can see that the peaks move to the left (lower wavelength) as the temperature increases. Consider a star heating up as it

starts its life. Its colour changes from red, through orange and yellow, to white. It is then a little hotter than our Sun. If the star continues to heat up it will become pale blue. Look at the downward slope of the right-hand side of the high temperature curves. It does not matter how hot the star becomes, the blue light will always be more intense than the other colours.

The relationship between the wavelength at the peak of the spectrum and the temperature of the blackbody is given by **Wien's displacement law**:

Peak wavelength × temperature = constant;

$$\lambda_{max}T = \text{constant} = 2.9 \times 10^{-3} \text{ m K}$$

where λ_{max} is the wavelength (in m) at the peak and T is the temperature (in kelvin).

(Be careful not to become confused by the units. They are metre kelvin, not millikelvin.)

Rearranging the formula gives:

$$\lambda_{max} \propto \frac{1}{T}$$

where T is in kelvin. In other words, peak wavelength is inversely proportional to the absolute temperature.

Q 2 If you take a photograph indoors using normal light bulbs, the image will look rather yellow. Use this fact to estimate the temperature of the light bulbs by referring to the Planck radiation curves.

An example of an indoor photograph taken using daylight film but illuminated by a tungsten filament bulb

3 A photographic flash gun produces a rather bright white light. Use the curves to predict the temperature inside the flash tube. Compare this to the temperature of the Sun's surface.

Stefan's law

It is possible to add up all the energy given out by one square metre of a blackbody. The energy from all wavelengths of the Planck radiation curve is summed and all the directions that the radiation can escape are taken into account. Thus the total energy radiated each second from a perfect radiator (blackbody) at an absolute temperature T is **the area under a Planck curve**. When all this is done, the result is Stefan's law (also called the Stefan–Boltzmann law):

$$M = \varepsilon\sigma T^4$$

where M is the **power** radiated per square metre, ε is the emissivity (1 for a blackbody and < 1 for real surfaces), σ is the Stefan constant (5.67×10^{-8} W m^{-2} K^{-4}) and T is the absolute temperature (in kelvin). The formula shows that a small rise in temperature means a large increase in the power emitted.

The original discovery was made in 1879 by the Austrian physicist Josef Stefan. He performed experiments that showed that the total radiant energy from a blackbody is proportional to the fourth power of its temperature. By 1889, another Austrian physicist, Ludwig Boltzmann, was able to derive this result from first principles using the laws of thermodynamics. This was an important step towards the quantum theory of radiation.

The inverse square law

The ancient Greeks had a wonderful model of the Universe (Fig. 3). They thought that all the planets and stars were fastened on to one of eight crystalline spheres. The inner spheres were the homes for the Moon, Mercury and Venus. The outer spheres held the other planets, with the outermost one holding the fixed stars. We can use this idea of the crystalline sphere to derive a formula for the intensity of a star.

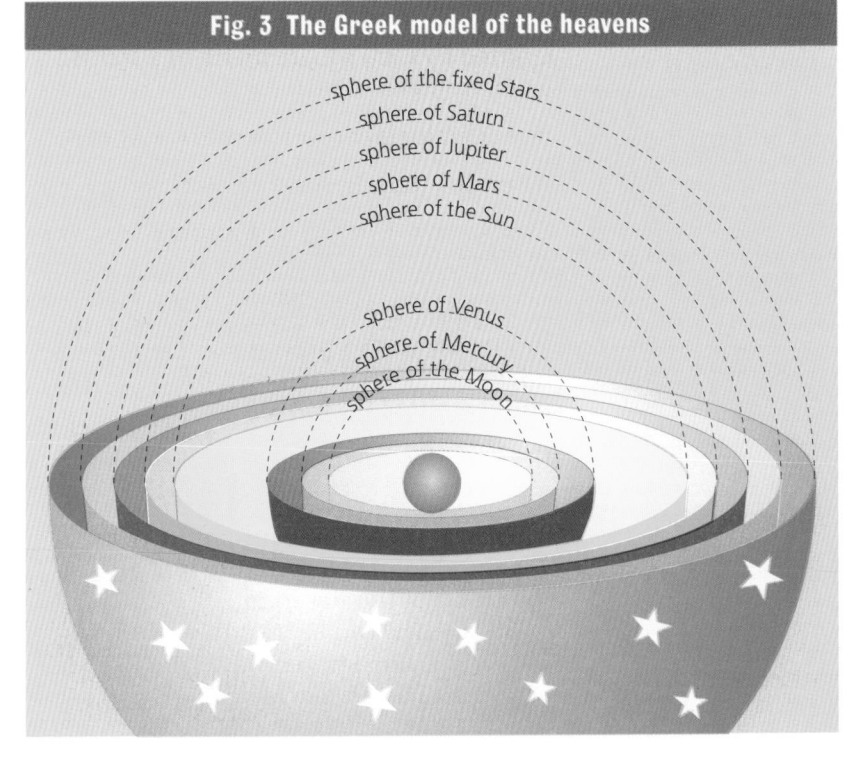

Fig. 3 The Greek model of the heavens

sphere of the fixed stars
sphere of Saturn
sphere of Jupiter
sphere of Mars
sphere of the Sun
sphere of Venus
sphere of Mercury
sphere of the Moon

43

Imagine a star at the centre of a glass sphere. All the radiation from the surface of the star must pass out through the sphere. The intensity of radiation from the star is defined as the power that falls on one square metre of the sphere. Now imagine the sphere to be twice the radius. Its area will be four times as large. The power falling on one square metre must have fallen to one-quarter of its original value. This illustrates the inverse square law. If you increase your distance from a source of radiation by a factor of two, then the intensity of the radiation you receive falls by a factor of four. If you increase your distance by a factor of ten then the intensity will be only one-hundredth of the original value.

- Area of sphere of radius $r = 4\pi r^2$
- Area of sphere of radius $10r = 4\pi \times (10r)^2$
  $$= 100 \times 4\pi r^2$$

These two spheres will receive the same amount of energy, so the intensity will be reduced by a factor of 100.

Fig. 4 Calculating the temperature of the Earth

1.37 kW falls on each square metre of the Earth

Total power received from the Sun
= area of Earth's disc × power per square metre
= πr^2 × power per square metre
= $\pi \times (6.37 \times 10^6)^2 \times 1.37 \times 10^3$
= 1.75×10^{17} W

The Earth radiates energy into space. If the surface of the Earth is taken to be a blackbody, then Stefan's law gives

power radiated $\quad=\quad$ surface area of Earth's sphere $\times \sigma T^4$
$\quad=\quad 4\pi r^2 \times \sigma T^4$
$\quad=\quad 4\pi \times (6.37 \times 10^6)^2 \times 5.67 \times 10^{-8} \times T^4$
$\quad=\quad 2.89 \times 10^7 \times T^4$

The Earth is at a constant temperature, so the power received must equal the power radiated, so:

$1.75 \times 10^{17} \quad=\quad 2.89 \times 10^7 \times T^4$

$T^4 \quad=\quad \dfrac{1.75 \times 10^{17}}{2.89 \times 10^7} \qquad$ (Hint: now take the square root twice)

$T \quad=\quad 279$ K
$T \quad=\quad 6\ ^\circ$C

We have ignored the small amount of heat coming from the Earth's core.

Intensity of a star

The intensity, I, of a star is defined as the power per square metre in W m^{-2} *arriving at the observer*. Using the imaginary sphere argument, the intensity of a star may be derived from the **total power output**, P, by:

$$I = \frac{P}{4\pi D^2}$$

where I is the intensity at the observer in W m^{-2}, P is the total power output in W and D is the distance from the observer to the source in m.

If the intensity of the source can be measured and its total output power estimated then its distance from Earth may be calculated.

4 **The solar constant (intensity of the Sun's radiation on Earth) is 1.37 $\times$ 10^3 W m^{-2} and the total output power (luminosity) of the Sun is 3.90 $\times$ 10^{26} W. Use these values to estimate the distance of the Sun from the Earth. Compare your answer with the value in the Appendix.**

It is useful to be able to calculate the total power output of a star from a knowledge of its temperature and radius. The power emitted by each square metre of a star is given by Stefan's law:

power emitted per square metre = $M = \varepsilon \sigma T^4$

Assuming that the star is a blackbody, $\varepsilon = 1$, so:

$M = \sigma T^4$

To calculate the total power, you multiply this by the star's surface area to give the total power output (P), defined as the total power emitted (in watts):

$P = 4\pi r^2 \times M$
$\quad = 4\pi r^2 \times \sigma T^4$

where σ is the Stefan constant in W m^{-2} K^{-4}, T is the absolute temperature in K and r is the radius of the star in m.

Stefan's law can be used to confirm why the Earth is not a frozen wasteland like Mars or a roasted desert like Mercury (Fig. 4).

The Sun has a surface temperature of 5700 K and a radius of 7.0×10^8 m. What surface area would a star of half this temperature need to radiate the same power as the Sun?

Answer: Using $P = \sigma A T^4$, if the power of the two stars is to be the same, then

$$\sigma A_{Sun} T^4_{Sun} = \sigma A_{Star} T^4_{Star}$$

Cancelling and using the formula for the surface area of a sphere:

$$\therefore 4\pi r^2_{Sun} \times T^4_{Sun} = A_{Star} T^4_{Star}$$

$$\therefore 4\pi (7.0 \times 10^8)^2 \times 5700^4 = A_{Star} 2850^4$$

$$\therefore A_{Star} = 9.85 \times 10^{19} \text{ m}^2$$

This area is sixteen times greater than the area for half the temperature.

Key ideas

- Wien's displacement law links the peak wavelength of light emitted by a blackbody to the temperature of the blackbody:

  $$\lambda_{max} T = 2.9 \times 10^{-3} \text{ m K}$$

- Stefan's law links the power emitted per unit area of a blackbody to the temperature of the body:

  $$M = \sigma T^4$$

- The power output of a star can be calculated:

  $$P = \sigma A T^4$$

  where A is the surface area of the star.

- The intensity of a star is inversely proportional to its distance, D, from Earth:

  $$I \propto \frac{1}{D^2}$$

4.4 Was there a big bang?

Have you ever wondered how the Universe began? Did it in fact begin or has it always been here? These two possibilities represented the opposing camps that astronomers occupied in the 1950s and early 1960s.

On the one hand there were the Continuous Creationists. Their story started in 1928 when Sir James Jeans, the English physicist and mathematician, proposed that matter is continuously created throughout the Universe. However, the real work did not start until 1948 when Hermann Bondi, Thomas Gold and Fred Hoyle proposed a detailed theory to overcome a major problem that had developed. The best prediction for the age of the Universe was only one or two billion years. This was clearly in conflict with the age of the oldest rocks on Earth (4.5 billion years) and the oldest stars (5 to 10 billion

years). By allowing matter to be continuously created throughout the Universe it was possible to increase the age estimate to agree better with the ages of the rocks and stars.

On the other hand were the Expansionists. They observed that the galaxies are moving apart and so argued that it must be possible to work back to a starting point. The beginning of the Universe would have been hot and dense. However long ago the big bang occurred, the theory predicted that there would still be some trace of the hot radiation. It is this radiation that the COBE satellite studied.

The original ideas were proposed by Alexander Friedmann and Abbé Georges Lemaître in the 1920s and the modern version was developed by George Gamow and colleagues in the 1940s. This is based on two assumptions: first that Einstein's

1917   Einstein's equations of special relativity.

1922   Einstein's equations solved by Friedmann.

1927   Lemaître suggests that the Universe is expanding from an explosive moment of creation.

1948   Bethe, Gamow and Alpher predict that background radiation will remain as evidence for the big bang. The high temperatures of the fire ball will allow chemical elements to be formed. The phrase 'big bang' was coined by Fred Hoyle, one of the opponents of the big bang theory.

1964   Penzias and Wilson discovered the existence of a uniform background radiation at a temperature of about 3.5 K. Later, more accurate measurement gave the value as 2.73 K.

1980s   Inflation theory. Up to a time just 10^{-34} s after the big bang, the Universe was so hot and dense that there were no separate forces of Nature and it expanded much more rapidly than it does today. This very rapid expansion allowed the Universe to reach its present size and to smooth out any large variations in density. If there had not been this inflationary phase, gravity would have slowed the expansion early on and the Universe would have been much smaller and less uniform.

1992   COBE satellite discovers 'ripples' in the background radiation.

general theory of relativity correctly describes the gravitational interaction of all matter, and second that an observer's view of the Universe depends neither on the direction of observation nor the location (the cosmological principle).

The first experimental evidence came in 1964, when Arno Penzias and Robert Wilson were preparing a microwave dish at Bell Laboratories in Holmdel, NJ, USA. They were working on a radio antenna associated with the first communications satellite. The 6 m long horn antenna was being tested at a wavelength of 7.35 cm. They were attempting to reduce the stray noise in their radio signal, but even with the best electronics and most careful preparation they still had unexplained background noise corresponding to a temperature of 3.5 K (see Fig. 2). Although their signal was very good for any radio receiver, they wanted to understand, and if possible eliminate, the remaining background noise, so they talked to a group of astronomers at the nearby Princeton University. The observations of Penzias and Wilson triggered an interest and soon the two research groups realised that they had found actual proof of the hot big bang theory.

This theory is based on the Universe starting with a fireball about 1.5×10^{10} years ago. The fireball has cooled down ever since, so that it is now only detectable in the microwave region of the spectrum (corresponding to very low temperatures).

When the results were made public, there was an explosion of interest and in a short time virtually all the astronomical community added their support to the hot big bang theory. The continuous creation theory was largely abandoned after the background radiation was detected. The results of the COBE satellite added to the evidence supporting the hot big bang theory.

There is a nice irony in the name 'big bang'. Fred Hoyle, a forthright Yorkshire astrophysicist, had strongly opposed the big bang theory. He was committed to developing the continuous creation theory. In a discussion, he had attempted to brush away the other theory by saying that he did not think creation would have happened in one big bang. It was such a good catch-phrase that it was adopted immediately by the opposing camp!

You can hear a little of the big bang noise on a VHF (FM) radio set. If the set has a mute control, switch it off and then tune to a place where no radio station is heard. A very small fraction of the random hiss you hear comes from the big bang! Modern radio astronomy observations of the cosmic microwave background give its temperature as about 2.7 K.

Stars in all their glory

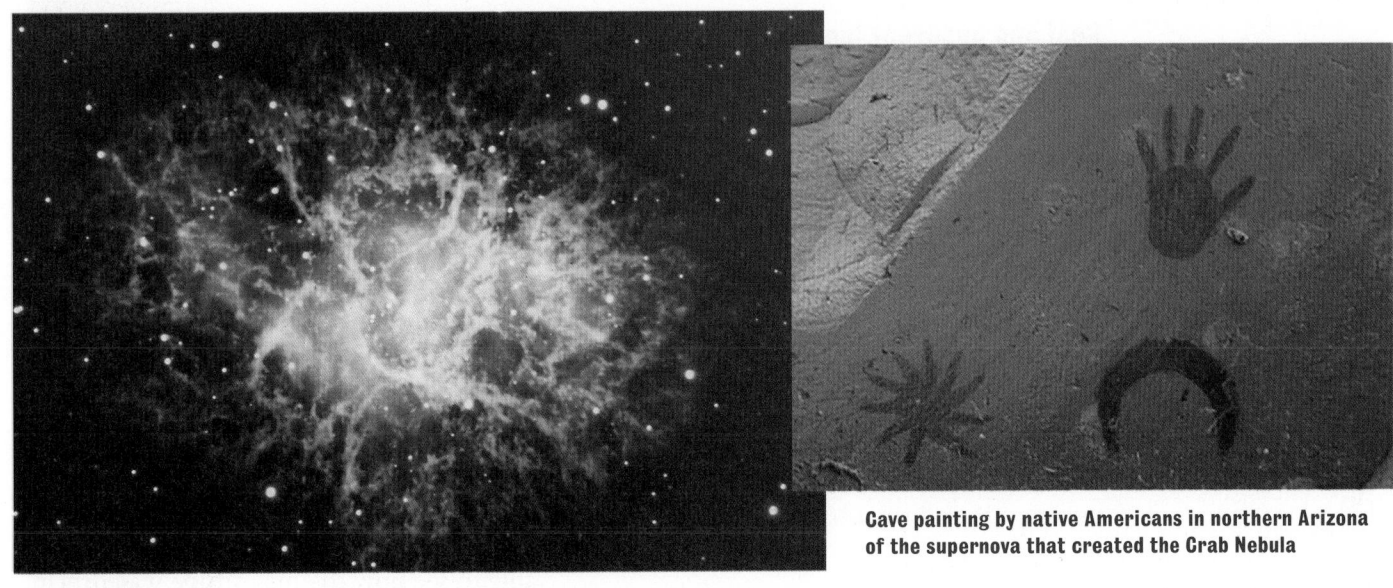

The Crab Nebula, the remnants of the supernova explosion of 4 or 5 July 1054

Cave painting by native Americans in northern Arizona of the supernova that created the Crab Nebula

Early in July 1054 a minor star in the constellation Taurus exploded. The resulting 'guest star', as it was termed by Chinese astronomers, was visible during the day for the following three weeks, initially being about as bright as the full moon, and was visible at night for most of the next two years as a reddish-white object. As well as the Chinese astronomers who made observations of the supernova, native Americans in northern Arizona recorded it in cave paintings. The next we hear of the remains of this supernova (which we now know as the Crab Nebula) is in 1731, when an amateur English astronomer, John Bevis, used a telescope to observe strings of gas and dust. It was named the 'Crab' in the middle of the nineteenth century because of its shape. But what caused the star to explode? How did the supernova behave, and what remains of the star today? Our Sun is a star – will it one day explode in a similar fashion? If it is likely to explode, then when? Astronomers have made observations of vast numbers of stars in all stages of their 'life cycle' and have been able to determine the sequence of events that a star will go through. Naked-eye supernovae are rare events: other supernovae have been observed in the years 185, 393, 1006, 1181, 1572, 1604 and 1987.

5.1 Learning objectives

After working through this chapter, you should be able to:

- **know** that stars can be described in terms of their apparent magnitudes;

- **work** with the units of distance used by astronomers;

- **calculate** the absolute magnitude of a star;

- **describe** the star classification system used by astronomers;

- **classify** a star when details of its spectrum are known;

- **place** stars on the Hertzsprung–Russell diagram;

- **understand** that most visible stars fall on the main sequence;

- **explain** how stars change as they run out of fuel.

5.2 Classification of stars by magnitude

Real and apparent luminosity

The brightness of a star is determined by the amount of radiation received from it. This will depend on both how powerful it is and how far away it is. Stars can be classified in this way to make naked-eye identification easy. Imagine you are at a sports stadium. Which is brighter, the 100 watt light bulb in the entrance kiosk or the stadium floodlights? The answer may seem obvious, but the single bulb will *appear* brighter close to, if compared to the floodlights at a distance of a few hundred metres. The apparent brightness depends on the power of the lamp and the distance between it and the observer. Similar problems apply to observations of stars.

Ever since the time of the ancient Greek astronomers, Hipparchus and Ptolemy, the visible stars have been divided into six magnitude groups. The brightest were called **first magnitude** and the ones that you can only just see with the unaided eye were called **sixth magnitude**. These magnitudes are called **apparent magnitudes** because they depend not only on how brightly the star is shining but also on how distant it is from the Earth.

The magnitude scale can be illustrated by studying the photograph of the 'W'-shaped constellation Cassiopeia. These stars are always visible in the night sky of the northern hemisphere. If you also study the accompanying map (Fig. 1), you will be able to see how the magnitude scale fits in with the image.

The five-magnitude difference between the brightest stars and the faintest stars was found to correspond to a factor of 100 in the intensity (power per unit area) detected by an observer. It was then proposed that all the magnitude steps should be in the same ratio, leading to a logarithmic scale. As five magnitude differences cover a factor of 100, each magnitude difference will cover a factor of the fifth root of 100:

$$100^{0.2}:1 = 2.512:1$$

As a result, a star of magnitude 2 is 2.512 times brighter than a star of magnitude 3, and a star of magnitude 1 is 2.512 times brighter than a star of magnitude 2.

Because of the way the apparent magnitude scale was set up, first magnitude stars have a magnitude of 1 and faint stars (those that are just visible without using a telescope) have a magnitude of 6 (Fig. 2). Initially magnitude was applied only to stars, and only to those stars visible without the use of telescopes. Therefore, the scale of 1 to 6 was quite reasonable. However, since the magnitude scale was introduced, it has been applied to objects brighter than the brightest stars. As a result, the scale now needs to involve negative magnitudes: for example, the Sun has an apparent magnitude of −26.7 and the full moon has an apparent magnitude of −11.

Fig. 1 Magnitude of stars in Cassiopeia

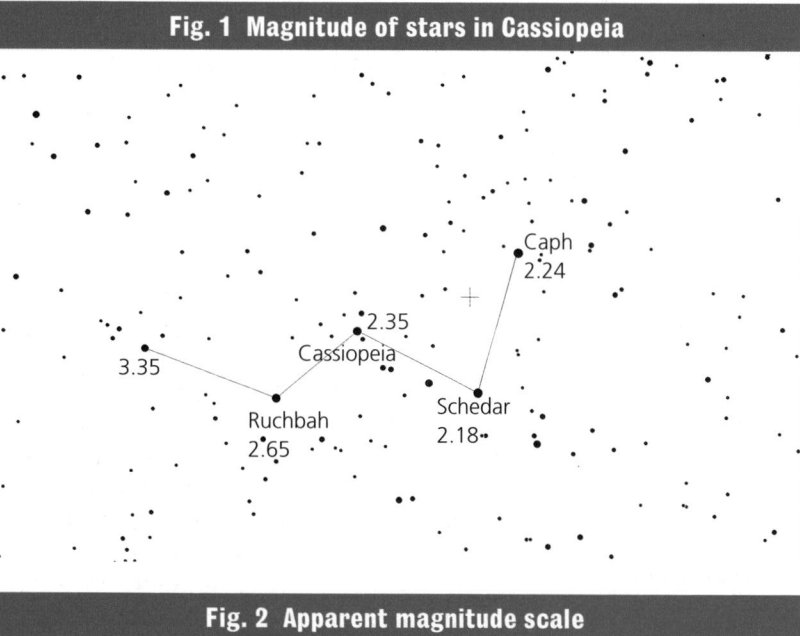

Fig. 2 Apparent magnitude scale

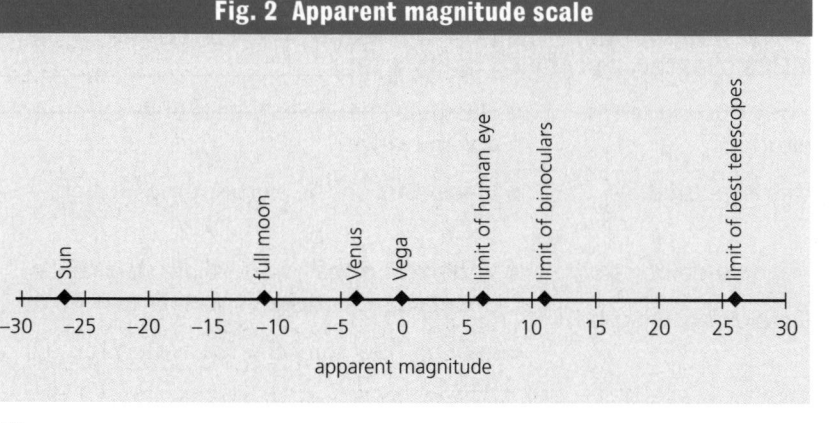

apparent magnitude

The magnitude scale has also been applied to objects so faint that they are only visible using telescopes. Such faint objects have magnitudes that are greater than +6. Objects of apparent magnitude +11 are the faintest observable using binoculars, while the faintest object observable with a large telescope has an apparent magnitude of about +26.

Absolute magnitude

If you want to compare the stars in the sky, the problem is that they are all at different distances from the Earth. To simplify matters

it is convenient to imagine that all stars are placed at one particular distance from the Earth. Astronomers have chosen a standard distance of 23.6 light-years or 10 parsecs (see Chapter 6 for the definition of a parsec). The apparent magnitudes of the stars are adjusted as if the star had been moved to a distance of 10 parsecs; this adjusted value is the **absolute magnitude** (M).

The difference between the apparent magnitude (m) and the absolute magnitude (M) can be used to calculate the distance between a star and the Earth (see Chapter 6, page 65).

Key ideas

- The magnitude of an astronomical body is a measure of its brightness.

- Apparent magnitude, m, is the magnitude as observed, corrected for atmospheric absorption.

- The brightest stars have $m = 1$, the faintest stars visible to the unaided eye have $m = 6$.

- Absolute magnitude, M, is the apparent magnitude a body would have at a distance of 10 parsecs from the observer.

5.3 Classification of stars by spectral type

The easiest way to classify stars is by their brightness. However, classifications can be made more useful by including details of the colour of the stars. The colour of a star is a good guide to its temperature: the hotter it is the bluer it looks (see Section 4.3); but just considering the colour of a star does not provide much information

about the star's chemical composition. For that you need a detailed spectrum.

It is easy to split sunlight into the colours of the rainbow using a prism (Fig. 3). There is little detail visible in such a solar spectrum, except that all the colours are of much the same brightness. However, if the sunlight falls on to a fine slit before it hits the prism, much more detail is apparent. The spectrum is full of fine dark lines parallel to the slit. These lines correspond to colours absorbed by the atoms of various elements. The spectrum is an **absorption spectrum** and the dark lines in the spectrum can be linked to particular elements.

The absorption occurs in the slightly cooler layer of gas and ions just above the visible surface of the Sun. The temperature in this layer is high enough to excite many hydrogen atoms to have their electron in the second level or shell ($n = 2$). From this state the electron can be excited by absorbing a photon from the Sun's surface. The electron moves up to a higher level

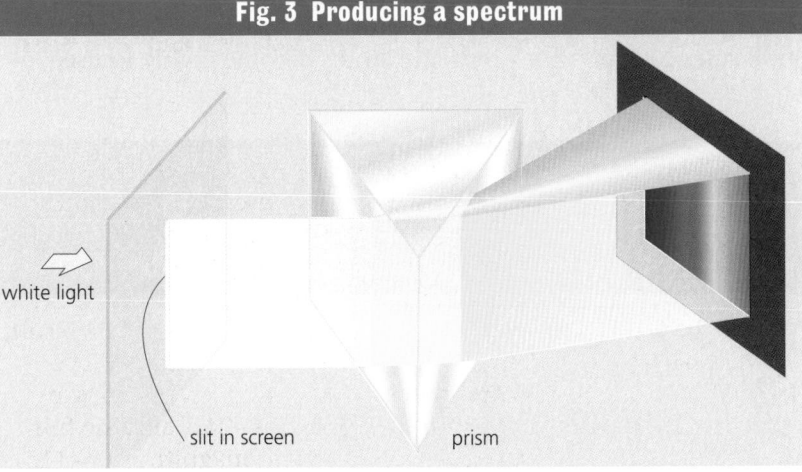

Fig. 3 Producing a spectrum

white light

slit in screen   prism

49

and in doing so produces the characteristic Balmer absorption spectrum of hydrogen. Jumps to levels 3, 4, 5 or 6 produce absorption lines in the visible part of the spectrum. See *CAMS Physics Core*, p. 138, Fig. 7.

Astronomers used a spectrometer (a sophisticated version of the fine slit and prism discussed above) to show that the gas surrounding the Sun contained atoms of most of the light elements. The experiment can also be carried out with the light from a star. Unfortunately, stars are so faint that you need a reasonable sized telescope and photographic film to capture a spectrum.

An absorption spectrum from the Sun

In early observations, absorption spectra from stars were of poor quality. The images were grainy and the spectral lines indistinct, but the main lines could be linked to gaseous hydrogen. With time, techniques improved and spectra were obtained for many bright stars. Astronomers were then in a position to create a detailed classification system for stars.

A good stellar spectrum can reveal the elements present in the stellar atmosphere and whether the elements are neutral or ionised. This is a further guide to the temperature of the gas. Broadly speaking, if the temperature is low, molecules can form. At higher temperatures molecules cannot

survive and only single atoms exist. At even higher temperatures all atoms are ionised.

The spectra of many stars were recorded and it became possible to identify a number of distinct classes. These were *originally* in alphabetical order. The classes were based on the complexity of the spectra and were placed in order of decreasing temperature. However, the classifications were modified as the understanding of stars improved, so the list became:

O, B, A, F, G, K, M, R, N, S.

(The mnemonic 'Oh, Be A Fine Girl, Kiss Me Right Now, Sweetheart!' is attributed to the American astronomer Henry Norris Russell, see below.)

Classes R and N have since been merged into class C. From class O to class M there is a steady decrease in temperature. After class M this pattern is lost. We will only consider classes O to M here.

Spectral classes

The details of the spectral classes are shown in Table 1. The continuum emission spectrum comes from the surface of the star (the photosphere) and is a good approximation to a blackbody spectrum at the temperature of the surface. For a star like the Sun it contains reasonably equal amounts of all colours.

The main trends disclosed are:
- All the spectral lines are seen in absorption against the continuum emission of the star.
- At high temperatures much ultraviolet light is emitted from the surface of the star and atoms become highly ionised.

A detailed high-resolution stellar absorption spectrum

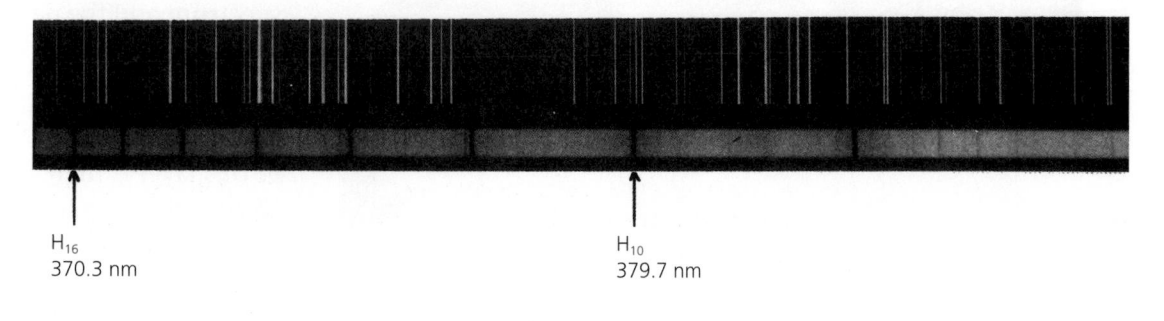

H₁₆
370.3 nm

H₁₀
379.7 nm

Table 1 Classification of stars by spectral type				
Type	Examples	Temperature	Colour	Absorption caused by
O	10 Lacertae	greater than 25 000 K	blue, with much ultraviolet radiation	• Hot enough to singly ionise He • C, N and O doubly ionised • Si is triply ionised
B	Rigel, Spica	11 000–25 000 K	blue, with ultraviolet radiation	• He neutral • Balmer lines seen for H ($n = 2$) • C and O singly ionised • Si is doubly ionised
A	Sirius, Vega	7500–11 000 K	blue, with some ultraviolet radiation	• H still excited • Mg and Si singly ionised (strong) • Ca singly ionised (weak)
F	Procyon	6000–7500 K	blue-white	• Ca, Fe and Cr singly ionised • cool enough for some neutral metals to exist • weak lines from H
G	The Sun, Capella	5000–6000 K	yellow-white	• Ca singly ionised (strong) • too cool for many metal ions to exist
K	Arcturus, Aldebaran	3500–5000 K	orange	• molecules of CH and CN absorb radiation • neutral metals predominate • blue continuum weak
M	Betelgeuse, Antares	less than 3500 K	red	• strong absorption by molecules, particularly TiO • neutral metals present • red continuum strong

- At medium temperatures, the ionisation is usually single and the continuum emission peak of the surface moves into the visible.
- At low temperatures, molecules are able to form and the continuum peak moves into the red.

The lines from isolated atoms and ions and the bands from isolated molecules extend from the ultraviolet region of the electromagnetic spectrum, through the visible and infrared regions, and into the radio spectrum. The spectral lines are studied because they provide important information about the temperature of the star, its density and its velocity (by calculating the Doppler shift of a particular line, see Chapter 3).

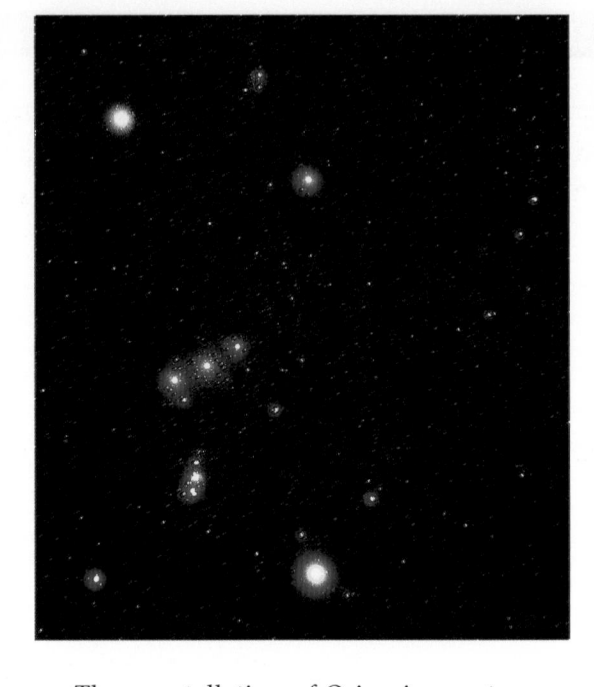

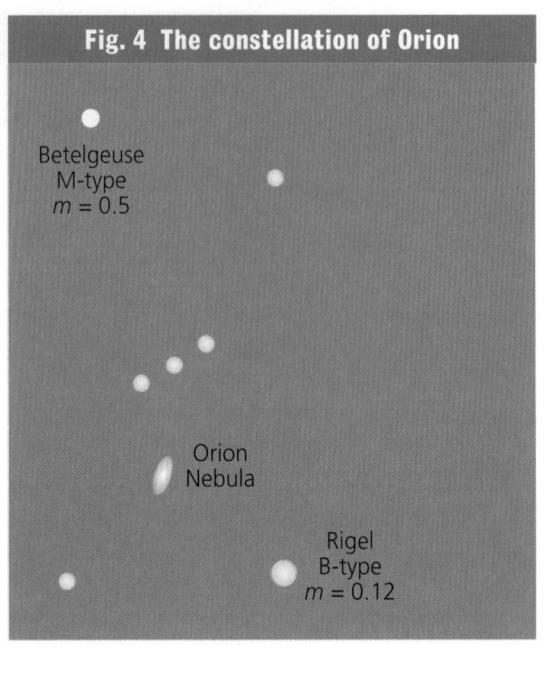

Fig. 4 The constellation of Orion

Betelgeuse
M-type
$m = 0.5$

Orion
Nebula

Rigel
B-type
$m = 0.12$

The constellation of Orion is easy to spot in the autumn and winter skies. It has two stars of particular interest: Betelgeuse is an M-class red giant (slightly variable) and Rigel is a B-class blue star (Fig. 4). Their apparent magnitudes (m) are very similar, but Betelgeuse is noticeably orange, even to the naked eye.

The Sun and its surroundings

The hot gaseous atmosphere surrounding the Sun (or any star) causes absorption and emission lines. The absorption lines were first reported by Fraunhofer in 1814. He saw them in sunlight, in moonlight and in the light from Venus. From this he correctly concluded that the Moon and Venus shone by reflecting light from the Sun.

The visible disc (photosphere) of the Sun emits yellow-white light with no spectral lines (Fig. 5). As the light passes through the slightly cooler 'reversing layer', absorption occurs. This layer is called 'reversing' because the temperature first falls and then rises again with increasing distance from the surface.

The chromosphere is seen at times of total eclipse as a thin pinkish band on the rim of the Sun. Both the chromosphere and corona are tenuous and have little effect except to add faint emission lines. These emission lines are only seen easily at times of total eclipse.

The discovery of helium was prompted by observations of the solar spectrum. Fraunhofer observed new absorption lines not previously seen during experiments on terrestrial materials. The discovery of these lines resulted in helium being identified on the Earth.

Fig. 5 The structure of the Sun

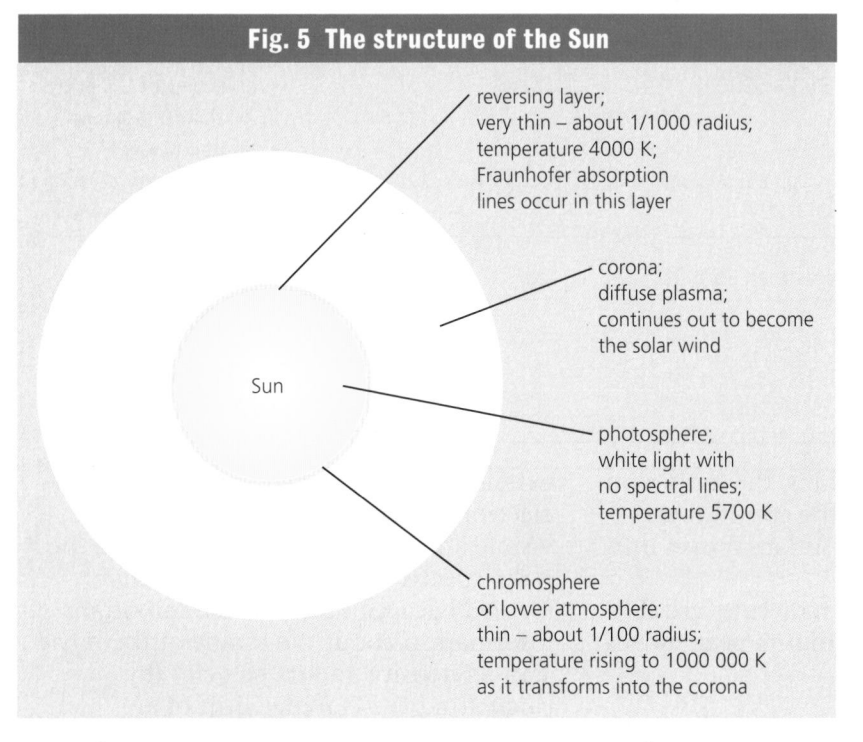

Sun

reversing layer;
very thin – about 1/1000 radius;
temperature 4000 K;
Fraunhofer absorption
lines occur in this layer

corona;
diffuse plasma;
continues out to become
the solar wind

photosphere;
white light with
no spectral lines;
temperature 5700 K

chromosphere
or lower atmosphere;
thin – about 1/100 radius;
temperature rising to 1000 000 K
as it transforms into the corona

Key ideas

- Stars can be classified according to their spectral details, which indicate their temperature and chemical composition.

- The classification is O, B, A, F, G, K, M from hottest to coolest.

- Type O are blue, are at over 25 000 K and are surrounded by ionised helium.

- Type M are red, are at less than 3000 K and are surrounded by molecules and neutral atoms.

5.4 The Hertzsprung–Russell diagram

It took astronomers many years to classify a large representative sample of stars in our Galaxy. The results can be plotted on a graph, with the vertical axis being the absolute magnitude of the stars and the horizontal axis being the spectral class of the stars (which is related to the temperature of the star). Ejnar Hertzsprung (1911) and Henry Norris Russell (1913) independently plotted this type of graph, so it has been named after them – the Hertzsprung–Russell (HR) diagram (Fig. 6).

There are four main regions in the HR diagram:
- the main sequence
- the giant region
- the supergiant region
- the white dwarf region.

Also plotted on the HR diagram are some bright stars that can be seen with the naked eye.

The life cycle of a star similar to our Sun can be traced using the HR diagram (Figs. 6 and 7). Briefly the stages are as follows.

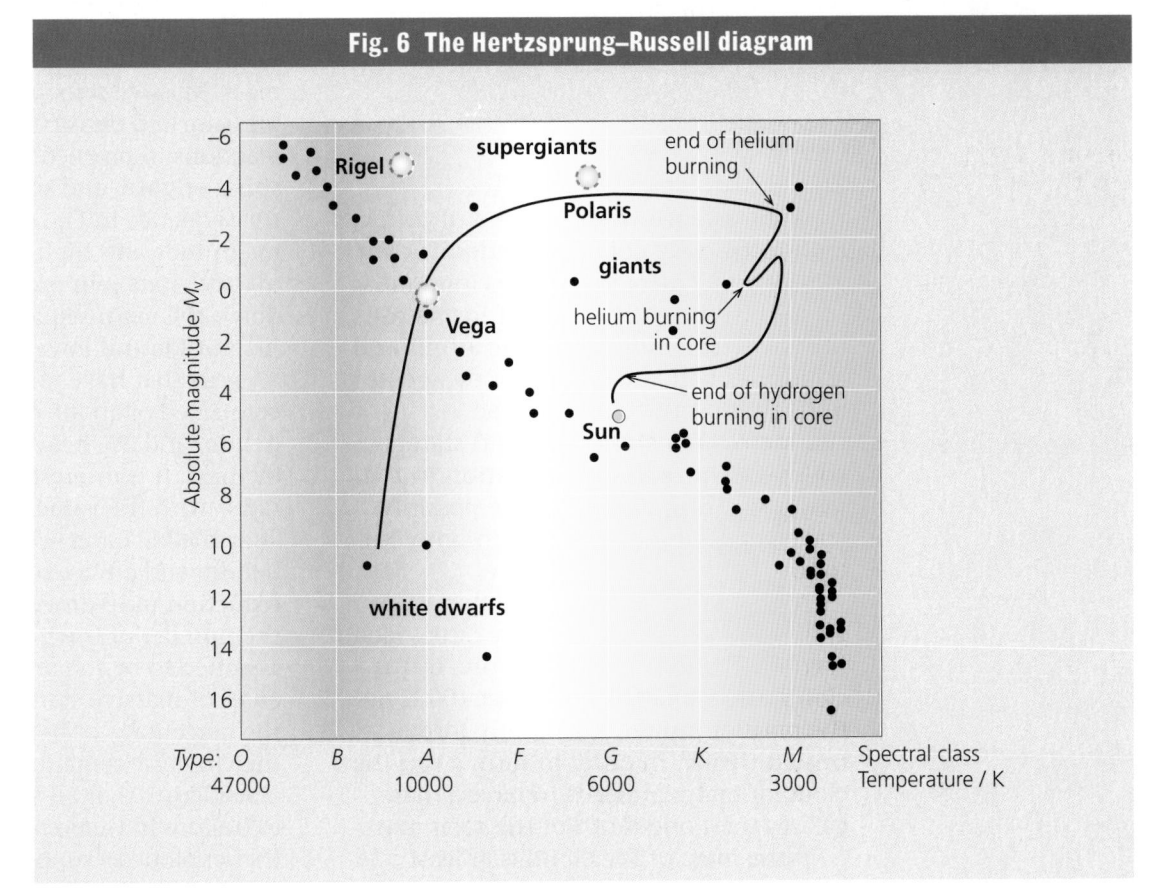

Fig. 6 The Hertzsprung–Russell diagram

Fig. 7 The life cycle of a star

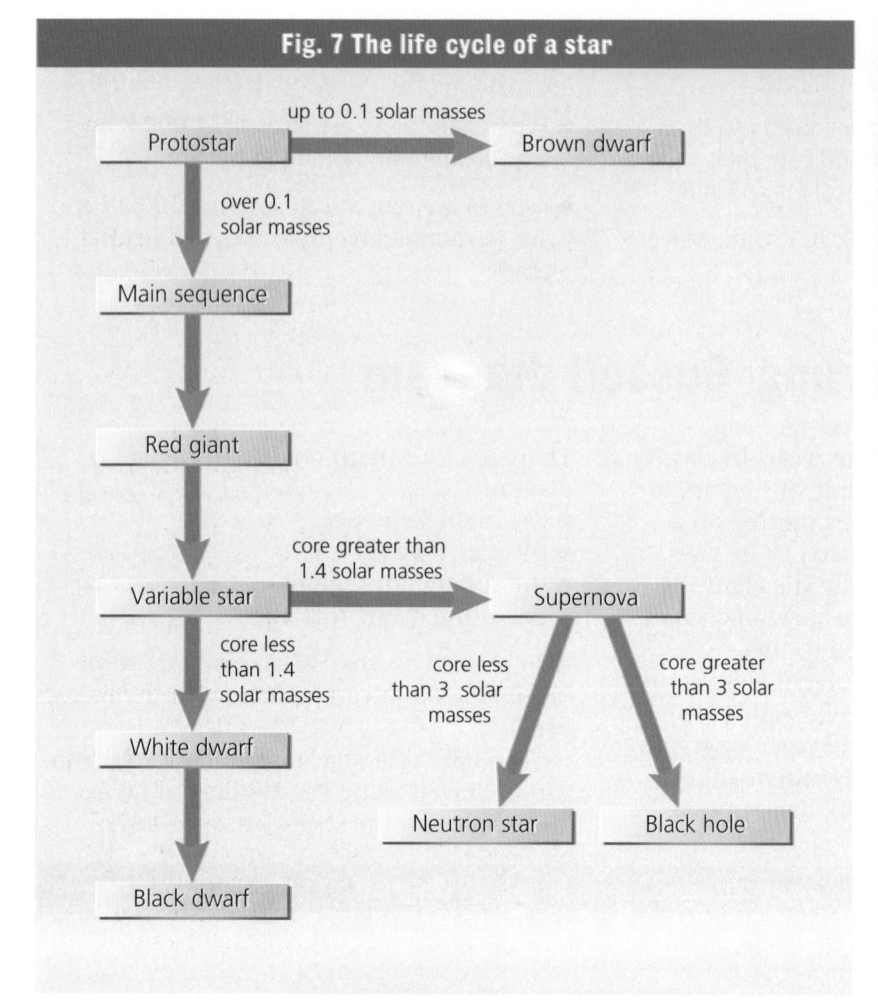

up to 0.1 solar masses
Protostar → Brown dwarf

over 0.1 solar masses
↓
Main sequence
↓
Red giant
↓
Variable star — core greater than 1.4 solar masses → Supernova

core less than 1.4 solar masses
↓
White dwarf
↓
Black dwarf

Supernova:
core less than 3 solar masses → Neutron star
core greater than 3 solar masses → Black hole

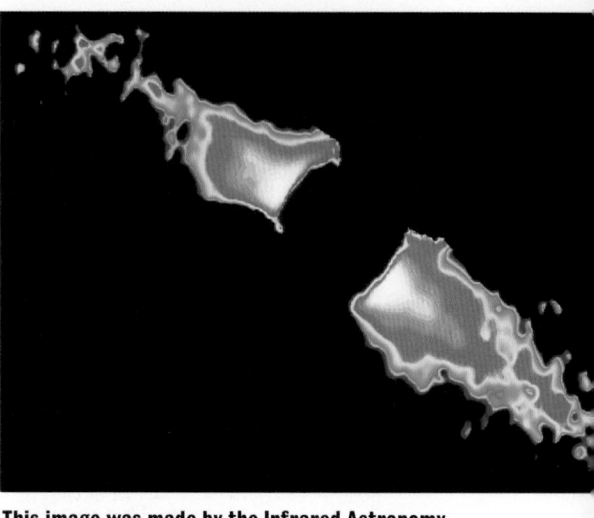

This image was made by the Infrared Astronomy Satellite (IRAS) and shows the cool emissions from the disc-shaped dust cloud round a nearby star; this dust cloud may form planets.

heat up at its centre sufficiently to allow nuclear fusion to start. For hydrogen to be fused into helium a temperature of about 4×10^6K is required. A star is born!

The main sequence

Newly formed stars join the **main sequence** at a point that relates to their mass. Massive stars have a high internal pressure and density. This allows the fusion reactions to proceed rapidly. These stars shine brightly and so join at the top left of the sequence in Fig. 6 (a large absolute magnitude and high temperature). Less massive stars join progressively further down the main sequence (lower absolute magnitude and lower temperature).

Stars that have formed recently are composed of about 73% hydrogen, 25% helium and 2% heavier elements, measured by mass. It is interesting to compare these ratios with the values predicted for just after the big bang – 75% hydrogen, 25% helium and a trace of lithium. The reduction in hydrogen and the growth in the number of the heavier elements is assumed to be the result of fusion in the cores of massive stars. Perhaps surprisingly, the percentage of helium in the free gas of the Universe remains fairly constant, considering that all stars convert hydrogen to helium in their cores. However, stars that explode as supernovae convert most of this helium into heavier elements. Stars

A star is born when a cloud of cold gas and dust slowly collapses under its own gravitational attraction. The cloud must be cold in the early stages of formation, otherwise the motions of the atoms and molecules will allow them to escape. It is unlikely that the cloud will be symmetrical or stationary as it starts to collapse. This will cause rotation in the newly forming star and quite possibly leave a disc of material that might go on to form planets.

As the collapse continues, the gravitational potential energy of the cloud is converted into heat at its core. If the cloud is too small, up to about 100 times the mass of Jupiter, it will only form a **brown dwarf**. In order to form a star the cloud of material needs to have a mass greater than one-tenth of the solar mass.

If the mass of the cloud is at least one-tenth the mass of our Sun, the material will that do not explode keep most of the helium locked up in their cores.

Stars spend most of their life on the main sequence and evolve off it when they finish their hydrogen-burning phase. For a star like our Sun the time on the main sequence will be about 10 billion years. For a star of 15 times the mass of our Sun, the lifetime will be as short as 10 million years.

Stars of up to about four solar masses are able to convert hydrogen to helium by nuclear fusion and, perhaps, convert some helium to carbon. Stars of greater mass, and hence with high internal temperatures, are able to create other elements in their cores, with iron the heaviest element created.

Leaving the main sequence

When a star like our Sun finishes the fusion of hydrogen to helium in its core, it will leave the main sequence. Its outer layers expand to form a red-hot gas cloud and it becomes a **red giant**. Fusion of hydrogen into helium and perhaps carbon continues part way out from the centre. The outer layers are red hot and have a large surface area. This explains why the position of the giants on the HR diagram is to the right (cool) and near the top (luminous).

Eventually the outer layers of the giant are pushed off into space, leaving behind the core of the star. The star is in the process of becoming a **white dwarf**. A white dwarf has finished generating heat from the fusion of helium from hydrogen, but it is still very hot and so is rather blue. It has probably lost more than half its mass and has become very dense under the force of its own gravity. This means that it has a small surface area and so is rather faint. These dwarf stars therefore occupy the lower (faint) left (hot) part of the HR diagram.

If the star is more than a few times the mass of the Sun, it will evolve off the main sequence and it too will become a red giant. However, its core goes on to fuse helium into carbon and heavier elements up to iron. At this point no further energy can be extracted from the fusion. The core then collapses and a massive explosion results – such as the Crab supernova.

The vast bulk of the star is blasted away, leaving a small core behind. The core is composed of pure neutrons – a **neutron star** – and is very dense. It emits so little light that it does not feature on the HR diagram. If the core is sufficiently massive it will collapse to form a **black hole**.

5.5 Types of star

The bright main-sequence star Sirius and its tiny companion, Sirius B; Sirius B is a white dwarf and is only about five times the diameter of the Earth, but it has a mass similar to that of the Sun.

White dwarfs

White dwarfs are at the end of their fusion lives. Although they have high surface temperatures they are using residual heat and gravitational potential energy to shine. Eventually they cool to be **black dwarfs**. As the dwarf state is the end point for all lower mass stars, dwarfs might well constitute a significant proportion of the mass of the Universe.

White dwarfs have densities of between $2.5 \times 10^7 \, kg \, m^{-3}$ and $6 \times 10^{11} \, kg \, m^{-3}$. (Compare this to the density of water which is $1.0 \times 10^3 \, kg \, m^{-3}$.) These very high values indicate that their material is so compressed that the electron shells have collapsed and the nuclei are almost touching each other. This is called 'electron degenerate' matter. The star is prevented from collapsing further by the pressure

caused as the electrons attempt *not* to occupy identical states. (Compare the situation of electrons in the shells of an atom and the Pauli exclusion principle.) The dwarfs must contain *less* than 1.4 solar masses of material (the Chandrasekhar limit), otherwise the gravitational forces overcome the electron degeneracy pressure and the collapse into a neutron star is inevitable. The absolute magnitude of white dwarfs is about +10 and they occur in classes O, B, A, F and G.

Brown dwarfs

Brown dwarfs are main-sequence stars of low mass and low luminosity. They have insufficient mass to raise their core temperatures to start nuclear fusion. Stars of less then 0.1 solar masses never start fusion reactions. They shine with energy released as the gas they are made of falls inwards under gravity, releasing gravitational potential energy. (Be careful in using the classification system. Not all red/brown stars are giants and not all dwarf stars are white.)

Giants

Giant stars are at least as massive as our Sun and are towards the end of their hydrogen-burning phase. They have an expanded outer gas shell, their core has collapsed a little and the temperature has risen to allow helium burning to begin. Hydrogen burning continues in the middle layers of the star. Giants have a large surface area and so can emit much energy, but their surface is quite cool for an active star. Their absolute magnitude is about 0 and they occur in classes F, G, K and M.

Supergiants

These massive stars are between eight and 100 times the mass of our Sun. The very high core temperatures (10^8K) cause the fuel to burn at a prodigious rate. The outer layers have expanded to many times the size of our Sun. Strong winds develop, ejecting material from the star –

particularly noticeable in carbon-rich stars. Once the central hydrogen is used up, helium is fused into carbon and so on up to iron. The carbon in our bodies and the iron we use in industry was made in these stars. Their absolute magnitude is about –10 and they occur in classes A, F, G, K and M.

Population I and Population II stars

Evidence for the existence of massive short-lived stars comes from the two distinct populations of stars found in our Galaxy. Population I stars are relatively young and are found in the spiral arms of the Galaxy. They contain relatively large proportions of heavier elements, indicating that they formed from materials that had undergone nuclear reactions in earlier generations of stars.

Population II stars are relatively old and are found in the spherical halo of the Galaxy. They contain relatively small proportions of the elements heavier than helium. This implies that they formed at an early stage in the lifetime of the Galaxy, before there was time for the heavier elements to be synthesised. They often have high velocities relative to the Sun and to the Galactic plane.

5.6 The death of a star

The size of a star is controlled by the balance between the gravitational attraction pulling inwards and thermal forces pushing outwards. The outward forces are made up of pressure from the hot material and the pressure generated by photons bouncing (scattering) off the particles of the material. A star similar in mass to our Sun will evolve from this equilibrium and enter the red giant phase after fusing the hydrogen and helium in its core.

If the star is greater than about four solar masses it will fuse most of its hydrogen, collapse a little, which will raise its temperature, and then start to fuse helium in its core. It develops an onion-like structure with the inner layers having higher and higher temperatures. In very massive stars, elements up to iron are created in the innermost layers. Synthesising elements

beyond iron requires an energy input, so this process cannot be a source of energy. Without further sources of nuclear energy the core starts to cool. The gravitational forces overcome the thermal forces and the star collapses very rapidly.

In the last few seconds of the collapse, the number of fast neutrons in the core is very high. Iron nuclei absorb the neutrons to create the heavy elements found in the rest of the Galaxy. To obtain the proportions of heavy elements found in our region of the Galaxy it is likely that the material has been through the supernova process about five times.

The compression in the collapsed core is so great that it may well produce a central neutron star. The infalling material collides at the centre and rebounds, throwing off much of the gas in the outer layers of the star. A spectacular explosion results in a billion-fold increase in the brightness of the star that lasts for several weeks. Initially the colour of the star is the red of the giant's gas envelope but, as the ejected material races away, the shock wave heats the debris and the star becomes quite blue. This type of supernova event creates objects such as the Crab Nebula, where the filaments of material are expanding away at over 1000 kilometres per second. The newly formed elements are flung into space and can go on to be included in new stars.

Nebulae, neutron stars and pulsars

The Crab Nebula is a example of a stellar core that must have been a little larger than 1.4 solar masses. As the core of the star collapsed it retained its angular momentum. Its speed of rotation increased, just as ice skaters spin more quickly by pulling in their arms. In the collapse it also retained its magnetic field. The original star would have had a field of about 0.01 tesla. In the compression this was increased to about 10^8 tesla, which is a massively strong magnetic field. (The strongest magnet in your laboratory is about 0.1 tesla.) The resulting core has a spin rate of 30 revolutions per second in an object of about 20 km across. The spinning star is surrounded by a large expanding cloud of debris. **Pulsar** activity occurs when the magnetic field of the core is not aligned with its spin axis. The rotation then causes major disturbances in the ionised debris, heating it strongly and causing the electrons to spiral round the magnetic field lines. This generates large quantities of energy called 'synchrotron radiation' that is identified by its characteristic spectrum. The rotation also acts like a lighthouse, producing pulses of energy that are detectable on Earth. The train of pulses led to the newly discovered objects being called pulsars.

Key ideas

- The Hertzsprung–Russell (HR) diagram plots stars according to their absolute magnitude and spectral class.

- The HR diagram shows a main sequence, a giant region, a supergiant region and a dwarf region.

- The HR diagram can be used to show the stellar evolution from star formation to white dwarf.

- A star may end as a supernova – a huge explosion which may then form a neutron star or a black hole.

5.7 The core of the Sun

Fusion reactions

The Sun creates 91% of its energy by fusing protons in a process called the PP I chain. In this process protons are combined to produce one helium nucleus, a positron, an electron neutrino, a gamma ray and two protons:

$$p^+ + p^+ \rightarrow {}_1^2H + e^+ + \nu_e$$

$${}_1^2H + p^+ \rightarrow {}_2^3He + \gamma$$

$${}_2^3He + {}_2^3He \rightarrow {}_2^4He + p^+ + p^+$$

where e^+ is a positron and ν_e is an electron neutrino.

The probability of two protons encountering each other with sufficient speed to start this reaction is surprisingly low. In the Sun each proton suffers about 10^{14} collisions per second and yet the average time for a fusion reaction to occur is about 10 billion years. However, there are many, many protons, so this is the main energy production route. When the positron-electron annihilation and all other energy is accounted for, the reaction releases 26.8 MeV (4.29×10^{-12} J). This is millions of times more than the energy output from a chemical reaction.

The age of the Sun

Stars of high mass spend a much shorter time on the main sequence than low mass stars. With about one solar mass a star would spend nearly ten billion years before evolving off it. With 15 solar masses it would spend as little as ten million years on it – a short bright-blue existence, a thousand times shorter.

Justifications for taking the age of the Sun to be ten billion years come from looking at the geology of the Earth and the Moon and of the composition of meteorites and comets. Using the half life of isotopes of heavy elements it is possible to estimate the age of the oldest rocks to be 4.55×10^9 years. The Solar System must have formed before this time.

Another check is the rate at which the Sun is emitting energy. If nuclear fusion is the energy source it is possible to use the famous Einstein equation $E = mc^2$ to calculate the rate at which mass is consumed.

 1 **The aim of this question is to show that the Sun has only used up a small fraction of its mass during its lifetime. Look up the solar luminosity in the Data Appendix and use $E = mc^2$ to work out the rate of consumption of mass. Use the mass of the Sun to calculate what percentage of its mass has been burnt, assuming an age of 1.0×10^{10} years.**

Answer:

$$\text{Mass per second} = \frac{\text{Luminosity}}{c^2}$$

$$= \frac{3.9 \times 10^{26}\ \text{W}}{(3.0 \times 10^8\ \text{m s}^{-1})^2}$$

$$= 4.3 \times 10^9\ \text{kg s}^{-1}$$

At this rate, the mass used up in 1.0×10^{10} years is given by:

Total mass consumed =

$4.3 \times 10^9\ \text{kg s}^{-1} \times (1.0 \times 10^{10}\ \text{years} \times 365.25 \times 24 \times 60 \times 60) = 1.37 \times 10^{27}\ \text{kg}$

This is only 0.07% of the Sun's mass of 2.00×10^{30} kg.

It was only about 80 years ago that astronomers and geologists were having intense arguments about the age of the Earth and the Sun. Just before the discovery of fission and fusion, it was argued that the Sun must be shining either by chemical reactions or by shrinking and using the gravitation potential energy released.

2 **An interesting exercise is to work out how long the Sun would shine if it were generating its energy by chemical reactions. Take the well-known energetic reaction of exploding hydrogen with oxygen to form water. Each mole of water produced has a mass of 0.018 kg and yields about 200 kJ of energy. Use the mass of the Sun and its luminosity to calculate the time it will take to run out of fuel. You should find that we should not be here to do the calculation!!**

Answer: The Sun generates 3.9×10^{26} joules of energy per second. This means that it must consume a mass of:

$$\text{Mass per second} = \frac{3.9 \times 10^{26}\ \text{W}}{200\ 000\ \text{J}} \times 0.018\ \text{kg}$$

$$= 3.5 \times 10^{19}\ \text{kg s}^{-1}$$

The time taken to consume the total mass of the Sun if chemical reactions were taking place would be:

$$\text{Total time} = \frac{2.0 \times 10^{30}\ \text{kg}}{3.5 \times 10^{19}\ \text{kg s}^{-1}} = 5.7 \times 10^{10}\ \text{s}$$

This is only 1800 years – far too short!

The temperature of the core

It is possible to estimate the temperature of the core of the Sun using simple physics. If protons are to come close enough to combine in nuclear fusion, they must overcome the electrostatic repulsion of their positive charges. This means that they must have a very high speed, which implies a very high temperature. The estimate is performed by equating kinetic and potential energy:

- The kinetic energy is that of a high-speed proton. For simplicity, the target proton is assumed to be fixed in space.
- The potential energy is that needed to climb the mountain created by the electrostatic repulsion of the two positive charges.

The kinetic energy (E) of a single particle in a gas is given by:

$$E = \frac{3}{2}\,kT$$

where k is Boltzmann's constant in J K^{-1} and T is the absolute temperature in K.

The potential energy (E) required for two charges to approach each other is given by:

$$E = \frac{1}{4\pi\varepsilon_0} \times \frac{QQ}{r}$$

where Q is the charge on the proton in C, r is the separation in m and ε_0 is the permittivity of a vacuum in F m^{-1}.

The distance of closest approach can be calculated by equating these two expressions. If we use 1.6×10^{-19} C as the charge and 2.0×10^7 K as the temperature, the distance can be calculated:

Equating the energies $\dfrac{3}{2}\,kT = \dfrac{1}{4\pi\varepsilon_0} \times \dfrac{QQ}{r}$

Rearranging gives $\;r = \dfrac{1}{4\pi\varepsilon_0} \times \dfrac{QQ}{T} \times \dfrac{2}{3k}$

$$= \frac{1.6 \times 10^{-19}\,\text{C} \times 1.6 \times 10^{-19}\,\text{C} \times 2}{(4 \times \pi \times 8.85 \times 10^{-12}\,\text{F m}^{-1} \times 2.0 \times 10^{7}\,\text{K} \times 3 \times 1.38 \times 10^{-23}\,\text{J K}^{-1})}$$

$$= \quad 5.6 \times 10^{-13}\,\text{m}$$

The size of a small nucleus is approximately 1×10^{-15} m. This answer agrees quite well with the distance of closest approach of single charged particles. Some particles will be travelling much faster than the average speed and so will get much closer. They can then fuse together and release energy.

Transfer of energy

The energy released in the core of the Sun makes its way to the surface by means of radiation and convection. Conduction plays little part in the transfer as the density of material, particularly in the outer layers, is too low.

In the Sun, the fusion core extends to a quarter of the way to the surface and beyond this there is a plasma region out to about 85% of the way to the surface. Radiation is the main means of transport in these regions but it is not easy for the photons to escape. A photon can only travel a fraction of a millimetre in the core before it scatters off a particle! The mean free path only increases to a few centimetres in the outer regions. The whole journey from the centre to the surface takes a photon about 10 million years!

The main transport mechanism for the energy in the last 15% of its journey is convection. In the outer layers the density is quite low, comparable with that of the air on Earth. The strong heating from below causes convection currents to form, carrying the energy outwards.

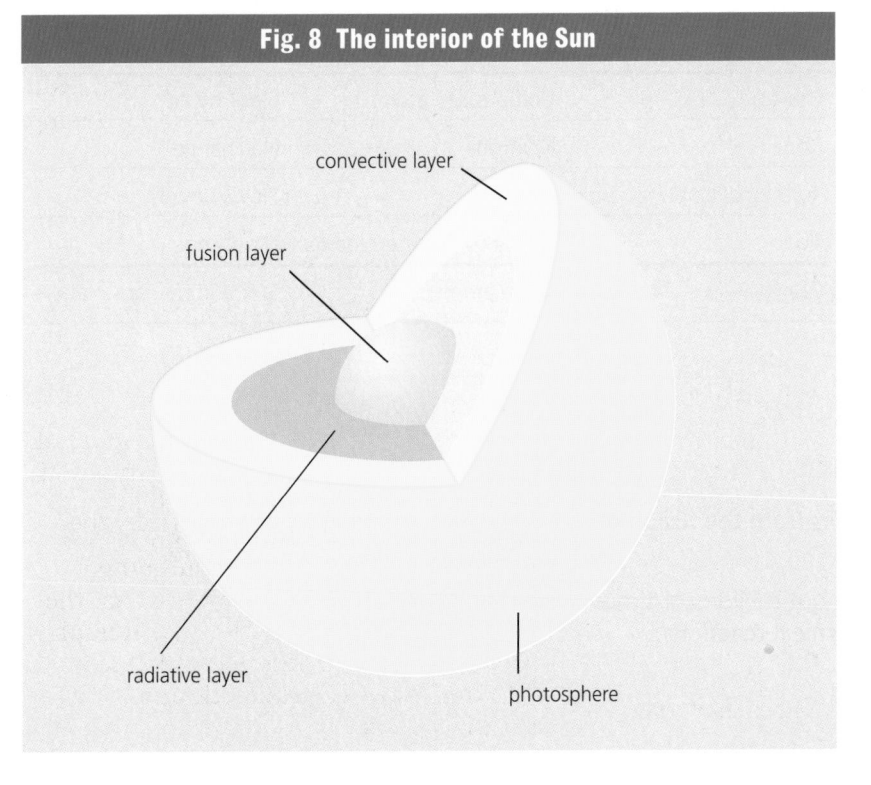

Fig. 8 The interior of the Sun

convective layer

fusion layer

radiative layer

photosphere

Pressure equilibrium

The layers of the Sun are supported against gravitational collapse by pressure from within. When particles collide they exchange momentum and so create a pressure. Although photons have no mass they do have momentum, so that they can also create a pressure during collisions.

The collisions of the particles create conventional gas pressure but the layers of the star are also supported by the pressure of the photons scattering off the particles. This is called radiation pressure.

In stars of about five solar masses the gas and radiation pressures are equal. In smaller stars like our Sun, the gas pressure is the larger, but not by much. In stars with 100 solar masses the radiation pressure dominates. As a star runs out of fuel these sources of pressure reduce and the star collapses.

Table 2					
Type	Mass (Sun = 1)	Place on HR diagram	Energy source	Composition	Will become
Massive star	50	Top left	H, He, C fusion	H, He atoms	Red supergiant
Sun	1	Middle	H fusion	H, He atoms	Red giant
Brown dwarf	0.1	Bottom right	Gravity	H, He atoms	Black dwarf
Red supergiant	>15	Top right	H, He, C fusion	H, He atoms	Supernova
Red giant	>5	Middle right	H, He, C fusion	H, He atoms	Supernova
Supernova	Core > 3	Briefly top left	Fusion of elements up to Fe	H, He plus traces of all elements	Black hole
Supernova	Core < 3	Briefly top left	Fusion of elements up to Fe	H, He plus traces of all elements	Neutron star or white dwarf
White dwarf	< 1.4	Bottom left	Gravity	Compressed atoms	Black dwarf
Neutron star	1.4 to 3	Too faint to plot	None	Neutrons	No change
Pulsar	1.4 to 3	Too faint to plot	Rotational kinetic energy	Neutrons	Slows down
Black hole	>3	No light output	None	Highly compressed matter	No change
Nebula	Many	Too faint to plot	Gravity	H, He atoms	Star and perhaps planets

Key ideas

- The Sun's energy comes from the fusion of hydrogen into helium.

- Nuclear reactions give out millions of times more energy than chemical reactions.

- The Sun is held at its present size by the balance of gravity and pressure.

Distances great and small

Voyager 2 was able to visit Jupiter, Saturn, Uranus and Neptune due to a rare alignment of these outer planets in the late 1970s and 1980s. The space probe will still be sending back data well into the twenty-first century.

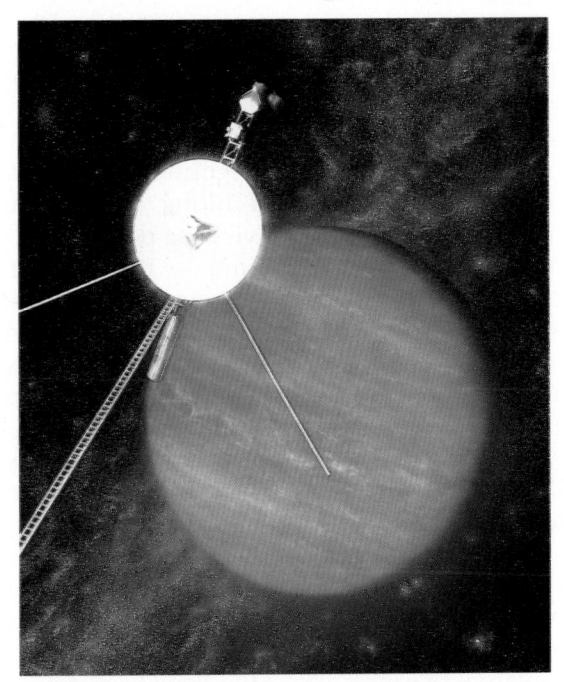

On Wednesday 15 October 1997 the spacecraft Cassini was launched from Cape Canaveral, Florida. Cassini, fuelled by plutonium-powered electrical generators, will reach Saturn in July 2004, having travelled about three billion kilometres. A journey of this length depends on using kinetic energy from other planets to boost the speed given to it by the Titan rockets that launched the spacecraft. Cassini will pass close to Venus (twice, in April 1998 and June 1999), the Earth (in August 1999)

and Jupiter (in December 2000). Each close pass to a planet enables Cassini to gain speed: whilst the spacecraft speeds up considerably, the planet slows down by a minute fraction.

This planetary 'swing-by' technique was used to allow the space probes Voyager 1 and Voyager 2 to travel to Saturn and beyond. Voyager 2 was launched on 20 August 1977, passed Jupiter (July 1979), Saturn (August 1981), Uranus (January 1986) and Neptune (August 1989), and is now heading out of our Solar System at 16 km s^{-1}. Voyager 1 was launched on 5 September 1977, passed Saturn in November 1980 and started to detect radio emissions from the heliopause in May 1993. The heliopause is the outer limit of the influence of the solar wind and is expected to be at least 1.5×10^{13} m from the Sun. Despite the large distances that the Voyager spacecraft have already travelled, and the high speed at which they are travelling, it will take them at least 78 000 years to reach the nearest star. The distances involved in planetary travel seem vast, but pale into insignificance when placed in the context of the distances between stars.

The methods used to measure both interplanetary and interstellar distances are discussed in this chapter.

6.1 Learning objectives

After working through this chapter, you should be able to:

- **explain** how astronomers use parallax to measure the distance to nearby stars;

- **calculate** the distance of stars using their spectra;

- **describe** how variable stars can be used to calculate the distances to nearby galaxies;

- **calculate** the distance to a planet using data from radar transmissions;

- **calculate** the speed of rotation of a planet from radar data.

6.2 Trigonometric (visual) parallax

The method used to measure a particular distance depends on the scale of distance to be measured. A micrometer is used to measure items of a few millimetres, a ruler for distances of a few centimetres, a measuring tape for distances of a few metres, and so on. Methods used to measure larger distances, including measuring distances to nearby stars, involve the use of parallax.

If you take a step sideways, most of the objects in your sight seem to move relative to each other. This apparent movement is called **parallax**. Although you may not realise it, you use parallax all the time to judge distances. You do this without thinking – it is part of the information your brain uses to create a three-dimensional world around you. If two objects are at exactly the same distance from you, they will not seem to move relative to each other when you move. Parallax has been applied to measuring the distances to the nearest stars.

The measurement of distance by trigonometric parallax relies on the Earth orbiting the Sun and so altering our viewing position. As an illustration, suppose that you are looking at an object (say a church spire) that is about a kilometre away against a background of distant hills. If you walk a few metres from side to side, the relative position of the church spire will alter with respect to the background hills. If you know how far you have walked between your two positions and can measure the change in angle between the church spire and a landmark on a distant hill, then you can calculate how far away the church is (Fig. 1).

The far-distant stars and galaxies form the fixed background for parallax measurements of closer stars. During the course of a year, stars within a few hundred light-years move one way, then the other, across this fixed background. This apparent movement is very small, but it is measurable.

Astronomers use several different units to record distance. For example, the nearest star is 4.07×10^{16} m away, a distance that can also be expressed as 4.3 light-years (ly) or 1.3 parsecs (pc). Another unit that is used is the astronomical unit (AU), which was originally defined as the distance from the centre of the Earth to the centre of the Sun, but is now defined as 149 597 870 km.

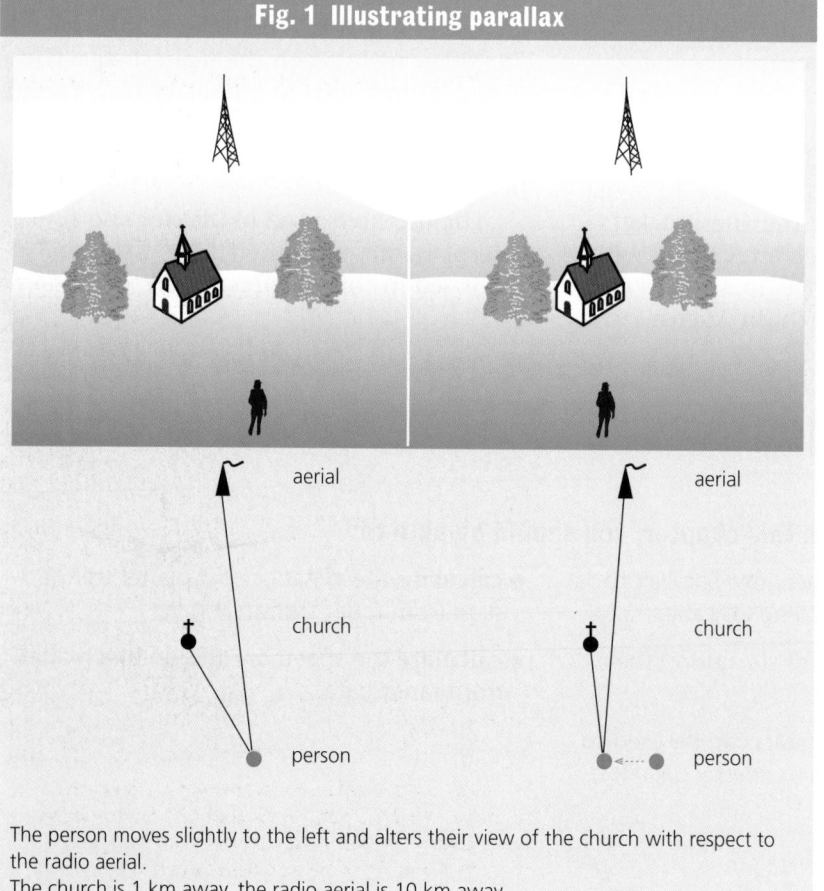

Fig. 1 Illustrating parallax

aerial

aerial

church

church

person

person

The person moves slightly to the left and alters their view of the church with respect to the radio aerial.
The church is 1 km away, the radio aerial is 10 km away

The astronomical unit (AU) used to be based on the distance between the Earth and the Sun

The best way of determining the very small angle involved in visual parallax measurements is to take two photographs, six months apart. The nearby stars seem to shift slightly from one photograph to the other when viewed against the far-distant stars (Fig. 2).

If the change in angle is one second of an arc, the object is said to be at a distance of one parsec (Fig. 3). The smallest angle that can be measured reliably for a single star is about 0.04 seconds of arc. This means that a distance of 25 pc is the maximum measurable distance for single stars using visual parallax.

The only way to measure greater distances is to work with clusters of stars. A globular cluster is a group of stars all quite close to each other relative to their distance from the Earth. The parallax of each individual star would not be accurate enough to be useful. The technique is to average the parallaxes of hundreds of stars in the cluster. Good results can be obtained by this method out to about 50 pc, although much better results can be obtained from the Hipparcos satellite and the Hubble Space Telescope (see photo below). Accuracies of about $\pm 5 \times 10^{-3}$ seconds of arc can be expected, corresponding to a distance of 200 pc.

The Hipparcos Space Astrometry Mission
Hipparcos was a pioneering space experiment dedicated to the precise measurement of the positions, parallaxes

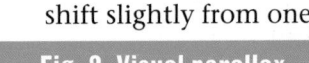

Fig. 2 Visual parallax

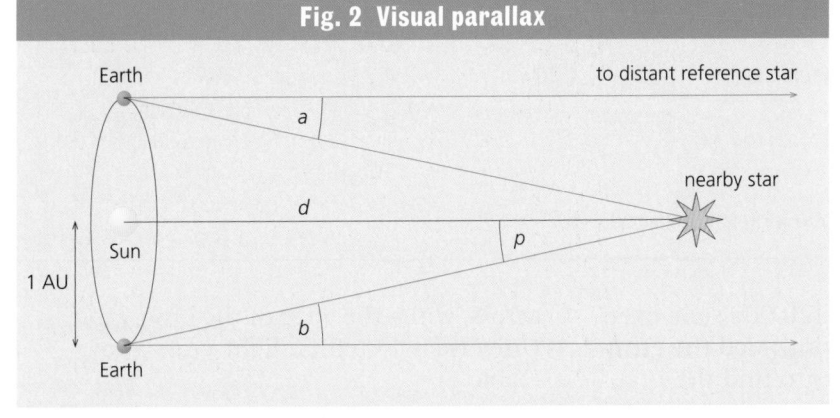

Earth

to distant reference star

a

nearby star

d

Sun

p

1 AU

b

Earth

Fig. 3 Distance units

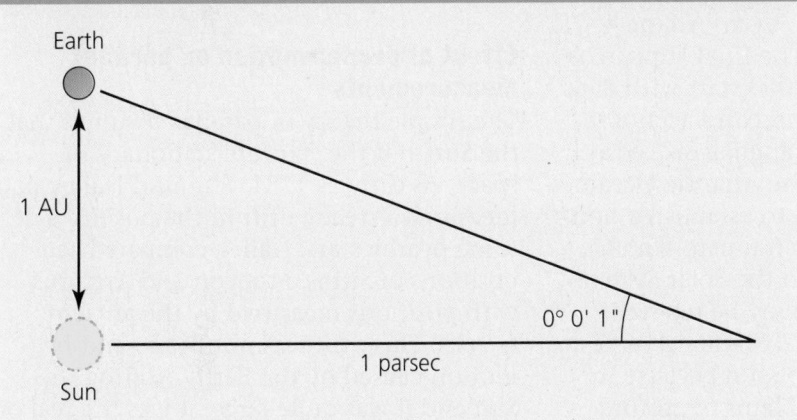

Earth

1 AU

0° 0' 1"

1 parsec

Sun

1 parsec is a unit of length equal to the distance at which a baseline of 1 astronomical unit subtends an angle of one second of arc.

$$\tan(0°0'1") = \frac{1\ AU}{1\ parsec}$$

$$1\ parsec = \frac{1\ AU}{\tan(0°0'1")}$$

$$= \frac{149\ 597\ 870\ km}{4.848 \times 10^{-6}}$$

$$= 3.086 \times 10^{13}\ km$$

$$= 3.086 \times 10^{16}\ m$$

$$1\ year = 365.26 \times 24 \times 60 \times 60\ s = 3.156 \times 10^7\ s$$

$$light\ speed = 2.997 \times 10^8\ m\ s^{-1}$$

$$1\ light\text{-}year = distance\ travelled\ by\ light\ in\ 1\ year$$

$$= 3.156 \times 10^7 \times 2.997 \times 10^8\ m$$

$$= 9.461 \times 10^{15}\ m$$

The Hubble Space Telescope was launched from the Space Shuttle Discovery on 25 April 1990; subsequent space shuttle missions have serviced the telescope, corrected a design fault and replaced various instruments

Table 1 Some astronomical distances			
Distance	Parsecs	Light travel time	m
1 parsec	–	3.26 yr	3.09×10^{16}
1 light-year	0.31	–	9.47×10^{15}
Earth to Sun (1 AU)	4.84×10^{-6}	8.31 min	1.50×10^{11}
Earth to Proxima Centauri (next star)	1.30	4.2 yr	
Earth to Sirius		8.6 yr	8.14×10^{16}
Across Milky Way		10^5 yr	
Earth to Andromeda (neighbouring spiral galaxy)	6.75×10^5		

The Hipparcos satellite

and proper motions of 120 000 stars over its four-year life. This continued the great tradition of astronomers to find the distances to the stars. The project was accepted by the European Space Agency in 1980 and the satellite was launched from Kourou, French Guyana, by an Ariane 4 rocket in August 1989. The final Hipparcos Catalogue contains 120 000 stars with data measured to one milliarcsecond accuracy. This corresponds to the angular size of a golf ball viewed across the Atlantic Ocean. The project has gone on to establish a non-rotating stellar reference frame to which the motions of objects in the Solar System and stars in the Galaxy may be referred. This is an improved Local Standard of Rest.

The satellite was successful because in space it avoided the problems of ground-based astronomical observatories, such as the perturbing atmosphere, lack of all-sky visibility, and gravitational and thermal bending of telescopes. Its sensors swept out one-degree-wide circles on the sky, over and over again. This allowed the positions of the stars in these strips to be measured tens of times. The data was carefully averaged and the final results have been published on CD-ROM for all astronomers to use. The remarkable accuracy of Hipparcos has allowed astronomers to measure, for the first time, distances of tens of thousands of stars in our Galaxy, and the motions of these stars through space.

The distances dealt with so far are still very small compared with those to the most distant objects. Two hundred parsecs is equal to about 650 light-years. The Milky Way, our Galaxy, is 100 000 light-years

across, while the edge of the observable Universe is 15 billion light-years away (Table 1).

 1   Fill in the missing values in Table 1.

Effect of proper motion on parallax measurements

The simple theory of parallax assumes that the Sun and the stars are stationary in space. As early as 1781, Edmund Halley had measured a steady drift in the positions of some nearby stars. Halley compared the positions of Sirius, Procyon and Arcturus with positions measured by the ancient Greeks. This drift was not the to-and-fro motion caused by the Earth orbiting the Sun and it was quite large; it was the real or **proper motion** of the stars. Modern results show the proper motions of Sirius, Procyon and Arcturus to be 1.324, 1.247 and 3.678 seconds of arc per year. These motions are caused by the stars themselves moving at high speed across our line of sight.

If we are to do parallax calculations we must be sure to take account of these **proper motions**. For these stars, their proper motion exceeds their parallax by a factor of ten. The proper motion must be subtracted from the motion of the star when calculating its distance.

It is possible to set up a reference frame from which to measure the motions of all the stars. We can do this by carefully averaging all the proper motions of the local stars. The result shows that the Sun has a velocity through space of 19.5 km s^{-1} relative to them. This is used to define the reference frame called the **Local Standard of Rest**. All astronomical data is adjusted to this frame of reference. It is worth mentioning that this frame does not represent the motion of the Sun round the Galactic centre. That is thought to be about 300 km s^{-1}.

Key ideas

- Visual parallax can only be used to measure distances to nearby stars.

- The limit to distance is 25 pc for single stars, 50 pc for globular clusters and 200 pc for measurements made by the Hipparcos satellite.

- The proper motion of some stars relative to the Earth needs to be allowed for in parallax measurements.

6.3 Spectroscopic parallax

Visual parallax can be used to measure distances directly up to a limit of about 200 pc. Beyond this distance indirect methods are needed. Spectroscopic parallax is one such method. Despite the name, the method does not involve any use of parallax; 'parallax' in 'spectroscopic parallax' merely relates to the idea of distance measurement.

Spectroscopic parallax uses measurements of the magnitude of a star and its spectrum to calculate the star's distance from an observer. It is possible to determine the **apparent magnitude** of a distant star by observing its intensity. By observing the spectrum of its light you can determine its temperature. Referring to the **Hertzsprung–Russell diagram** you can find the **absolute magnitude** of a star of that spectral class (see Chapter 5, page 53).

The equation that links the distance of the star from Earth to its absolute and apparent magnitudes is:

$$m - M = 5 \log \frac{d}{10}$$

where m is the apparent magnitude of the star, M is the absolute magnitude of the star and d is the distance to the star (in pc). You have to be careful with the signs of the magnitudes in this equation.

You may also find this equation quoted as:

$$m - M = (5 \log d) - 5$$

This is just the same equation, but with the log term rearranged. The equation comes from the inverse square law and the definition of magnitude.

Q2 **A star has an absolute magnitude of +3. When observed from Earth it has an apparent magnitude of +11. Calculate its distance from Earth.**

Some care has to be taken when using this method of calculating distances. The distance estimate can be affected by dust and gas in the path between the star and the Earth. Absorption can make the star seem dimmer (reduce its apparent magnitude) and so the calculation will give an incorrectly large value for the distance.

A further problem can occur if the gas and dust do not dim all colours equally. If the blue light is scattered more than the red light, then the star will look too red. This will make the estimate of the star's temperature too low. When plotted on the Hertzsprung–Russell diagram this will lead to an estimate of the absolute magnitude that is larger (more positive) than the true value. In this case the calculation will give an inaccurately reduced distance.

Q **3 a** Repeat Q2, but for the situation if the value of the apparent magnitude is incorrectly given as +10. What value is calculated for the distance?
  b Repeat Q2, but use an incorrectly measured value of the absolute magnitude of +2. What value is calculated for the distance?

Spectroscopic parallax is accurate out to about 10 Mpc (3.2×10^7 ly) and so can be used to determine the distances of nearby galaxies if it is possible to identify suitably luminous stars in them.

Another method for determining distance is to consider a cluster of stars within a galaxy. **Galactic** or **open clusters** are found in the thin disc of the Milky Way and have nearly circular orbits round the centre of the Milky Way. If the stars in a galactic cluster were all formed at about the same time then, by random chance, their masses should be distributed over a range similar to that of the stars in the Galaxy as a whole. A Hertzsprung–Russell (HR) diagram plot of the stars in the cluster can then be made, using the apparent magnitudes of the stars in the cluster, and this can then be compared with the overall HR diagram (Fig. 4).

For a local galactic cluster, such as the Hyades, its main-sequence stars are sufficiently well defined on the HR diagram to allow direct comparison with the main sequence. A particular point on the main sequence may be chosen, for example the Sun at $M = 5$, which is a Class G star. The apparent magnitude (m) of corresponding Class G stars (identified spectoscopically) can be found on the Hyades plot. This then enables $m - M$ to be found; for Hyades it is 3.30 ± 0.04. The equation:

$$m - M = 5 \log \frac{d}{10}$$

can be used to calculate the distance to the galactic cluster; for Hyades it is 45.7 pc. Once this distance is known, the absolute magnitudes of all the stars in the cluster can be found.

This method can also be applied to **globular clusters** – clusters of stars that are to be found in a spherical halo round the Milky Way and which have highly elliptical orbits. However, it is not obvious that all the stars in globular clusters have evolved in quite the same way as the stars in the spiral arms of the Galaxy as a whole and so this method has to be used with care.

A better method for use with globular clusters is to locate the position of the 'giant branch' of the HR diagram and to compare it with the branch in our Galaxy's HR diagram (Fig. 5). This is particularly appropriate for distant clusters, since the giants stars will probably be the only stars sufficiently luminous to observe individually.

Fig. 4 Hertsprung–Russell diagram for a galactic cluster

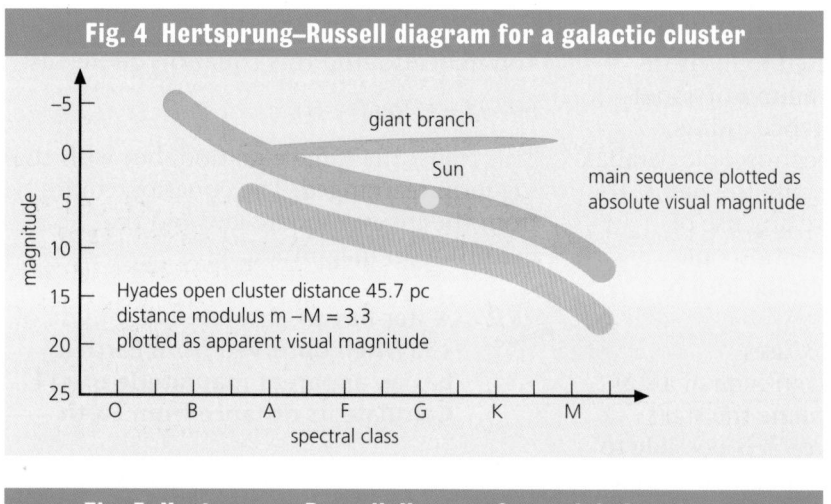

Fig. 5 Hertsprung–Russell diagram for a globular cluster

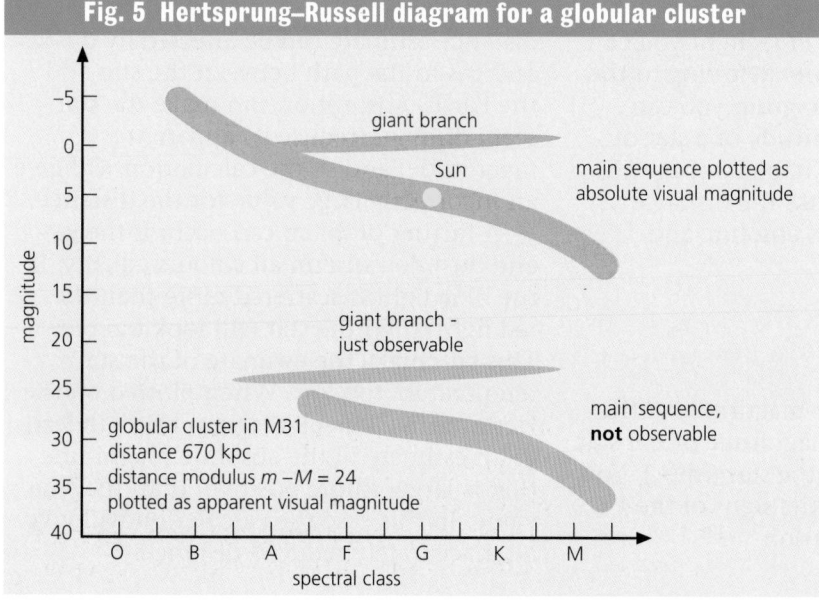

6.4 Cepheid variable stars

Cepheids are high-luminosity intrinsically variable stars which can be identified nearby in our own Galaxy and in galaxies up to a few tens of megaparsecs away. Their apparent magnitude is seen to alter in a regular manner. A graph of apparent magnitude against time shows the period of variability (Fig. 6). However, their period is straightforwardly related to their absolute magnitude (Fig. 7).

To find the distance to a newly discovered Cepheid you need to find its period. This is done by studying images of it taken over a span of several weeks. The images also allow you to measure its mean apparent magnitude (Fig. 6). With a knowledge of the period you can find the

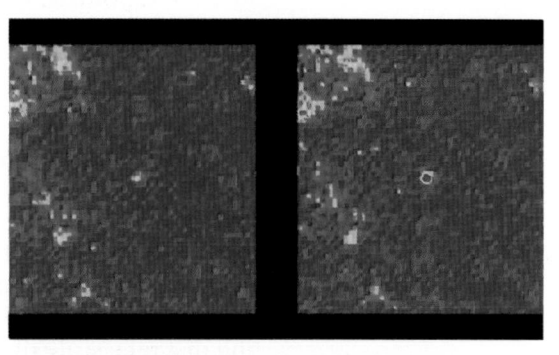

A pair of photographs taken by the Hubble Space Telescope showing a newly discovered Cepheid in the distant galaxy M100.

absolute magnitude (Fig. 7). The distance can then be calculated using the standard formula:

$$m - M = 5 \log \frac{d}{10}$$

The light curve shown here is for a distant Cepheid in the galaxy designated M100. The period of the variable star can be read off the light curve as being about 51 days and the mean apparent magnitude as being +24.9. From the period-luminosity graph (Fig. 7), this period can be seen to relate to an absolute magnitude of about −6.3.

Substituting into:

$$m - M = 5 \log \frac{d}{10}$$

$$24.9 - (-6.3) = 5 \log \frac{d}{10}$$

$$\log \frac{d}{10} = \frac{31.2}{5}$$

$$\frac{d}{10} = \text{antilog}(6.24)$$

$$d = 17.4 \text{ Mpc}$$

This is just about on the limit of observation for Cepheids from the Hubble Space Telescope. Nearer to home, the Pole Star is a Cepheid with apparent magnitude variation from +2.09 to +2.13 and a period

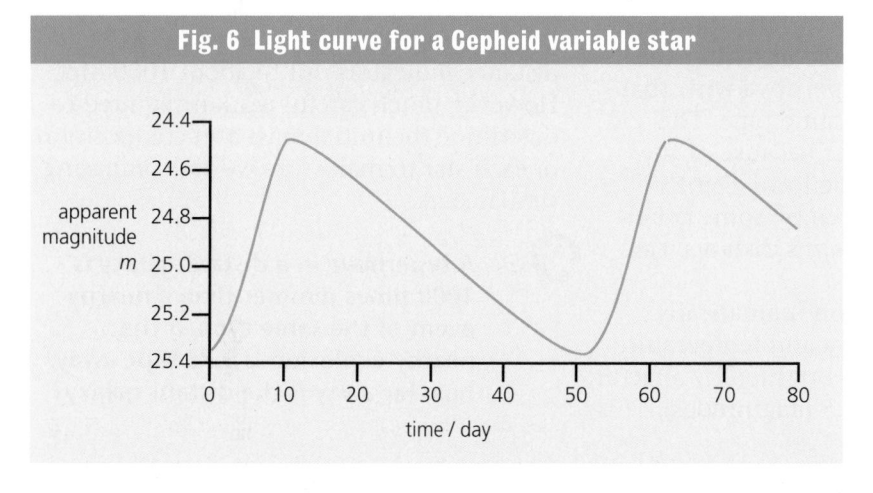

Fig. 6 Light curve for a Cepheid variable star

apparent magnitude *m* (y-axis: 24.4, 24.6, 24.8, 25.0, 25.2, 25.4)

time / day (x-axis: 0, 10, 20, 30, 40, 50, 60, 70, 80)

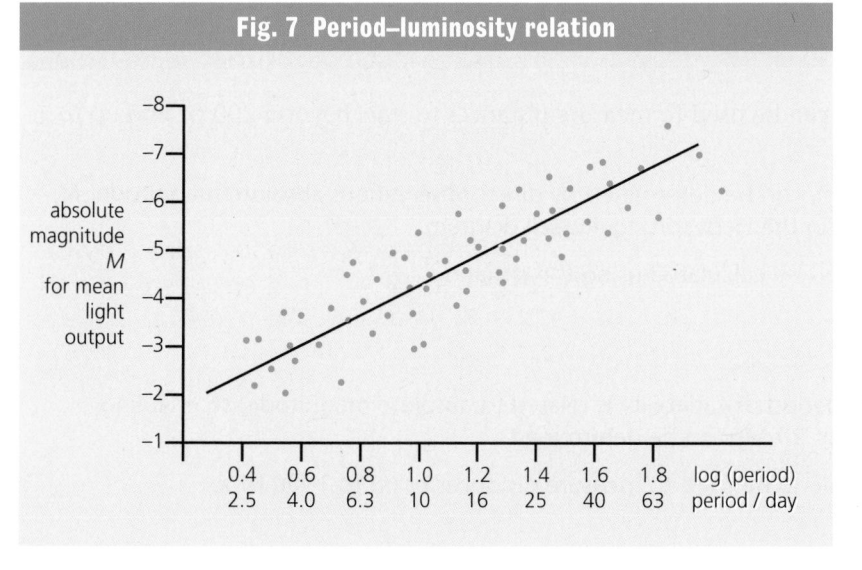

Fig. 7 Period–luminosity relation

absolute magnitude *M* for mean light output (y-axis: −8, −7, −6, −5, −4, −3, −2, −1)

| log (period) | 0.4 | 0.6 | 0.8 | 1.0 | 1.2 | 1.4 | 1.6 | 1.8 |
| period / day | 2.5 | 4.0 | 6.3 | 10 | 16 | 25 | 40 | 63 |

of four days. Although this slight variation is not visible to the naked eye, it can be measured photographically.

 4   Calculate the distance of the Pole Star from the Earth.

Other variable stars

W Virginis stars (Type II Cepheids) are similar to Cepheids but are about two magnitudes fainter. They were not originally identified as a separate class of variable star. This led to early estimates of the distance scale of the Universe being out by a factor of ten, which resulted in some cosmologists creating the steady state theory to explain the Universe seeming to be younger than the oldest stars.

Supernovae as distance indicators

If you want to measure very great distances, you need very bright **standard candles**. This is done by comparing the brightness of a local supernova with that of a distant one of the same type. The distant one looks fainter because of the inverse square law. If the local event's distance can be measured by some other method, the distant event's distance can be determined by ratios.

A supernova explosion dramatically increases the surface area and temperature of the star, causing it to brighten by a factor of a billion or more (22.5 magnitudes). This is equivalent to a star in the night sky suddenly approaching the brightness of the Sun! The peak absolute magnitude is expected to be similar for all stars of a given mass and composition, so their distances can be compared using the inverse square law.

The distance that a supernova can be observed may be estimated using the inverse square law; it is:

$$\frac{d_a}{d_b} = \sqrt{\frac{10^9}{1}} = 3.2 \times 10^4$$

times further away than the star before the explosion, where d_a is the distance of visibility *after* the explosion and d_b is the distance of visibility *before* the explosion.

The distance of visibility is increased by a factor of 32 000 times over the distance that the unexploded star can be seen. In fact, it is hoped to use supernovae as distance indicators out to about 1000 Mpc. However, much careful work is required to determine the initial mass and composition of each star to make sure we are comparing similar stars.

 5   A supernova in a distant galaxy is 1000 times dimmer than a nearby event of the same type. If the nearby explosion is 0.75 Mpc away, how far away is the distant galaxy?

Key ideas

- Spectroscopic parallax can be used to measure distances to stars beyond 200 pc and up to 10 Mpc.

- Apparent magnitude, m, can be determined by direct observation; absolute magnitude, M, can be determined using the Hertzsprung–Russell diagram.

- The distance to stars can be calculated using the equation

$$m - M = 5 \log \frac{d}{10}$$

- For variable stars, the period of variability is related to absolute magnitude, so enabling distances of up to about 20 Mpc to be determined.

- Supernovae may be able to be used to measure distances of up to 1000 Mpc.

6.5 Distances to the planets – radar astronomy

Ground-based observations

In the years immediately following the Second World War, Bernard Lovell set up surplus radar equipment at Manchester University, which is located near to the centre of Manchester. He was seeking echoes from cosmic ray showers. Unfortunately the interference from the overhead electrical equipment of passing trams was so great that he was forced to look for a radio-quiet site. Manchester University offered a field in Cheshire at their Botanical Research Station. From there he was able to detect radar echoes from the ionised trails left by meteors burning up in the top of our atmosphere. The site is now known as Jodrell Bank and is of international importance in radio astronomy.

Ground-based radar studies of nearby planets were very popular in the 1950s and 1960s, but have been somewhat overtaken by space probe investigations. However, good-quality radar maps of the cloud-covered surface of Venus were made and its period of rotation measured. Using long wavelength radar, sub-surface maps of the Moon gave valuable information before space probes were able to soft-land.

To measure the rotation of Venus, short radar pulses were directed towards the planet. When they returned, the radio signals were seen to be Doppler shifted. Signals from the approaching side of the planet had a higher frequency than the transmitted signal and signals from the receding side had a lower frequency. This allowed the rotation speed of the equator to be found and hence the period of rotation. The result was a surprise, as Venus was found to rotate in the opposite sense to the Earth and with the very long period of 243 days.

Distance and rotation have been measured for all the inner planets and these results have led to our present estimate of the astronomical unit (AU).

The planet Mercury has only been visited by one spacecraft and it only made a map of the surface from far away. There are no plans to visit the planet again in the near future, so it is left to radar to discover more about this small world. In 1991 workers at Caltech directed a 500 kW, 3.5 cm wavelength pulsed radar at Mercury for eight hours. The faint echoes were picked up by the Very Large Array in New Mexico and carefully averaged. The resulting maps seemed to show that the poles of the planet were made of highly fractured ground containing water ice – an unexpected result considering the 430 °C temperature of its daylight-side equator!

Asteroids and collisions

There have been some quite near misses between asteroids and the Earth. Radar studies of about 70 nearby asteroids have led to interesting discoveries. In particular

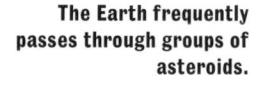

The Earth frequently passes through groups of asteroids.

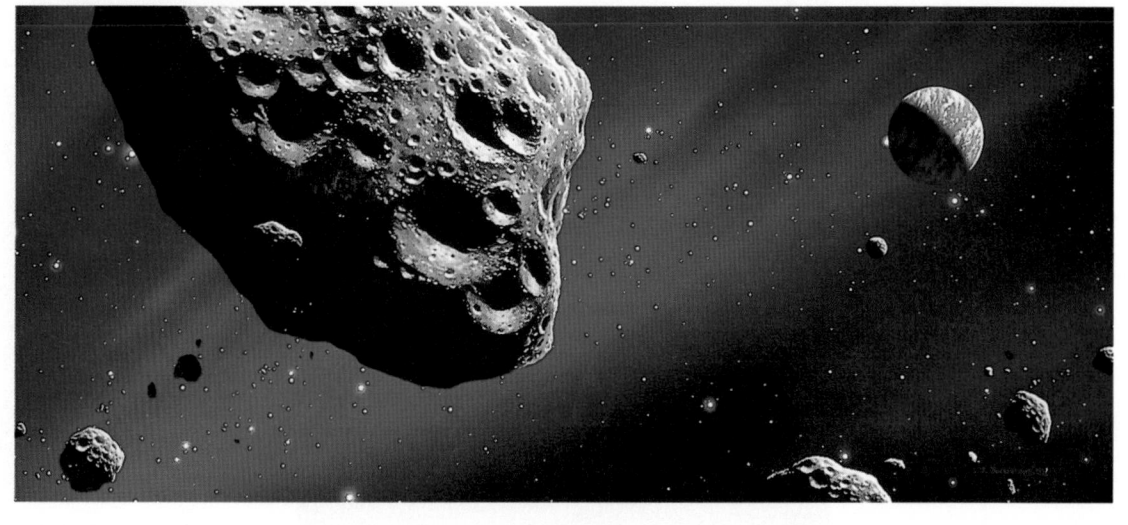

one asteroid is such a good reflector that its surface must have a very high proportion of metals. This asteroid passed within 20 million kilometres of the Earth in 1986! It was illuminated with 3.5 cm wavelength radar pulses from a large radio telescope in California. The echoes were received by the 27-dish VLA where detailed maps of the asteroid were produced as it tumbled through space. It is fortunate that it did not hit us as it was far too large to burn up in our atmosphere.

The outer planets are rather too distant for observation by Earth-based radars because the echoes would be too faint, while radar echoes from the stars are out of the question, not only because the echo would be too faint to detect, but it would take years to return, even from the closest star.

Space-based observations
Recently the radar probe Magellan was placed in orbit round Venus. Its observations were a great success. The radar system was able to penetrate the cloud cover and map the whole surface down to a scale of a few hundred metres. It also accurately measured the rotational period of planet.

The word 'radar' implies radio waves, but light beams may also be employed. Using a cat's-eye reflector placed on the Moon by NASA astronauts, pulsed lasers on Earth can determine the Earth–Moon separation to within a few tens of millimetres.

6 Many laser pulses of light are sent in quick succession towards the reflector on the Moon. Using a telescope with a large collecting area the reflections of the pulses are received and the time from launching to reception is measured. After averaging thousands of pulses, the time of flight is found to be 2.85 s. How far was the Moon from the telescope at the time of the measurement?

Accurate measurement of the Earth–Moon distance has improved our understanding of the tidal forces in the Earth–Moon system. These forces are causing the Moon to slowly recede from us by about 40 mm per year.

Calculations using the Doppler effect
Care must be taken to use the double Doppler effect formula for radar echoes. The target senses a changed frequency due

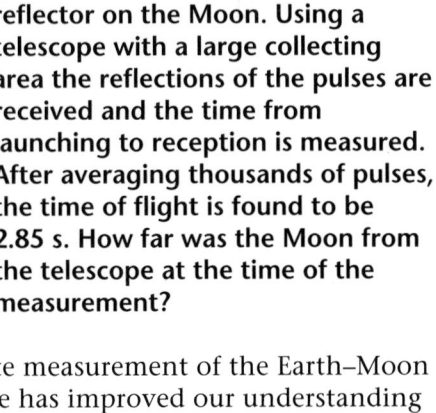

This reflector has enabled the distance to the Moon to be measured to about the same accuracy as you could measure your height

The probe Magellan was launched from the Kennedy Space Center, Florida, on 4 May 1989, arriving at Venus on 10 August 1990. The probe mapped the surface of Venus three times, enabling a three-dimensional map to be created. It then collected data on the gravity of Venus, enabling a gravity map to be produced.

Part of the radar map of Venus produced by Magellan

to the relative motion between the source and the target. The waves are reflected at that new frequency. The observer then sees that new frequency shifted again by the relative motion between the observer and the target. As a result, a factor of two is needed in the standard formulae (see Chapter 3, page 33):

$$\frac{\Delta f}{f} = \frac{2v}{c} \quad \text{and} \quad \frac{\Delta \lambda}{\lambda} = -\frac{2v}{c}$$

As discussed in Chapter 3, the maximum Doppler shift will be found in echoes that return from the limbs of the rotating object, where the relative velocity is greatest. The tangential velocity is measured in this way.

The time of flight of the pulse to the object and back gives a very accurate measurement of target to observer distance. Again, a factor of two is needed as the echo travels twice the distance to the object:

$$s = \frac{u \times t}{2}$$

where s is the distance (in m), u is the velocity (in m s^{-1}) and t is the time (in s).

Consider the following example (Fig. 9). An asteroid is observed in a series of photographs. Its diameter is too small to measure from the photographs but its reflected light varies with a regular period of 20.0 hours. This is interpreted as evidence that the asteroid is gently spinning as it proceeds through space. Radar pulses are aimed at the asteroid and the returning echoes are analysed. The transmitted frequency is 2.50 GHz. The returned signal is at a higher mean frequency and is spread over a range of frequencies. The signal ranges from 4091 to 5009 Hz above the transmitted frequency. This information can be used to find the following (Fig. 8):

- the relative velocity of the asteroid as measured from the Earth
- the radius of the asteroid.

Fig. 8 Using the Doppler effect with radar

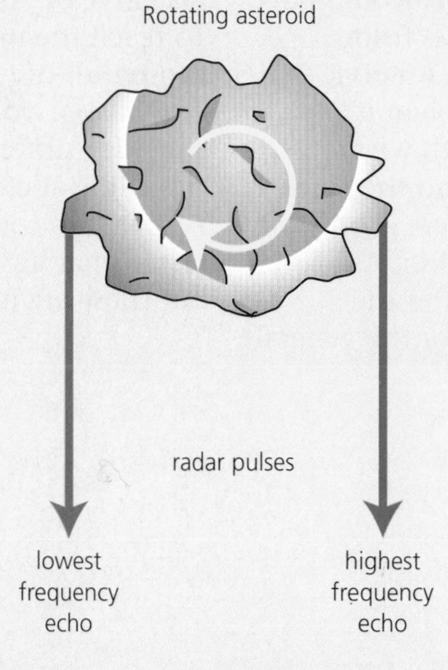

Rotating asteroid

radar pulses

lowest frequency echo

highest frequency echo

The transmitted frequency is 2.50 GHz
Frequency range of the echoes above the transmitted frequency is 4091 to 5009 Hz. Hence the mean frequency increase is 5000 Hz.

Using the double Doppler shift formula,

$$\frac{\Delta f}{f} = \frac{2v}{c} \quad \text{so} \quad v = \frac{c\,\Delta f}{2f}$$

$$v = \frac{3.0 \times 10^8 \text{ m s}^{-1} \times 5000 \text{ Hz}}{2 \times 2.50 \times 10^9 \text{ Hz}} = 300 \text{ m s}^{-1}$$

The range of frequencies is due to rotation. The increase over the mean frequency = 9 Hz, so

$$v = \frac{c\,\Delta f}{2f} = \frac{3.0 \times 10^8 \text{ m s}^{-1} \times 9 \text{ Hz}}{2 \times 2.50 \times 10^9 \text{ Hz}} = 0.54 \text{ m s}^{-1}$$

Since $T = 20$ hours (72000 s), we can use the rotational formulae, $v = r\omega$ and $T = \frac{2\pi}{\omega}$ to find the radius of the asteroid, r.

$$r = \frac{vT}{2\pi} = \frac{0.54 \text{ m s}^{-1} \times 72000 \text{ s}}{2\pi}$$

$$r = 6200 \text{ m}$$

Q 7 The shortest distance between Mars and the Earth is about 7.8×10^{10} m. The radius of Mars is 3.4×10^6 m and the time for one rotation of the planet is 24.6 hours.
If a radar pulse is sent towards Mars, how long will it take the echo to return?
If the frequency of the radar pulse is 9 GHz, what is the highest frequency signal found in the echo?

Key ideas

- Radar astronomy allows the distances to planets and the radius and period of rotation of planets to be measured.

- Radar echoes undergo a double Doppler shift.

6.6 Manned expeditions in space

The problems of getting a manned mission as far as Mars are enormous. It is expected to take three years to visit the surface of the planet and return safely. The most obvious problem is a lack of food and oxygen. Then there is the reliability of such a complex set of equipment. A rescue mission is unlikely, so problems have to be solved as they occur. Even radio conversations would have a delay of at least eight minutes from asking a question to receiving a reply! A more serious long-term problem is exposure to radiation. On Earth we are shielded by the atmosphere and the Earth's magnetic field but in space there is only a thin layer of metal for protection. An astronaut might receive 20 times the maximum exposure allowed for the general public. If there was a powerful solar flare that shot fast protons towards the astronauts, then some sort of shelter would be essential as the radiation dose would be lethal.

Now consider the problems of exploring Europa, the ice-covered satellite of Jupiter and a place where life might exist. It would take at least 20 years to do the return trip. To reach the nearest star would take tens of thousands of years. To reach the edge of our Galaxy would take too long to consider, unless we could find a way of travelling at close to the speed of light. Perhaps we could find a way of travelling faster than light, at warp speed perhaps, but these are just dreams!

7 The changing Universe

If you had no knowledge of astronomy, you could look up at the stars in the night sky and believe they had always been there and would never change. Earlier in this book you discovered that stars do not shine for ever. So how did the

The Hubble Deep Field shows some of the most distant galaxies ever seen. Because of their distance, they are among the earliest galaxies to form after the big bang.

Universe begin and how might it end? If the Universe is so large, is there intelligent life out there?

Here on Earth we orbit a quiet, long-lived star. If the Earth had been in orbit round the star that exploded to make the Crab Nebula, we would not have had time to evolve. How many civilisations have developed and then been destroyed by their own sun?

On the grand scale, how long is it since the Universe came into being and how long will it last? Perhaps the Universe will collapse into a 'big crunch' or perhaps it will expand for ever, cooling down to a frozen wilderness.

7.1 Learning objectives

After working through this chapter, you should be able to:

- **explain** how Hubble discovered that the Universe was expanding;

- **estimate** the age of the Universe;

- **discuss** the problems raised by the discovery of the quasars;

- **describe** how quasars are used to probe the edges of the Universe;

- **explain** how a black hole is formed;

- **calculate** the size of the event horizon of a black hole.

7.2 The expanding Universe

The American astronomer Edwin Hubble (1889–1953) invested years of effort into photographing the spectral lines of distant **galaxies**. All the spectra showed a red shift (see Chapter 3). Hubble converted these red shifts into velocities, using the **Doppler effect formula**, and found that there was a link between the velocities and the distances of the galaxies (Fig. 1). The galaxies that were moving away fastest were also the most distant ones. By the late 1920s Hubble had shown that the Universe was expanding.

Some researchers thought that part of the red shift might be caused by the gravitational field of the galaxies, but now most astronomers believe that gravity makes almost no contribution.

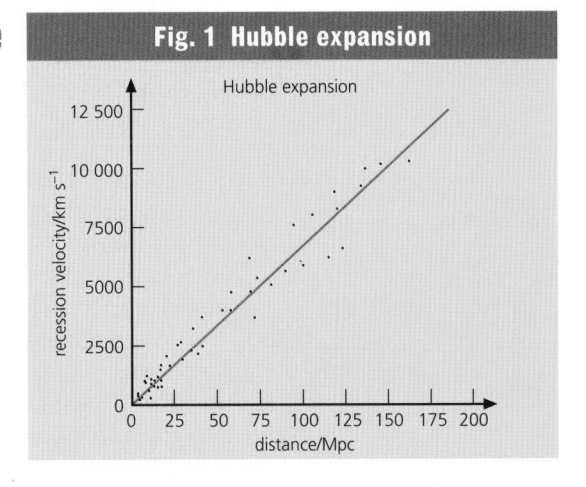

Fig. 1 Hubble expansion

Hubble expansion

(graph: recession velocity/km s⁻¹ on vertical axis from 0 to 12 500; distance/Mpc on horizontal axis from 0 to 200)

The points on the graph are rather scattered but the best-fit line has a gradient of about 67 km s⁻¹ Mpc⁻¹. This defines the Hubble constant (*H*). The data only extend out to a distance of 200 Mpc, as distance measurements beyond that point are almost impossible (see Chapter 6). The edge of the observable Universe is thought to be about 20 times this distance. Recent results give values of the Hubble constant clustered around 60 and 70 km s⁻¹ Mpc⁻¹. (Note that the syllabus uses 100 km s⁻¹ Mpc⁻¹.)

distance the recession velocity will equal the speed of light. Beyond this distance the light from a galaxy would never reach us. We cannot know if there are any galaxies beyond the speed-of-light limit. All we can do is to calculate the size of the *observable* Universe.

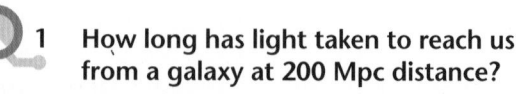

1 How long has light taken to reach us from a galaxy at 200 Mpc distance?

2 What speed would you substitute into the Hubble law equation to calculate the distance to the edge of the observable Universe?

3 What is the distance to the edge of the observable Universe? Use a value of 67 km s⁻¹ Mpc⁻¹ for the Hubble constant.

Part of the Virgo Cluster of Galaxies. This group is about 19 Mpc away from us.

It is relatively easy to measure the velocities accurately using the Doppler effect, but it is rather more difficult to measure the distances accurately. The Hubble expansion graph is a good straight line for the closer distances. It leads to an equation for **Hubble's law**:

velocity of recession = Hubble constant × distance

$$v = Hd$$

where v is the recession velocity in km s⁻¹, d is the distance in Mpc and H is the Hubble constant in km s⁻¹ Mpc⁻¹.

There still remains a possibility that the Hubble constant may not have been constant throughout the expansion of the Universe, but no satisfactory way has yet been found to test for variations. For the present we may assume that Hubble's constant is constant.

Size of the observable Universe
The more distant the galaxy you observe, the faster it is receding. At some great

The age of the Universe
From the Hubble constant and equation you can calculate the age of the Universe:

$$\text{time} = \frac{\text{distance}}{\text{velocity}} = \frac{1}{H}$$

First we must change the units of the Hubble constant from Mpc to pc and km to m:

$$H = 67 \text{ km s}^{-1} \text{ Mpc}^{-1} = 67 \times 10^{-3} \text{ m s}^{-1} \text{ pc}^{-1}$$

One parsec is 3.26 light years, so the length of 1 parsec in metres is:

$$3.26 \text{ pc} \times 3.0 \times 10^{8} \text{ m s}^{-1} \times 365.25 \times 24 \times 60 \times 60 \text{ s}$$

$$= 3.09 \times 10^{16} \text{ m}$$

So $H = \dfrac{67 \times 10^{-3} \text{ m s}^{-1} \text{ pc}}{3.09 \times 10^{16} \text{ m pc}}$

$$= 2.17 \times 10^{-18} \text{ s}^{-1}$$

Age of the Universe $= \dfrac{1}{H} = 4.6 \times 10^{17}$ s

All galaxies are moving away from us on Earth, so the galaxies must have been closer together in the past. Early in the history of the Universe the density of matter must have been very high; all matter must have originated from the same point, expanding away from this point since the start of the Universe. The explosion that started this expansion of space and time is known as the 'big bang'.

7.3 Quasars

The objects we see in the sky emit electromagnetic radiation in the visible portion of the spectrum. However, astronomers use telescopes that detect in other parts of the electromagnetic spectrum, including the radio spectrum (see Chapter 2). Early radio maps of the sky showed many objects that emitted radio waves, most of which could be associated with our galaxy. More puzzling were the radio sources that did not obviously correspond to any optical sources on the sky survey plates. What objects could be good emitters of radio energy but be hard to identify in the visible part of the spectrum? There were so many objects on the survey plates that precise positions were needed to make further progress.

Much effort was put into identifying the exact position of the strong radio source 3C273 – so named because it was the 273rd source in the Third Cambridge Radio Source Catalogue. In 1963 the Moon was due to pass in front of the region of sky where 3C273 was thought to be located. Astronomers know the orbit of the Moon very precisely, so a special effort was made to observe the times at which the radio signal disappeared and reappeared, as the radio signals were blocked by the Moon. This allowed the position of 3C273 to be found to a very high degree of accuracy.

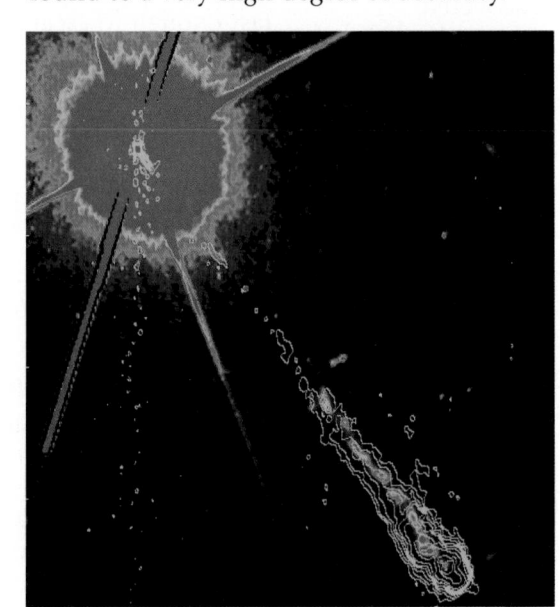

Optical image of the radio source 3C273, with the radio image overlaid; though this source looks like a very faint star, it is a very strong radio emitter.

When the location of the radio source was studied on an optical map of the sky, all that was seen was a faint star. This was unexpected for such a strong radio source. It led to the name 'QUAsi-StellAr Radio source' or **quasar**, because in visible light it looked like a star but obviously was something rather different.

The optical spectrum was even more of a puzzle. It contained a few faint emission lines that were not immediately identifiable with known elements. Careful measurement showed that the lines were from neutral hydrogen and ionised oxygen gas, but had been shifted to the red end of the spectrum. The red shift gave the recession velocity of the quasar.

The source 3C273 is now probably the best-known quasar. When observed in visible light, 3C273 consists of a 14th magnitude 'star' with a faint narrow jet about 10 seconds of arc long. One part of the radio image is centred on the end of the jet and the other on the 'star'. The elongated jet is thought to be caused by **relativistic** electrons, that is electrons moving at speeds near to the speed of light, spiralling in the local magnetic field. In doing so, the electrons emit bright beams of **synchrotron radiation**. The quasar's optical spectrum shows hydrogen emission lines with a red shift of 0.16. This corresponds to a recession velocity of approximately 4.4×10^7 m s^{-1} and a distance of roughly 660 Mpc (2.2×10^9 light years) using $H = 67$ km s^{-1} Mpc^{-1}. It certainly is not in our Galaxy. When first measured, this great distance caused theoretical problems: If the source was distant and fairly bright, it must be giving out a great deal of energy. But if the source was very small then it would not be possible to generate so much energy in such a small volume.

The output power of 3C273 is 10^{39} watts. This is 1000 times the entire power output of our Galaxy. The power is being generated in a region the size of our Solar System. There is no known energy source that could produce this, so 3C273 could not be a star.

When the images of several of these sources had been analysed, astronomers realised that they had found a new class of objects. Our Galaxy emits very little radio energy. By contrast, there are significant numbers of galaxies that have been disrupted, probably by close encounters with their neighbours. A small fraction of these go on to become quasars.

The nuclei of these active galaxies eject powerful beams of charged particles along their polar axes. When these particles spiral in the magnetic fields, they emit narrow beams of radio energy. If a beam happens to be pointing in our direction we see a bright compact radio source.

Active galactic nuclei are now thought to be powered by massive black holes. Stars, gas and dust near the centre are accelerated and crushed as they are drawn inwards under gravity. This process accelerates the material close to the speed of light and releases energy in a way that is perhaps ten times more efficient than the fusion process in our Sun. However, once the central region of the galaxy is cleared of material, the quasar switches off. It might only shine for 50 million years before it has used up all the central material, so there must have been many more quasars in the past than we can now observe. Recent research has also shown that up to 90% of quasars are radio quiet.

There was considerable controversy when quasars were first discovered.

● Perhaps their spectra were reddened by scattering of blue light as it passed through **interstellar dust clouds**? This would be similar to the scattering of light when the Sun is low in the sky. It looks redder because the blue light has been scattered by many air molecules.

● Perhaps the red shift was caused by the photons having to escape from intense gravitational fields?

The optical spectrum of a quasar is poor and ill defined; it was difficult to be certain about the information in it, particularly when only a few examples were known. Now, many examples are known and very detailed and beautiful radio maps have been made. Astronomers agree that the red shifts are caused only by the speed of the galaxies. However, measuring the extreme distances is still very hard. As mentioned in Chapter 6, waiting for a supernova to occur in a galaxy and then using it as a standard candle is a good way to measure distances approaching 1000 Mpc. This would allow 3C273's distance to be measured accurately.

Quasars and the fate of the Universe

Some quasars are so bright that they are the most distant objects observed. This is the only way to extend the top end of the Hubble graph. The shape of the very end of the plot is an important guide to the fate of the Universe. If the graph turns upwards, the most distant galaxies are moving away faster than is needed for the Universe to expand for ever. If the graph turns down, the galaxies are not moving fast enough to escape and gravity will eventually pull all the galaxies together into the big crunch.

7.4 Supernovae, neutron stars and black holes

When a star burns up the last of its available hydrogen and can no longer carry out nuclear fusion reactions it can either become a red giant or a supernova (see Chapter 5). There are three possible end points for the remains of the star:

● If the core of the star contains less than 1.4 **solar masses**, a white dwarf is left behind.

● If the core of the star contains between 1.4 and about 3 solar masses, a neutron star is formed.

● If the core of the star contains over 3 solar masses the material collapses into a black hole.

A white dwarf has sufficient mass to create a very large gravitational pressure. The gravitational forces are strong enough to partially collapse the electron shells of the atoms, creating a fluid of electrons and nuclei. It is the **electron degeneracy pressure** that stops the white dwarf from collapsing further (Chapter 5).

Neutron stars

If the mass of the core of the dying star is greater than 1.4 solar masses, then even the pressure from the electrons can be overcome and the core will collapse into a fluid with many free neutrons. The mean density rises to about 5×10^{17} kg m^{-3} and the core will have a radius of about 15 km. In this state the pressure that prevents further gravitational collapse is provided by the neutrons attempting not to occupy identical states – **neutron degeneracy pressure**. A **neutron star** has been formed.

To illustrate the massive value of the density in a neutron star, consider the ink in one of the full stops on this page. If it were made of neutron star material, it would have a mass of about 1000 tonnes.

The core of a neutron star is in fact a series of layers. The outer crust is almost certainly a crystalline solid composed of metal nuclei (mainly iron) with many free electrons. Beneath that there is a layer of crystalline material with many free electrons and neutrons. Then there is a large region of neutron superfluid and at the centre there might be a truly solid core (Fig. 2). What state that solid might be in is very uncertain, since the pressure and density are well beyond the limits of experiment and present-day theory.

The acceleration due to gravity at the surface of a neutron star is massive. It can be calculated using Newton's law:

$$g = \frac{GM}{r^2}$$

where g is the acceleration due to gravity in m s^{-2}, G is the gravitational constant in

N m^2 kg^{-2}, M is the mass of the star in kg and r is the radius of the star in m.

4   Calculate the value of g for a neutron star of 1.4 solar masses and radius of 15 km. (solar mass is 2.00×10^{30} kg, G is 6.67×10^{-11} N m^2 kg^{-2}.)

5   Calculate the work done by a person of mass 60 kg climbing a step 1 mm high on this neutron star.

6   An adult human can generate 200 watts of power continuously. Use this to calculate the time taken to climb this step on a neutron star. (Hint: It is a very long time.)

Black holes

If the mass of the core of the dying star is greater than 3 solar masses, nothing can stop it collapsing to an even greater extent than a neutron star. The star collapses down towards a point, called a **singularity**, where the laws of physics as we know them break down. The gravitational forces near the singularity are so great that neither matter nor radiation can escape.

We can work out the critical radius inside which light is trapped. It is called the **Schwarzschild radius**. Newton's laws of gravitation show that the energy required by an object of mass m to escape to infinity from the gravitational field of an object is given by:

$$\text{energy} = \frac{GMm}{r}$$

where G is the gravitational constant in N m^2 kg^{-2}, M is the mass of the star in kg and r is the distance from the centre of the star in m. Imagine that this energy is available as a single pulse, as in the case of a bullet travelling with an initial velocity v. Its kinetic energy can be equated to the energy required to escape:

$$\tfrac{1}{2}mv^2 = \frac{GMm}{r}$$

where v is the velocity in m s^{-1}. This equation should contain relativistic corrections on each side, because the velocity being considered is the speed of

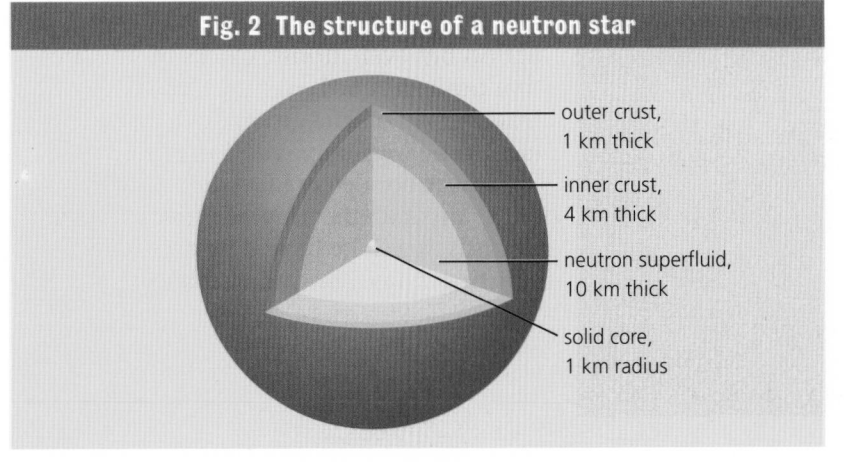

Fig. 2 The structure of a neutron star

- outer crust, 1 km thick
- inner crust, 4 km thick
- neutron superfluid, 10 km thick
- solid core, 1 km radius

light, but fortunately the corrections cancel out. Simplifying, it becomes:

$$v = \sqrt{\frac{2GM}{r}}$$

The critical point is reached when this velocity equals the speed of light, c, in m s^{-1}. The formula then becomes:

$$c = \sqrt{\frac{2GM}{r}} \quad \text{or} \quad r = \frac{2GM}{c^2}$$

This equation defines the Schwarzschild radius (r). Any object closer to the black hole than this distance would require a velocity greater than the velocity of light to escape from the gravitational field of the black hole – an impossibility. The Schwarzschild radius defines a sphere that is called the **event horizon** of the black hole. Inside this sphere nothing is visible and *nothing* escapes.

Q7 Calculate the Schwarzschild radius for a 3 solar mass star. (Use the values given in question 4.)

The gravitational effects of the black hole are just the same as if the star had not collapsed. The mass is still present and the pull of its gravity is unchanged; it is just that you cannot see the black hole.

Falling into a black hole
Imagine you are on the first expedition to a black hole; your ship has gone into orbit 1000 000 km from the centre of the black hole. Your orbital period is only about 3 hours and your speed is over 600 km per second. A not-so-lucky crew member enters

the expedition capsule and fires the retro-rocket to slow down for the descent. As the capsule falls inwards, you notice that the clock on the capsule appears to be running a little slow and the capsule looks slightly red. Then the effects change rapidly. The clock slows down until it seems to have almost stopped, and the capsule grows fainter and fainter and redder and redder. In the next second it has vanished; it is lost for ever.

These effects may seem fanciful. The reddening of light by a strong gravitational field was first predicted by Einstein and was then observed a few years later in 1925. The bright star Sirius is in fact a binary star system. The strong gravity of the larger star, Sirius A, affects the light from its smaller companion Sirius B (Ch 5, p. 55). By analysis of the spectrum of Sirius B it is possible to detect the gravitational reddening.

Back to the story. What happened to the crew member? When you get close to any massive object, gravity becomes much stronger at your feet than at your head, assuming that your feet are closer to the massive object than your head is. At a distance of 10 000 km from a black hole the force on a mass of 1 kg is about 1 N greater at your feet than at your head. At 100 km, the difference in force is a million times greater, enough to pull you completely apart.

Time travel
Close to a *rotating* black hole the nature of space and time is significantly altered. You could perhaps travel through time if you were able to survive the close pass that is required. This might seem like science fiction but even atomic clocks in satellites that orbit the Earth run slightly faster than when tested on the ground before launch due to the weaker gravitational potential.

We cannot detect black holes directly, but if any material around a black hole falls inwards, it will be heated by collisions, emitting X-rays, uv and visible light.

The film 'Black Hole' depicts a hazardous journey into the unknown

7.5   Explaining the Universe as we see it

In Section 4.2 we discussed microwave background radiation, the radiant heat of the big bang, cooled down to just 2.7 K. The COBE satellite was launched in 1989, painstakingly recorded the intensity and the spectrum of the microwave background. The data were an excellent fit to the 2.7 K blackbody curve. This is a very important piece of supporting evidence for the big bang theory.

The COBE satellite then went on to check the evenness of the microwave signal across the sky. By April 1992 the team, led by George Smoot, announced that they had found slight differences in the signal from place to place in the sky. The results show that the microwave background has variations of a few parts in 100 000 in its intensity. This variation is very important. The 'hot big bang' theory predicts that the Universe was very dense for the first 300 000 years. The particles and radiation collided so often that they shared the available energy. At the end of this time, the Universe had expanded sufficiently to allow the particles and radiation to go their own way. The radiation took away a fingerprint of the Universe 300 000 years after the big bang. Most importantly, it took information about how the matter was distributed at that time.

Hubble flow
To speculate effectively about the fate of the Universe you need to link theory with observation. The most secure observations relate to the Hubble flow: the more distant the galaxy, the faster it is receding. The Hubble expansion graph of speed against distance is quite a good straight line for the middle-distance galaxies. Unfortunately, information about the most distant galaxies (red shift greater than 4) is scanty. It is difficult to be sure whether the line continues straight or curves away.

If the most distant galaxies are found to be moving away rapidly, then the Universe will expand for ever. If they are moving too slowly, then gravity will pull them back to the big crunch. If the velocities are just right for the density of matter, then the Universe will come to rest at infinite size.

Dark matter
A much harder problem is to estimate the total amount of matter in the Universe. Only visible matter can be measured directly; stars, gas and dust clouds and galaxies. Dark matter, i.e. black holes, brown dwarfs, molecular hydrogen, very diffuse gas and dust, neutrinos and other elementary particles, is very difficult to measure. At present, the estimated mass of visible matter falls short by between 10 and 100 times of that needed to halt the expansion of the Universe and so ensure a big crunch.

Significant progress in the search for dark matter came in 1979. A pair of quasars that looked very similar and were very close together turned out to be images of the same source. As there are only a few thousand quasars (down to 22nd magnitude) in the sky, the chance of finding two of them so close together was remote. Optical spectra showed the quasers to be effectively identical. The proposed explanation is that the light and radio signals from a very distant quasar have been deflected by a massive galaxy between us and the quasar. The result of this lens action is a double image. In the processed photograph it is just possible to see the intervening massive galaxy.

This type of observation allows us to estimate the total mass in the lensing galaxy and thus the total amount of matter in the Universe. Results obtained recently using the Hubble Space Telescope hint that the final amount of matter located might just balance the expansion, leading to a stable Universe of infinite size.

Before the big bang?
If a Universe existed before the big bang then it probably suffered the big crunch. All its mass and energy combined and became indistinguishable. It appears that the sum of mass and energy would be carried over to create the new big bang. Unfortunately for historians, all other information was lost. At the instant of the big bang, there was no space and no time. If a new big crunch occurs, nothing of our civilisation will be known to any future Universe.

The gift of sight

The human eye is a remarkable optical system, like a living video camera. It contains 130 million light-detecting cells. These are sensitive enough to form an image in the darkness of night and adaptable enough to cope with summer sunshine, when the light can be ten million times brighter. With perfect eyesight you can see details as small as 1 mm up to 6 m away and switch your focus from a 20 cm 'close-up' to infinity in less than one tenth of a second.

Unfortunately, not everyone has perfect eyesight. Diseases such as cataracts, glaucoma and macula degeneration, cause blindness in millions of people throughout the world.

New techniques can restore sight to patients affected by these conditions. Lasers are used to treat glaucoma by improving fluid drainage from the eye. Artificial plastic lenses are inserted into the eyes of cataract patients. Now, doctors in Baltimore have devised spectacles which carry a miniature video camera and TV screen that can 'fill in' the gap in vision caused by macula degeneration. This could be one step on the way to creating an artificial retina.

A scene as viewed by a person with good vision

(a) Cataracts are responsible for 23% of all blindness. The lens of the eye becomes cloudy and may need to be removed.

(b) People suffering from glaucoma have increased pressure within the eye. This damages the cells and leads to a gradual, but irreversible loss of vision.

(c) Macula degeneration is a disease affecting the light-sensitive cells of the retina. It leads to a 'hole' in the centre of vision.

8.1 Learning objectives

After working through this chapter, you should be able to:

- **describe** the structure of the eye;

- **draw** ray diagrams to **explain** how the eye produces a focused image;

- **use** the lens formula to calculate the positions of images formed by a convex lens;

- **explain** how the eye detects light;

- **define** visual acuity and **explain** some of the factors that affect it;

- **state** what is meant by depth of focus and depth of field;

- **describe** common defects of vision and **explain** how these can be corrected using lenses.

8.2 Creating an image

Fig. 1 The eye–brain system compared with the video camera–TV system

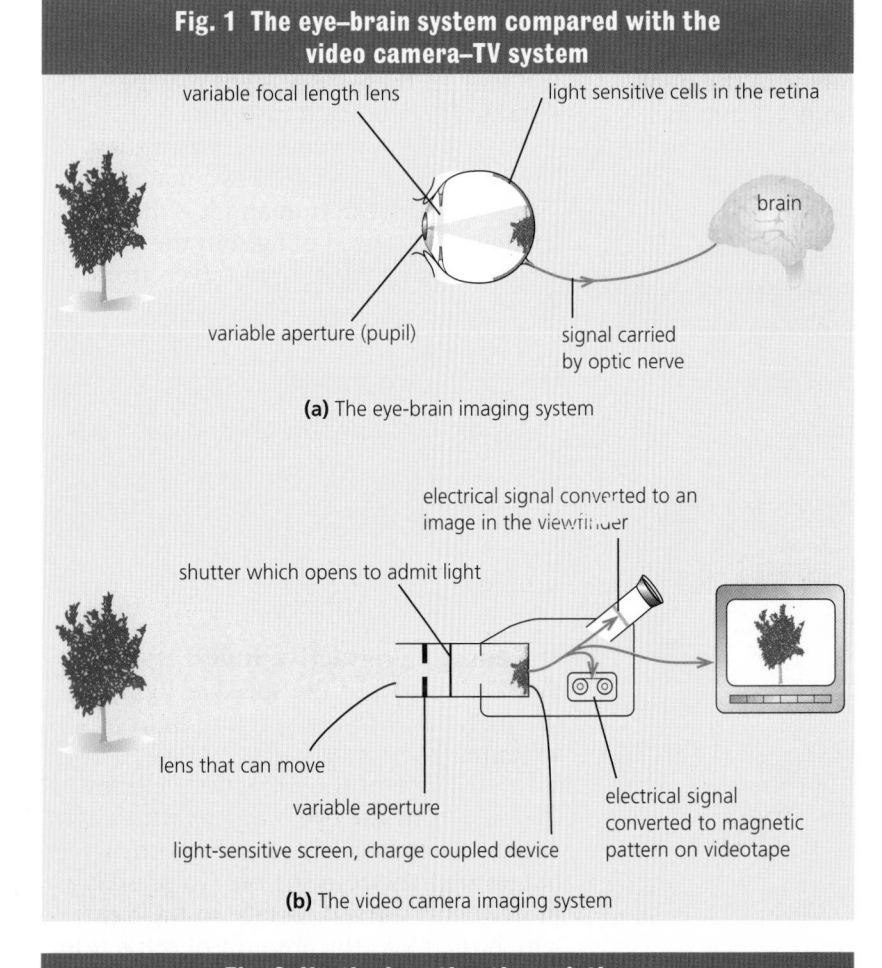

variable focal length lens

light sensitive cells in the retina

brain

variable aperture (pupil)

signal carried by optic nerve

(a) The eye-brain imaging system

electrical signal converted to an image in the viewfinder

shutter which opens to admit light

lens that can move

variable aperture

light-sensitive screen, charge coupled device

electrical signal converted to magnetic pattern on videotape

(b) The video camera imaging system

Fig. 2 Vertical section through the eye

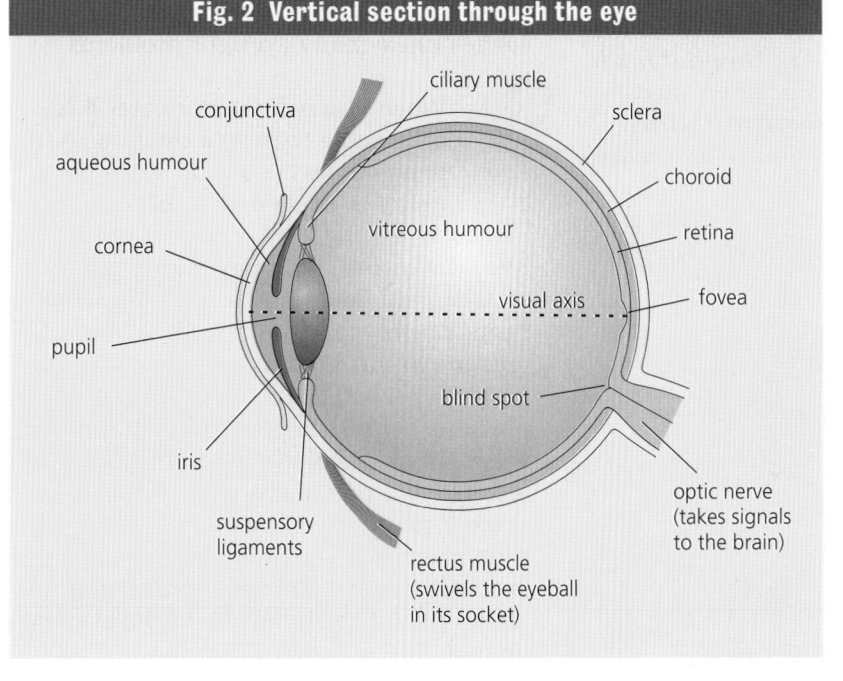

ciliary muscle

conjunctiva

sclera

aqueous humour

choroid

vitreous humour

retina

cornea

visual axis

fovea

pupil

blind spot

iris

optic nerve (takes signals to the brain)

suspensory ligaments

rectus muscle (swivels the eyeball in its socket)

The living camera

The idea of using video technology to restore sight to the blind is exciting, but is it realistic? Can a modern camera perform as well as the human eye?

Digital camcorders are capable of producing impressive images. The zoom lens can change from a focal length of about 6 mm to around 60 mm. The lens, typically around 50 mm diameter, will admit much more light than a human eye and can produce a highly detailed image, even in low-light conditions.

The eye and the video camera face similar demands. They need to:

- produce an image in 'real-time', which means updating the image at least 25 times per second;
- automatically adjust the focus from close-up to infinity;
- automatically adapt to changing light conditions.

There are similarities about the way that the eye and the camera meet these demands (Fig. 1). They both admit light through a variable **aperture** and they both use a convex lens to focus an image on a light-sensitive surface, which then produces an electrical signal.

Controlling the brightness

The amount of light entering a video camera is controlled by a variable aperture between the lens and the light-sensitive screen. In the eye, the aperture is in front of the lens and is known as the **pupil** (Fig. 2). Its diameter is varied by a ring of smooth muscle known as the **iris**. The iris is the coloured part of your eye; the colour comes from a pigment that absorbs light. People with darker coloured eyes simply have more pigment in their iris.

Some of the muscle fibres in the iris run radially like bicycle spokes. Other muscle fibres encircle the pupil. When the circular fibres contract, the pupil becomes smaller (constricts). When the radial muscles contract, the pupil opens wider (dilates). Both sets of muscles are governed by the autonomic nerves which control reflex actions within our bodies (Fig. 3).

 **1** **The eye can increase its sensitivity to light by a factor of about one million. The diameter of the pupil can vary from about 1.5 mm in bright light to about 8.0 mm in low-light conditions. Work out whether the increase in sensitivity is due entirely to the change in area.**

Fig. 3 The iris and pupil in bright light and in dim light

If the intensity of light reaching the retina increases, the pupil automatically constricts (the circular muscles contract).

If the intensity decreases, the eye's reflex system causes the pupil to dilate (the radial muscles contract).

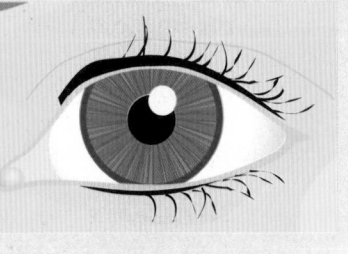
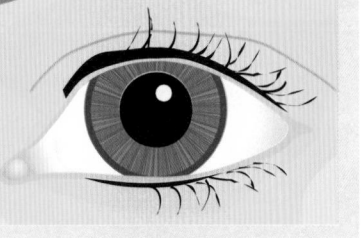

Which set of eyes do you prefer? Dilated pupils are said to be more attractive. Light is not the only factor affecting the pupil – some drugs can make the pupil dilate or constrict. Adrenaline causes your pupil to dilate, so when you are excited or frightened your pupils may give you away!

Getting things in focus
'My body kept rejecting donated corneas so surgeons at the Sussex Eye Hospital made me a new cornea from one of my own teeth. A ring of tooth was fitted with a plastic lens. This new 'cornea' was placed under the skin of my cheek for two months to allow some soft tissue to grow onto it and then it was stitched in place in my eye.'

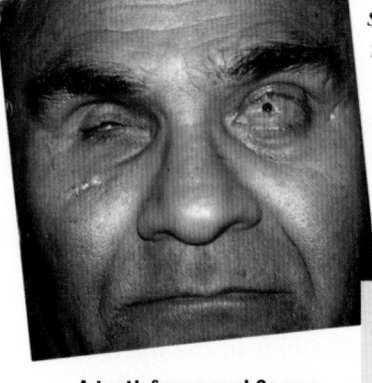

A tooth for an eye! Cornea transplants are an excellent way of restoring sight to some people.

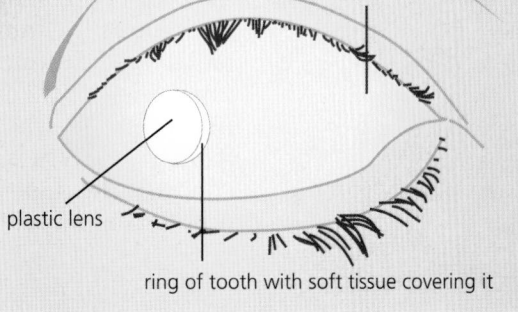

damaged cornea

plastic lens

ring of tooth with soft tissue covering it

Light rays enter the eye through the **cornea**, the transparent membrane which covers the front of the eye. If the cornea gets scratched, it can repair itself but it can become opaque as a result of illness or accident. In these cases, sight may be restored by a cornea transplant.

Rays of light are deviated when they cross a boundary between two materials. This is called **refraction** and it is due to the change in the speed of light in the different media. When a ray of light travels from medium 1 to medium 2, the refractive index, $_1n_2$, is defined as:

$$_1n_2 = \frac{\text{speed of light in medium 1}}{\text{speed of light in medium 2}}$$

The refractive index from air to water is therefore given by:

$$_{air}n_{water} = \frac{2.98 \times 10^8 \text{ m s}^{-1}}{2.24 \times 10^8 \text{ m s}^{-1}} \approx 1.33$$

The **absolute refractive index** of a material compares the speed of light in the material with the speed of light in a vacuum.

About 60% of the refraction of light that occurs in the eye happens when light strikes the cornea (Fig. 4). The cornea bulges slightly from the eye, to present a more highly curved surface to the light which increases the amount of refraction. Variations and defects in the shape of the cornea cause many eyesight problems.

2 **When you swim underwater it is impossible to form a clear, focused image unless you wear swimming goggles. Explain why this is so.**

After the cornea, light passes through a clear, watery fluid known as the **aqueous humor** before reaching the **lens**. The pressure in this fluid, normally about 15 mmHg (2000 Pa) above atmospheric pressure, helps the eyeball to maintain its shape. In a normal eye, aqueous humor is secreted and then reabsorbed at the rate of about 2 ml per day. In a patient suffering from glaucoma, the drainage system becomes blocked and the increase in fluid causes the internal pressure in the eye to increase. If the pressure gets too high, it

Fig. 4 Refraction and the eye

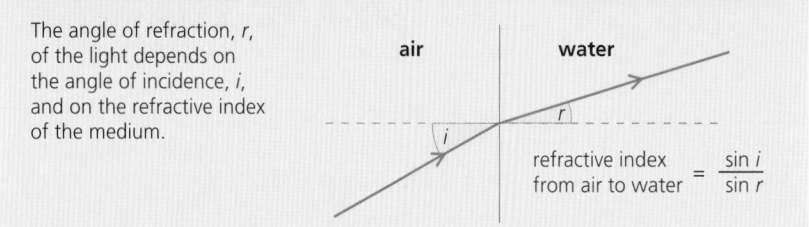

The angle of refraction, r, of the light depends on the angle of incidence, i, and on the refractive index of the medium.

$$\text{refractive index from air to water} = \frac{\sin i}{\sin r}$$

As a ray of light passes through each part of the eye it is refracted at each boundary between media. A large change in the refractive index causes more refraction. In the eye, the largest deviation will occur as the light passes from air into the cornea.

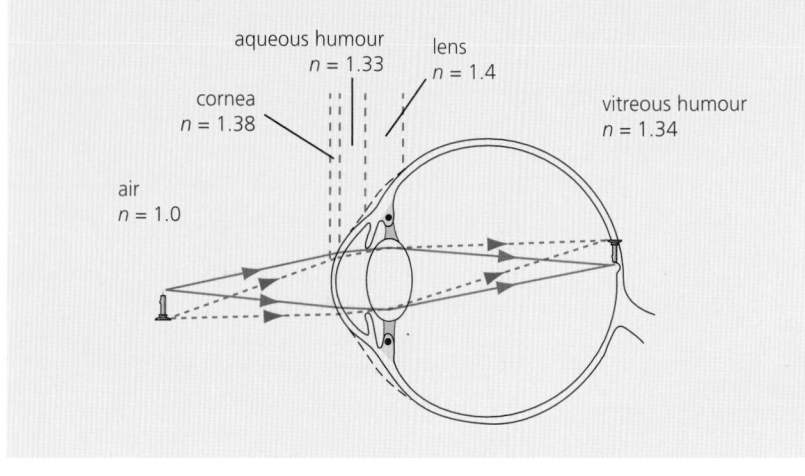

aqueous humour $n = 1.33$

lens $n = 1.4$

cornea $n = 1.38$

vitreous humour $n = 1.34$

air $n = 1.0$

will destroy the cells at the head of the optic nerve by restricting their blood supply.

The lens makes the small adjustment to the direction of the light rays to produce a focused image (Fig. 5). The bi-convex lens is formed entirely of transparent cells, each one measuring about 1.0 cm in length but

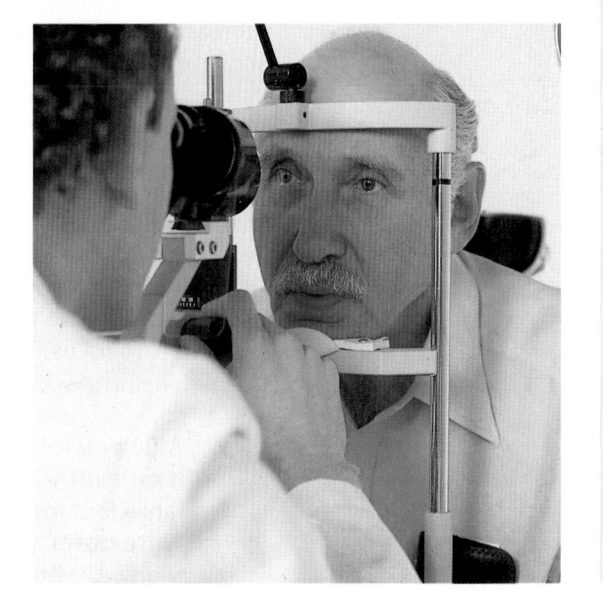

An optician assesses the pressure within the eye using a non-contact tonometer. The tonometer directs a gentle blast of air against the surface of the eye, allowing the opthalmologist to assess the internal pressure of the eye. A high pressure could indicate glaucoma.

with a thickness of only 2 μm. With ageing, the cells become less elastic and the lens becomes less flexible, losing its ability to focus at different distances.

The lens is held in tension by about 70 suspensory ligaments which are connected to the ciliary muscle. As this muscle contracts and relaxes, the lens changes shape (Fig. 6). The ability of the lens to change its focal length automatically, so that objects at different distances are brought into sharp focus on the retina, is called **accommodation**.

When the lens adopts a highly curved surface it increases its focusing **power**. The power of a refracting surface is measured in **dioptres**, D, and is defined as:

$$\text{power (dioptres)} = \frac{1}{\text{focal length (metres)}}$$

By convention, a converging lens has a positive power, whilst a diverging lens has a negative power (Fig. 7).

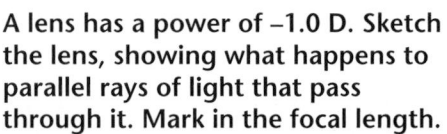 **3** A lens has a power of –1.0 D. Sketch the lens, showing what happens to parallel rays of light that pass through it. Mark in the focal length.

Fig. 5 Cross section through the lens

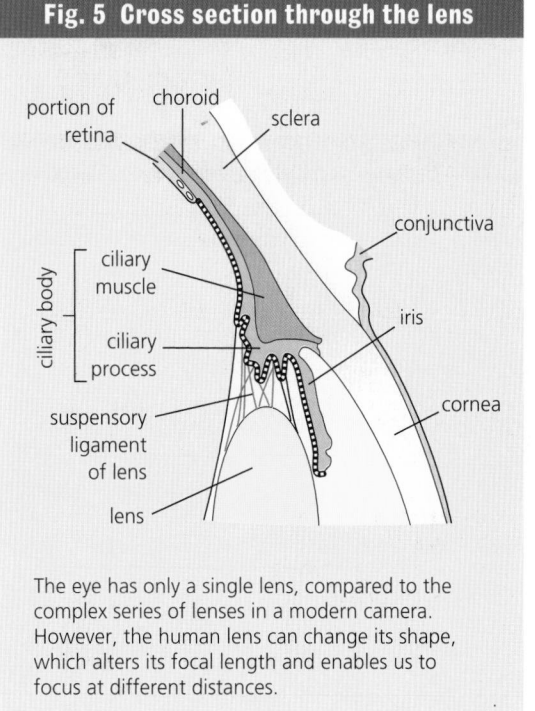

portion of retina

choroid

sclera

ciliary body

ciliary muscle

ciliary process

conjunctiva

iris

suspensory ligament of lens

cornea

lens

The eye has only a single lens, compared to the complex series of lenses in a modern camera. However, the human lens can change its shape, which alters its focal length and enables us to focus at different distances.

83

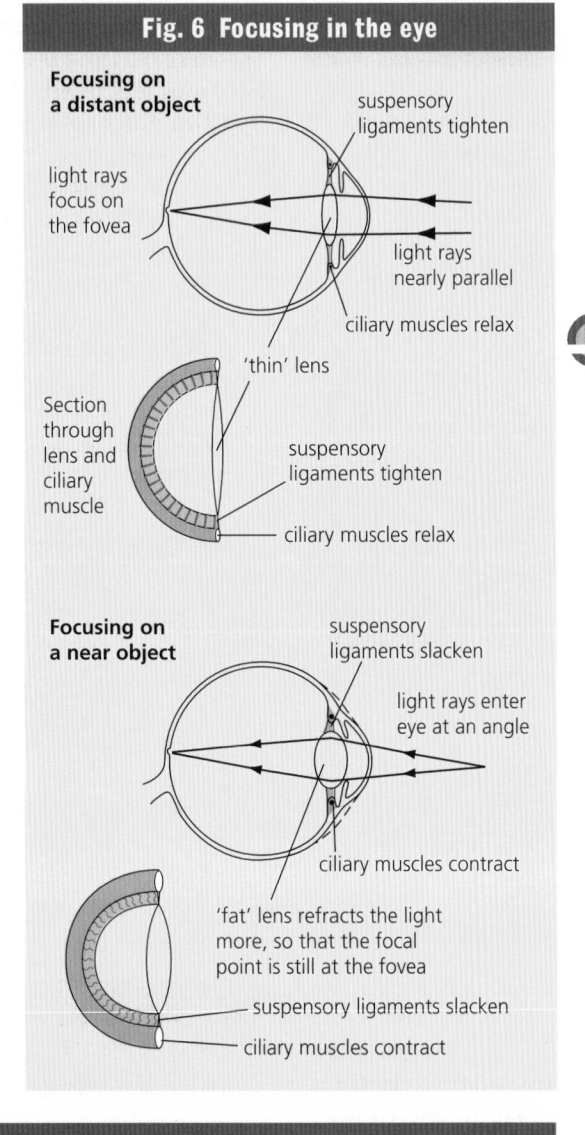

Fig. 6 Focusing in the eye

Focusing on a distant object

suspensory ligaments tighten

light rays focus on the fovea

light rays nearly parallel

ciliary muscles relax

'thin' lens

Section through lens and ciliary muscle

suspensory ligaments tighten

ciliary muscles relax

Focusing on a near object

suspensory ligaments slacken

light rays enter eye at an angle

ciliary muscles contract

'fat' lens refracts the light more, so that the focal point is still at the fovea

suspensory ligaments slacken

ciliary muscles contract

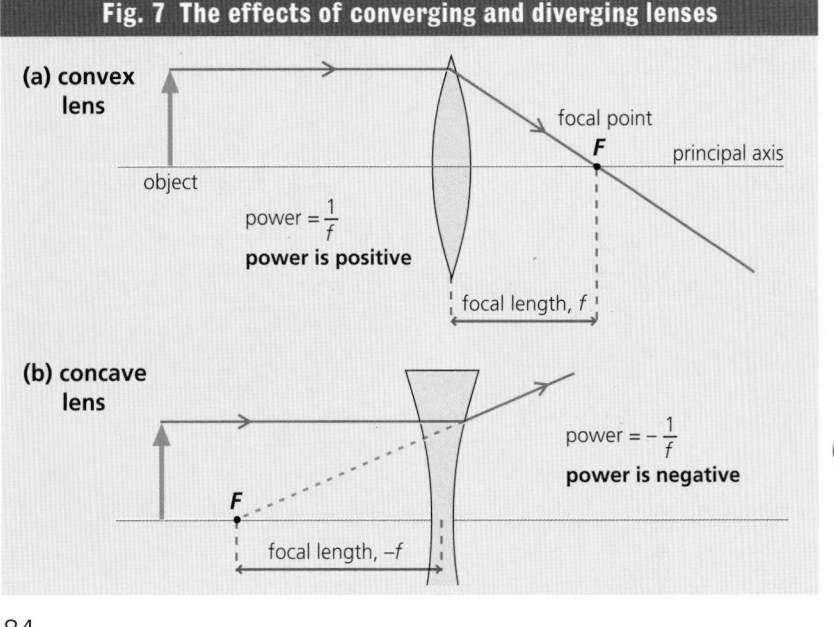

Fig. 7 The effects of converging and diverging lenses

(a) convex lens

object

focal point

F

principal axis

$$power = \frac{1}{f}$$

power is positive

focal length, f

(b) concave lens

F

$$power = -\frac{1}{f}$$

power is negative

focal length, $-f$

The total refracting power of a combination of lenses, or surfaces, is the sum of their powers. The human cornea has a refracting power of about +43 D. The power of the lens varies from +17 D when it is in its flattest, unaccommodated state to about +31 D when it is in an accommodated state. The total power of the eye therefore varies from about +60 D to +74 D.

4 A concave lens of power –5 D is to be used as a spectacle lens for a person whose eye has an overall power of 50 D when the lens is in an accommodated state. What is the focal length of the combination?

The power of the zoom lens system in a video camera can be changed from about 170 D to 17 D. This increases the magnification of the image, but reduces the field of view. The image is brought into focus by moving the lens towards, or away from, the light-sensitive screen. Both the eye and the camera have a limit on the range of distances that they can focus on. The **near point** is the closest distance at which they can produce a sharply focused image. If you close one eye and bring this page close to your other eye, you should be able to find your near point.

For a young, healthy eye the near point is about 25 cm. You may be able to get closer than this for a short time but you will feel a strain as your muscles tire. As you get older things will get worse! The increasing stiffness of the lens makes accommodation more and more difficult. A baby's lens can become almost spherical, but by the age of forty the lens has a much flatter shape and without glasses many people need to hold a book at arm's length in order to read it. This loss of accommodation is known as **presbyopia**.

The **far point** of the eye or camera is the furthest distance at which an object can be brought into focus. For both a camera and a normal, healthy eye the far point is infinity.

5 A 50-year-old mature student finds it difficult to read the board of a large lecture theatre and then to write notes. Explain why this is so.

In the eye, the lens brings rays of light from an object to a focus on the **retina**. For a lens of a known power, it is possible to find out where an image will be formed by constructing a ray diagram (Fig. 8). We simplify the situation by representing the lens as a straight line. The line that passes through the optical centre of the lens at right angles to it is called the **principal axis**. The object is represented as an arrow and the diagram is drawn to scale. The **focal point**, *F*, of the lens is marked in on the principal axis on both sides of the lens.

A converging lens, such as that used in spectacles for long-sight, could have a power of 3 D. The focal length of such a

Fig. 8 Ray diagrams of light passing through convex and concave lenses

Rays of light leave the tip of the object in every direction. For three specific rays, we can predict their passage through the lens and locate the focused image.

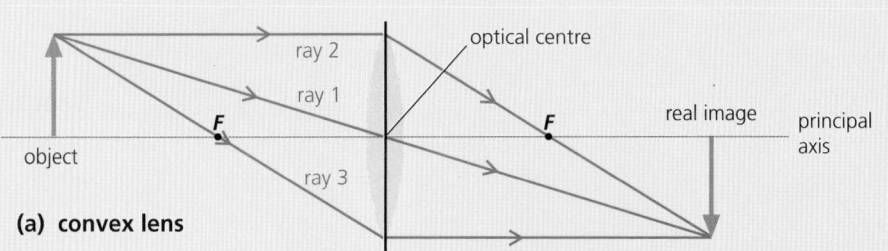

(a) convex lens

Ray 1 Any ray of light that passes through the optical centre will be undeviated.

Ray 2 A ray of light that travels parallel to the principal axis will be refracted through the principal focus.

Ray 3 A ray of light that passes through the principal focus will be refracted so as to travel parallel to the principal axis (this is rule 2 in reverse).

The focused image is formed where the rays of light from the tip of the object meet again. This is referred to as a real image because rays of light actually pass through it – an image would be formed on a screen placed at this point.

(b) concave lens

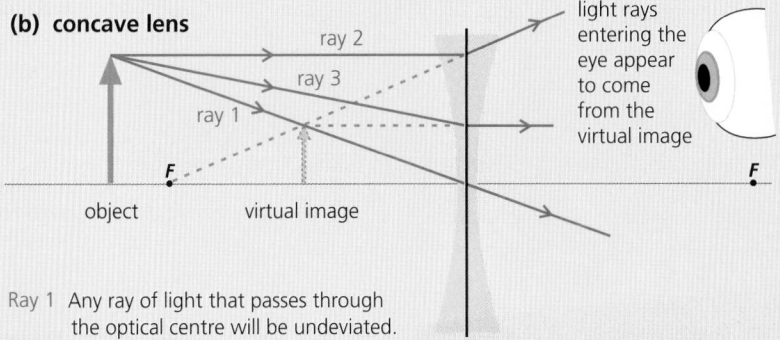

Ray 1 Any ray of light that passes through the optical centre will be undeviated.

Ray 2 A ray of light that travels parallel to the principal axis will be refracted away from the axis, so that it appears to have come from the principal focus.

Ray 3 A ray of light that would have passed through the principal focus will be refracted so as to travel parallel to the principal axis (this is rule 2 in reverse).

The focused image forms where the rays of light from the tip of the object appear to have come from. This is known as a virtual image because no rays of light actually pass through it. It is not possible to form an image on a screen placed at this point.

At the centre of the lens, there is no curvature; the two surfaces of the lens are parallel. The refracted ray leaves the lens at the same angle as it entered. For a thin lens, the deviation is negligible.

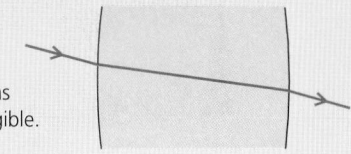

lens is $\frac{1}{3}$ = 0.33 m or 33 cm. A ray diagram can be used to find out where this lens would produce a focused image of an object that is 1 metre from the lens (Fig. 9).

Fig. 9 Using a ray diagram to locate an image

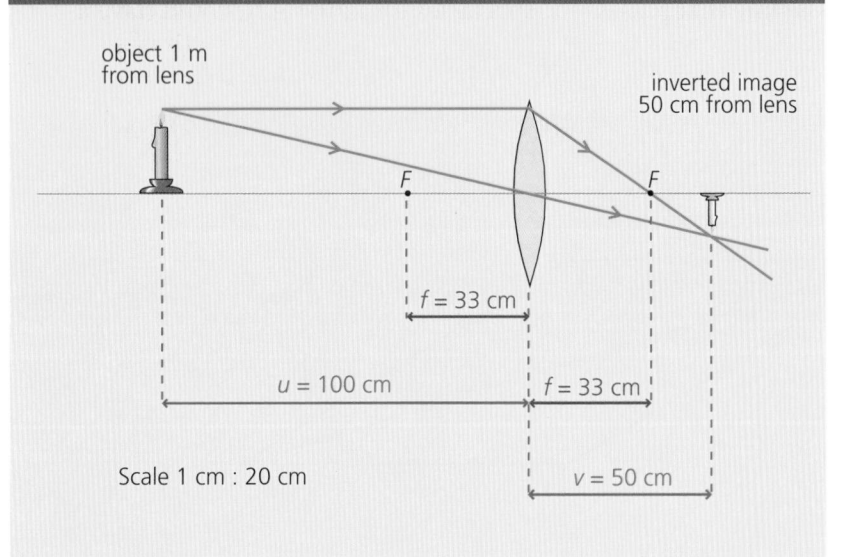

object 1 m from lens

inverted image 50 cm from lens

f = 33 cm

u = 100 cm

f = 33 cm

Scale 1 cm : 20 cm

v = 50 cm

Fig. 10 Depth of field and the circle of confusion

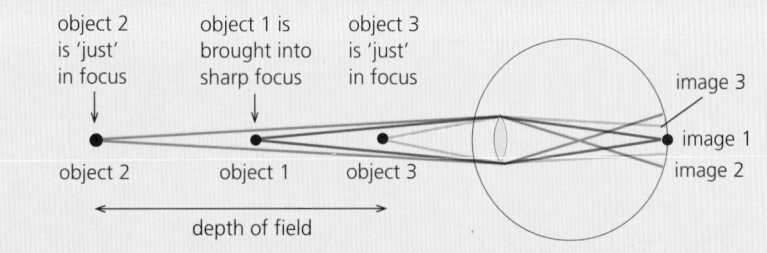

object 2 is 'just' in focus

object 1 is brought into sharp focus

object 3 is 'just' in focus

image 3
image 1
image 2

object 2

object 1

object 3

depth of field

The lens is adjusted to bring the image of object 1 sharply into focus. Object 2 cannot also be exactly in focus. Light leaving a point of object 2 will form a circle on the retina. This circle is called the **circle of confusion**. The distance on either side of the object where the circle of confusion is small enough so that the image is not noticeably blurred, is called the **depth of field**.

6 A camera lens has a focal length of 50 mm.
   a Use a ray diagram to find out how far away the lens has to be from the film if an object is placed 0.5 m from the camera.
   b How far does the lens have to move to focus on objects at infinity?

7 A convex lens cannot produce an image on a screen when the object is closer to the lens than the focal length. Draw a ray diagram to help you explain why this is the case.

Depth of field and depth of focus

In any scene filmed by a camera, not everything can be in focus at the same time. This is also true for your eyes, though we tend not to notice it, because whatever we choose to look at is brought into focus almost instantly by the rapid change of shape of the eye's lens. Close one eye and hold your hand about 30 cm from your eyes. Now fix your gaze on your middle finger and you should be aware that objects in the background are blurred. If you switch your gaze to the background, your fingers will be blurred.

Strictly speaking, only objects at one particular distance can be exactly in focus at any given time. But there is a range of distances over which things are *acceptably* sharp. This range is called the **depth of field** (Fig. 10).

A camera in 'portrait' mode uses its largest possible aperture to give a small depth of field (a). This makes the subject stand out against a blurred background. The depth of field increases if the camera is focused further away (b), or if the aperture is smaller (c).

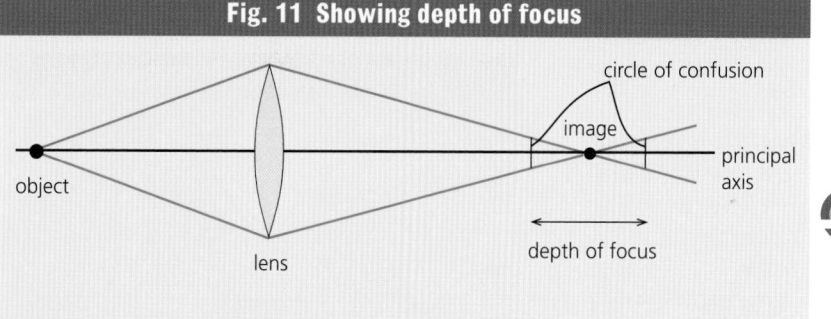

Fig. 11 Showing depth of focus

circle of confusion

image

object

lens

principal axis

depth of focus

A convex lens brings light from a point source to a point image. The distance on either side of that image where the circle of confusion is small, so that it is not noticeably blurred, is called the **depth of focus**.

The depth of field varies with aperture. In bright sunlight, when your pupil is small, you have a greater depth of field. You can simulate this by looking through a small hole; you should notice that nearby objects and distant ones are all in focus.

8 **Your pupil will automatically constrict when you look at nearby objects. Explain why it does this.**

Fig. 12 The effect of aperture size on depth of field and depth of focus

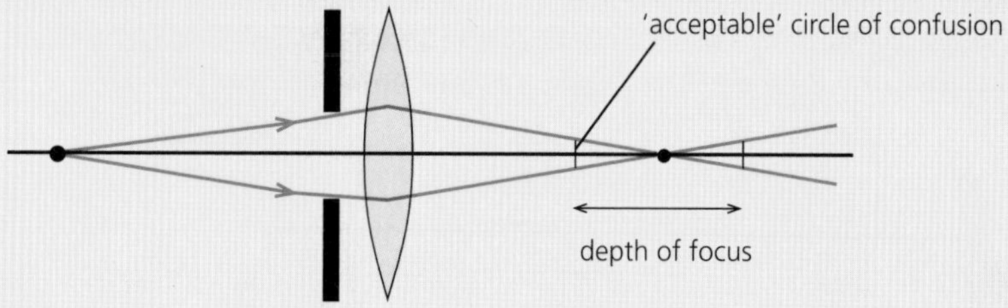

'acceptable' circle of confusion

depth of focus

a   A large aperture allows highly divergent rays of light to reach the lens. These diverge rapidly after the focus and the depth of focus is small.

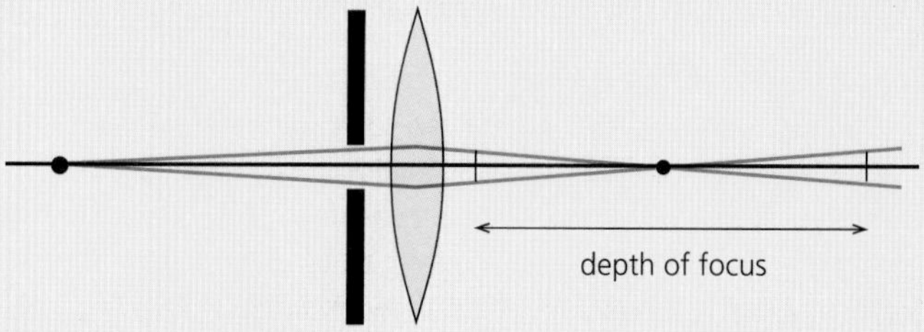

depth of focus

b   A small aperture only admits rays of light which are less divergent. The depth of focus and the depth of field are increased.

Key ideas

- The amount of light entering the eye is controlled by the iris.

- Light is refracted as it passes through the cornea and the lens, so that a focused image is produced on the retina.

- The power (in dioptres) of a lens is:

$$\frac{1}{\text{focal length (in metres)}}$$

- The eye can focus on objects at different distances because the lens can change its curvature, and hence its power. This is called accommodation.

- The range of distances that can be brought into acceptable focus by a lens is called the depth of field.

8.3 Out of focus

20/20 Vision

The most common type of eye test is actually a test of **visual acuity**. Someone with good visual acuity can distinguish smaller details in a scene than someone with poor acuity (Fig. 13). But even a normal eye has a limit on the size of the detail that it can detect. Try reading this book from a distance of two to three metres and the text will become indistinct. This is due to the spacing of the **receptor cells** on the retina (see section 8.4) and the fundamental limit on visual acuity that is set by the diffraction of light (Fig. 14).

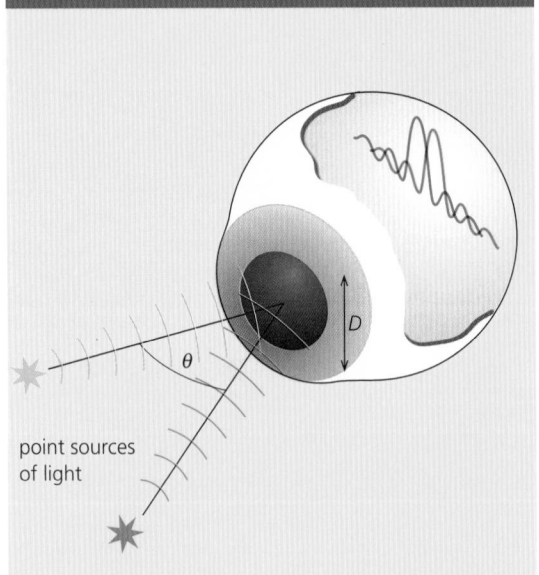

point sources
of light

Fig. 13 The test for visual acuity

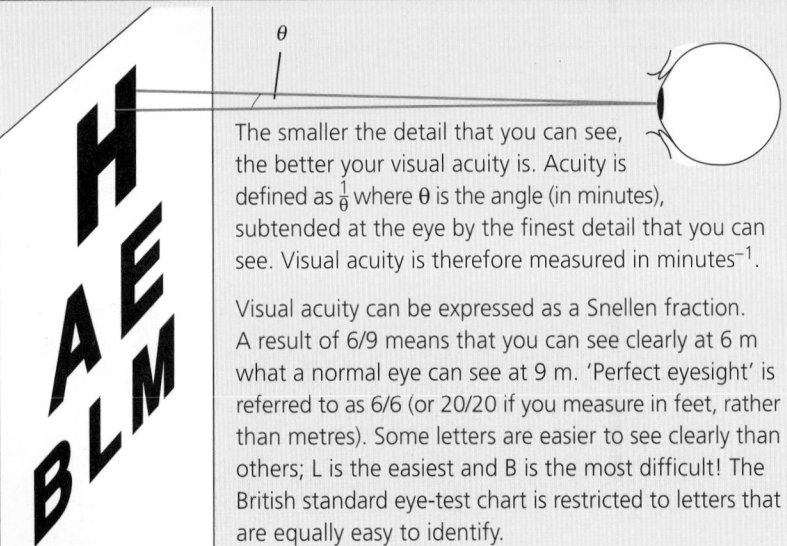

The smaller the detail that you can see, the better your visual acuity is. Acuity is defined as $\frac{1}{\theta}$ where θ is the angle (in minutes), subtended at the eye by the finest detail that you can see. Visual acuity is therefore measured in minutes^{-1}.

Visual acuity can be expressed as a Snellen fraction. A result of 6/9 means that you can see clearly at 6 m what a normal eye can see at 9 m. 'Perfect eyesight' is referred to as 6/6 (or 20/20 if you measure in feet, rather than metres). Some letters are easier to see clearly than others; L is the easiest and B is the most difficult! The British standard eye-test chart is restricted to letters that are equally easy to identify.

When you look at two separate point sources of light, diffraction can cause their images to overlap on the retina. When this happens the two images blur into one and the images are said to be **unresolved.**
The Rayleigh criterion (see chapter 2) says that two images are *just* resolved when the central maximum of one diffraction pattern falls over the first minimum of the other diffraction pattern. The Rayleigh criterion leads to a formula for the minimum angle, θ in radians, that can be resolved:

$$\theta = \frac{1.22\lambda}{D}$$

where D is the diameter of the aperture and λ is the wavelength of the light.
If the diameter of the pupil is about 4 mm and we take a value of λ in the middle of the visible range (about 550 nm), this gives:

$$\theta = \frac{1.22 \times 550 \times 10^{-9}}{4.0 \times 10^{-3}}$$

$$= 1.7 \times 10^{-4} \text{ rad}$$

$$= 0.009° \text{ or } 0.6 \text{ min}$$

This is a visual acuity of $\frac{1}{0.6} = 1.7$ min^{-1}. This means that you should just be able to resolve two objects that are 1 mm apart when they are about 6 m away.

Under ideal conditions, a normal eye could see details that subtend an angle of just over half a minute (see Fig. 14). This is a visual acuity of just under 2 min^{-1}. In practice the actual performance of the eye depends on the brightness and the contrast of the image – the actual acuity may be less than this optimum value.

 9 **The critical detail on a letter H can be taken as the width of its vertical lines. On a car number plate this width is about 1.5 cm. What is the maximum distance at which a person with normal vision could read the letter?**

Short-sightedness

I am short-sighted. I can see nearby objects very clearly, so I can read without my glasses, but more distant objects are blurred. I visit the opticians twice a year so that my lens prescription can be checked.

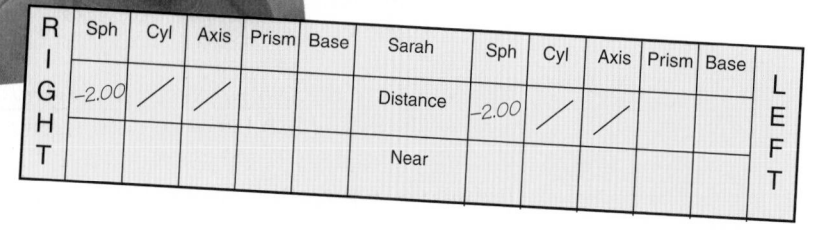

R I G H T	Sph	Cyl	Axis	Prism	Base	Sarah	Sph	Cyl	Axis	Prism	Base	L E F T
	-2.00	/	/			Distance	-2.00	/	/			
						Near						

It is quite common for the eye's refracting power to be badly matched to the length of the eye-ball. When this happens, the image on the retina is out of focus and the visual acuity is much reduced. People who are shortsighted or **myopic** have a lens and cornea that are too powerful, or an eye-ball that is too long. Although a nearby object may be focused properly, the image of a distant object is brought to a focus in front of the retina.

A concave lens can be used to diverge the light, enabling the myopic person to focus on distant objects. However, some people need stronger lenses than others. The **lens formula** is used to calculate the focal length of the required lens.

The lens formula connects the focal length of a lens, f, to the image distance, v, and the object distance, u.

$$\frac{1}{f} = \frac{1}{u} + \frac{1}{v}$$

We can use this formula to calculate where a lens with a 10.0 cm focal length will form an image of an object that is 30.0 cm away.

$$\frac{1}{v} = \frac{1}{f} - \frac{1}{u}$$
$$= \frac{1}{0.100} - \frac{1}{0.300}$$
$$= 10.0 - 3.33$$
$$= 6.67 \text{ m}^{-1}$$

So $v = \dfrac{1}{6.67} = 0.15$ m

The image will be formed 15 cm away from the lens.

It is possible for the image distance to be negative. If the object in the example above was placed 5.0 cm from the lens the calculation would become:

$$\frac{1}{v} = \frac{1}{f} - \frac{1}{u}$$
$$= \frac{1}{0.100} - \frac{1}{0.050}$$
$$= 10.0 - 20.0$$
$$= -10.0 \text{ m}^{-1}$$

So $v = \dfrac{1}{-10.0} = -0.10$ m

In fact, this lens is not powerful enough to bring the image to a focus at all. If we looked through this lens towards the object, the light rays would appear to come from a point –0.1 m from the lens. We say that a **virtual image** has been formed. No light rays actually pass through this image and it could not be formed on a screen. A negative value of the image distance, v, means that a virtual image has been formed on the *same* side of the lens as the object (as in Fig. 8b).

Fig. 15 The short-sighted, or myopic, eye

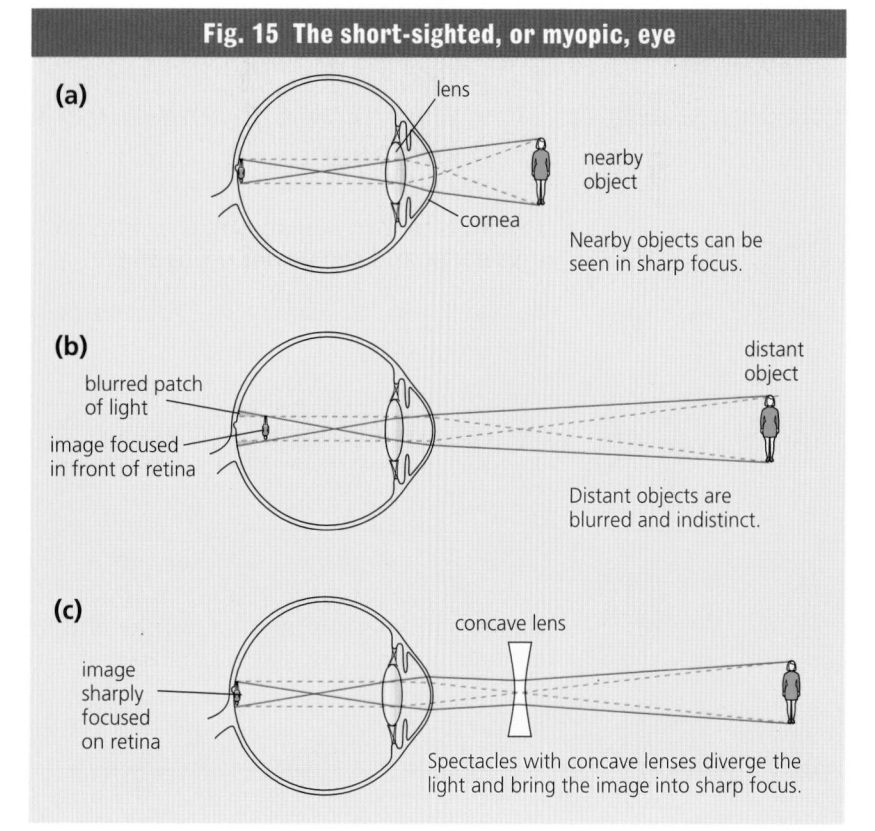

(a) lens, nearby object, cornea

Nearby objects can be seen in sharp focus.

(b) blurred patch of light, image focused in front of retina, distant object

Distant objects are blurred and indistinct.

(c) image sharply focused on retina, concave lens

Spectacles with concave lenses diverge the light and bring the image into sharp focus.

89

Fig. 16 Finding the image from the lens formula

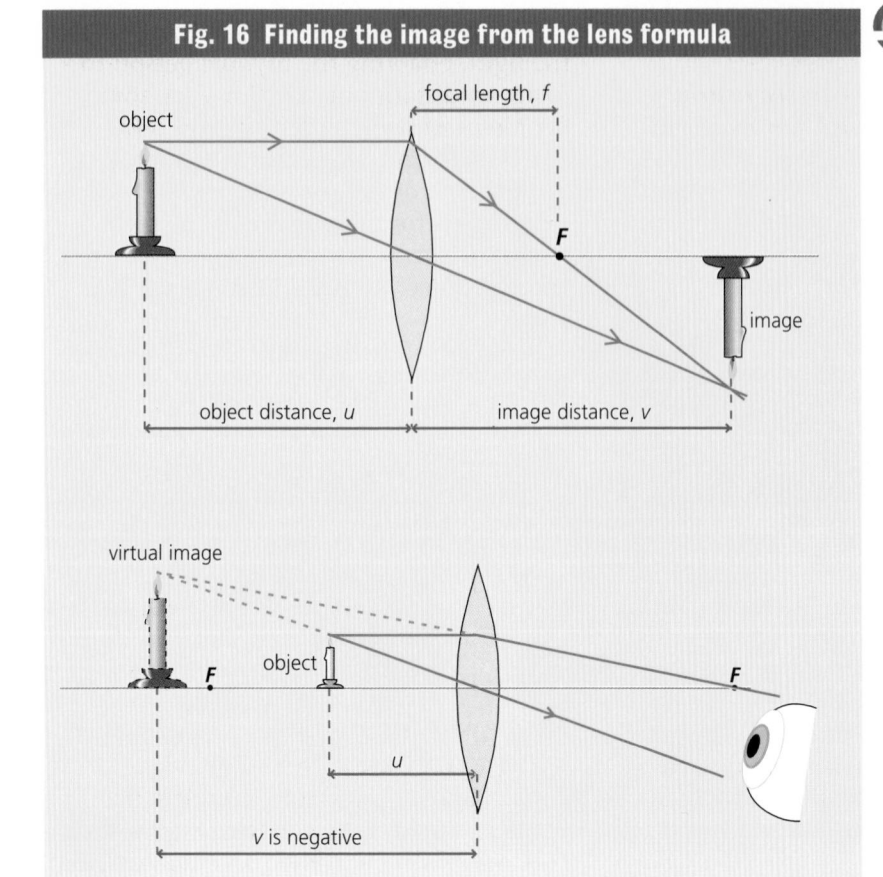

focal length, *f*

object

F

image

object distance, *u*

image distance, *v*

virtual image

F object *F*

u

v is negative

Fig.17 Ray diagrams to show long-sightedness

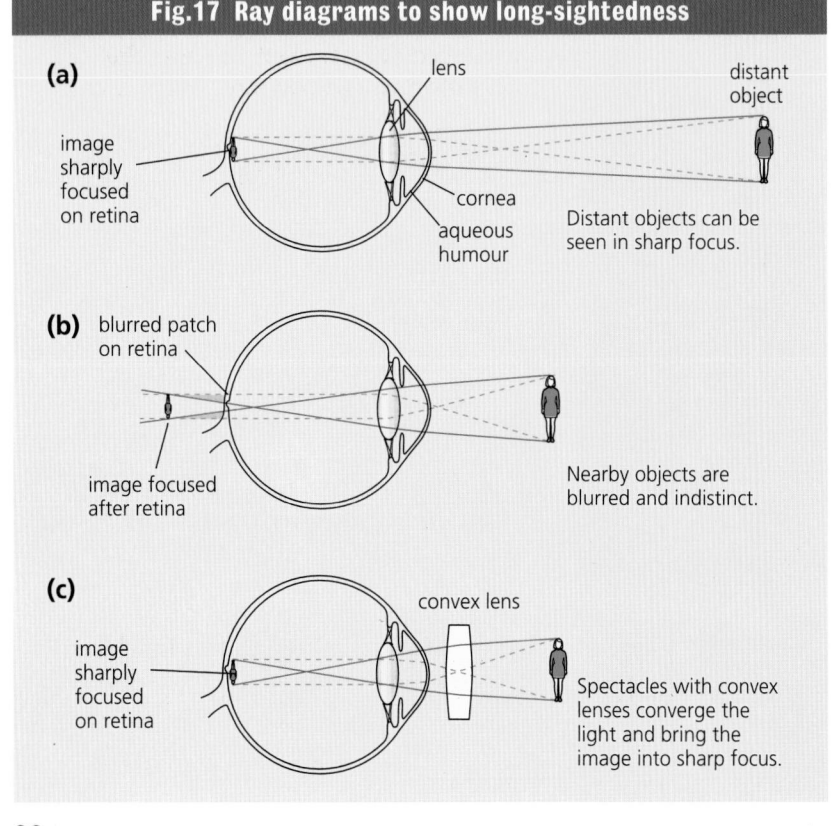

(a)

lens

distant object

image sharply focused on retina

cornea

aqueous humour

Distant objects can be seen in sharp focus.

(b) blurred patch on retina

image focused after retina

Nearby objects are blurred and indistinct.

(c)

convex lens

image sharply focused on retina

Spectacles with convex lenses converge the light and bring the image into sharp focus.

10 A convex lens with a focal length of 20 cm is to be used to produce an image of an object. Where will the object be formed when the object is:

a 40 cm from the lens;
b 20 cm from the lens;
c 10 cm from the lens?

Comment on your answers to parts b and c.

The lens formula also works for **diverging** lenses. To distinguish between converging and diverging lenses, we use a positive number to represent the focal length of a converging (convex) lens and a negative number to represent the focal length of a diverging (concave) lens.

Sarah is very short-sighted, without glasses the furthest object that she can comfortably focus on is 50 cm. This is her **far point**. The distance between the lens and the retina is 20 mm. This gives $u = 0.500$ m and $v = 0.020$ m. We can use this information, together with the lens formula, to calculate the refracting power of her eyes, and then the necessary power of the corrective lens.

$$\frac{1}{f} = \frac{1}{u} + \frac{1}{v}$$

$$= \frac{1}{0.500} + \frac{1}{0.020}$$

$$= 52 \text{ D}$$

If Sarah is to focus on an object at infinity, then $u = \infty$, and the power needs to be:

$$\frac{1}{f} = \frac{1}{\infty} + \frac{1}{0.020}$$

$$= 50 \text{ D}$$

We need to reduce the total refracting power of her eyes from 52 D to 50 D. She can do this by wearing glasses with concave lenses of refracting power –2 D. These glasses will also increase her near point distance (see section 8.2), but this is not usually a problem as myopic people tend to have near points that are very close.

Long-sightedness

When the lens–cornea combination is not powerful enough, the light from nearby objects cannot be brought to a focus before the retina. This condition is called long-sight or **hypermetropia** (Fig. 17). A person with long sight can focus on objects at infinity but cannot focus on nearby things. Convex lenses are needed to converge the light more and to reduce the person's near point.

Q11 A long-sighted person has a near point of 1 m, the distance between their lens and retina is 25 mm.

a Calculate the refracting power of their eyes when they are focused at 1 m.

b What lens power would be needed to enable the person to focus on objects at 25 cm?

Astigmatism

Corneas are not spherical in shape. They have different curvatures in the horizontal and vertical directions. When this difference in curvature is large, or there are irregularities in the cornea, the image formed on the retina can be unevenly focused. This condition is known as **astigmatism**.

Astigmatism can be corrected by using a cylindrical lens (Fig. 18). If the astigmatism is mild, an ordinary contact lens can be used to correct the vision, since the surface of the contact lens can be made perfectly spherical.

The end of spectacles?

About 3 million people in Britain now use contact lenses. Modern contact lenses are made of plastic and are only about 1 mm thick. The latest are soft and oxygen-permeable, making them far more comfortable to wear. However, rigid lenses are still needed by people with severe astigmatism.

Contact lenses can also be useful for people who have had treatment for cataracts, a condition in which the lens becomes opaque. Cataracts can occur due to illness or exposure to radiation, but the most common cause is simply old age.

The only way to restore sight is to remove the patient's lens altogether. A plastic replacement lens is often inserted. When this is not possible, the patient has to wear aphakic spectacles, spectacles with thick convex lenses, to compensate for the loss in refractive power. These tend to make the image larger than normal because the lenses are further from the retina. The **magnification** of an image is defined as:

$$\text{magnification} = \frac{\text{image height}}{\text{object height}}$$

Fig. 18 Correcting astigmatism

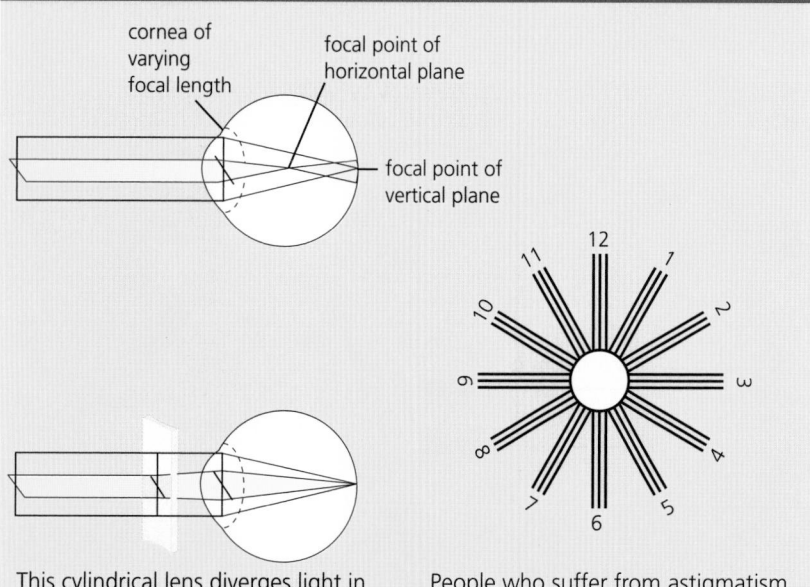

cornea of varying focal length

focal point of horizontal plane

focal point of vertical plane

This cylindrical lens diverges light in the horizontal plane, so that the image is correctly focused on the retina.

People who suffer from astigmatism can see some of these lines clearer than others.

Tinted contact lenses allow you to change the colour of your eyes at will.

Magnification is also given by the ratio:

$$M = \frac{\text{image distance}}{\text{object distance}} = \frac{v}{u} \quad \text{(Fig. 19)}$$

The magnification produced by the eye is always less than one, which means that the image is **diminished**. When aphakic spectacles are used, the image distance (v) is greater than in a normal eye because the lens is further from the retina. The magnification, $\frac{v}{u}$, is increased. Larger images are difficult for the patient to adapt to. It can be difficult to converge the images from both eyes. Contact lenses help because they are worn closer to the retina.

12 A convex lens with a focal length of 20 cm is to be used to produce an image of an object.
  a What will the magnification be when the object is 1 m from the lens?
  b Where will the object be when the magnification is 1 (i.e. the object and the image are the same size)?

Prolonged use of contact lenses can lead to severe eye problems. A new technique which uses a laser to reshape the cornea may be the answer (Fig. 20). Thousands of people have already had the treatment, known as photo-refractive keratectomy, to cure moderate short sight. Under a local anaesthetic a pulsed laser is used to burn away sections of the cornea, each pulse vaporises a layer about 0.25 micrometres thick. A disc about 50 µm deep, half the thickness of a human hair, is eventually carved out. The new profile of the cornea is designed to bring light to a focus exactly on the retina.

Fig. 19 Ray diagram to show image formed by lens

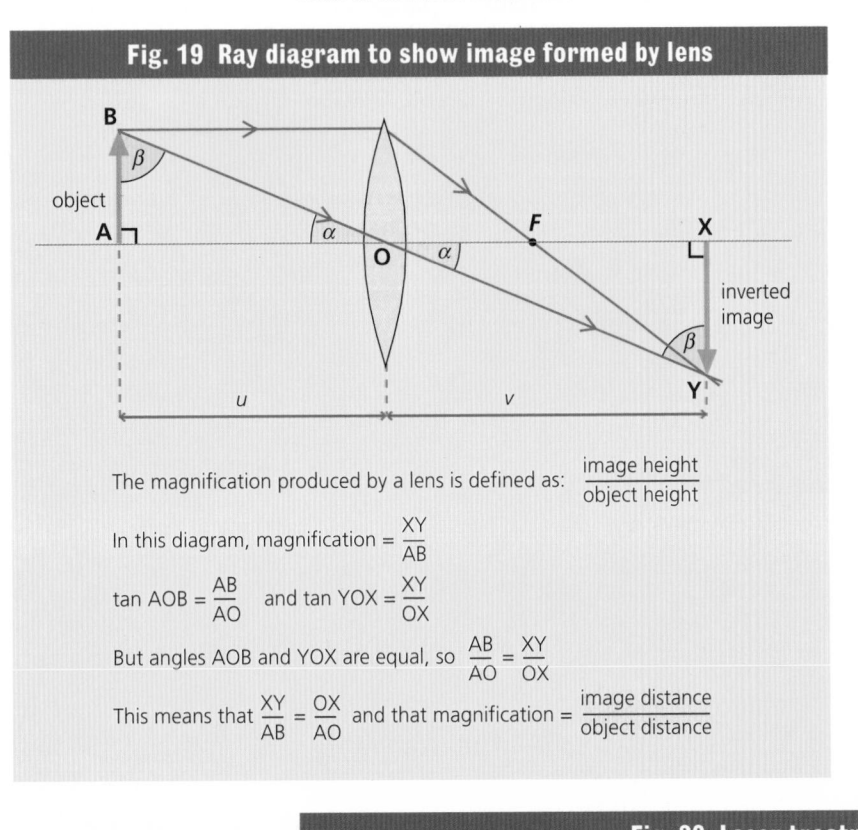

The magnification produced by a lens is defined as: $\frac{\text{image height}}{\text{object height}}$

In this diagram, magnification $= \frac{XY}{AB}$

$\tan AOB = \frac{AB}{AO}$ and $\tan YOX = \frac{XY}{OX}$

But angles AOB and YOX are equal, so $\frac{AB}{AO} = \frac{XY}{OX}$

This means that $\frac{XY}{AB} = \frac{OX}{AO}$ and that magnification $= \frac{\text{image distance}}{\text{object distance}}$

Fig. 20 Laser treatment of the cornea

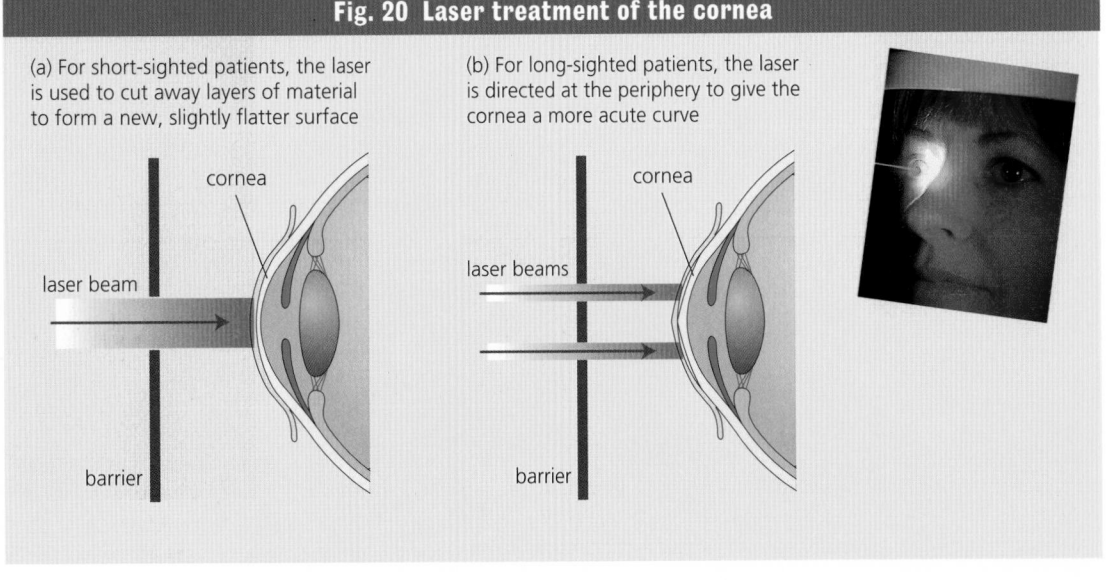

(a) For short-sighted patients, the laser is used to cut away layers of material to form a new, slightly flatter surface

(b) For long-sighted patients, the laser is directed at the periphery to give the cornea a more acute curve

Key ideas

- Myopia, or short sight, means that an image of a distant object is brought to a focus in front of the retina. It can be corrected by wearing concave lenses.

- Hypermetropia, or long sight, means that an image of a nearby object is brought to a focus behind the retina. It is corrected by wearing convex lenses.

- Astigmatism means that images are focused differently in different directions, usually because the cornea is not spherical.

- The lens formula allows you to calculate where an image will be for a lens of focal length f:

$$\frac{1}{f} = \frac{1}{u} + \frac{1}{v}$$

- The magnification of an image is:

$$M = \frac{\text{image height}}{\text{object height}} = \frac{\text{image distance}}{\text{object distance}}$$

- Lasers can be used to reshape the cornea.

8.4 Light detection

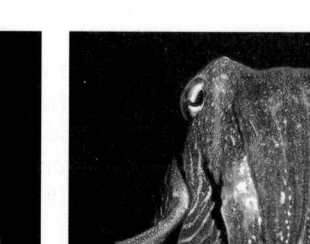

Unpolarised

Cuttlefish can see polarised light. Cuttlefish use patterns of polarised light, reflected from their bodies, to communicate with each other.

The eyes of living creatures vary enormously in their design, from the compound eyes of insects to the complex, camera-like eyes of most animals.

At the heart of all these different eyes are light-sensitive cells. In humans, these are found on the back surface of a tissue called the **retina** (Fig. 21) which lines the inside of the eyeball. The retina contains about 130 million light-sensitive cells, compared with a video camera which forms an image with around 400 000 **pixels**. Each

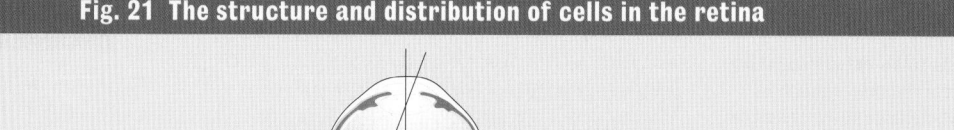

Fig. 21 The structure and distribution of cells in the retina

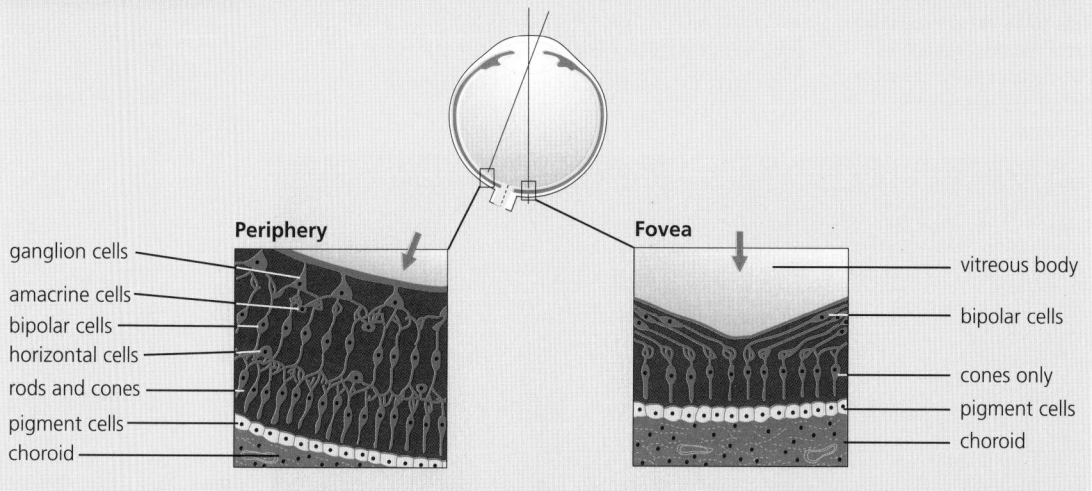

ganglion cells
amacrine cells
bipolar cells
horizontal cells
rods and cones
pigment cells
choroid

Periphery

Fovea

vitreous body
bipolar cells
cones only
pigment cells
choroid

The centre of the field of view falls on the **macula lutea**, or **yellow spot**, where there are only cone cells. In the centre of this region is a small depression called the **fovea**. Peripheral vision uses the edge of the retina where rods outnumber cones 16 to 1.

Fig. 22 Rod and cone cells

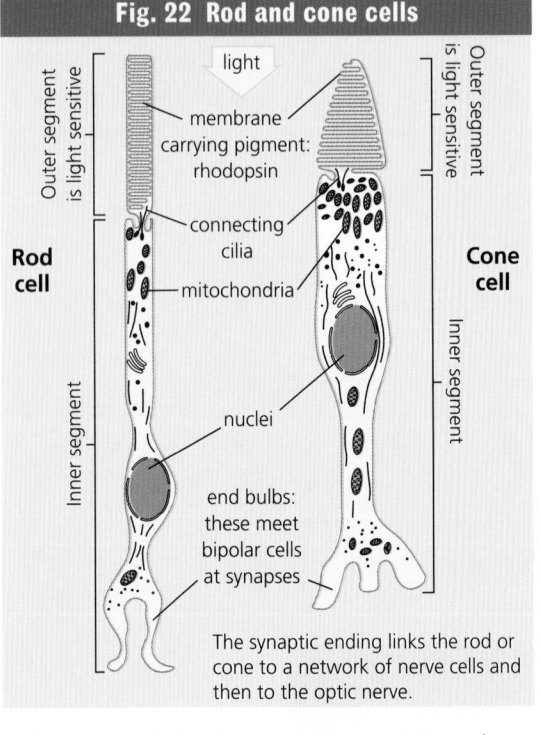

light

Rod cell

Cone cell

Outer segment is light sensitive

Outer segment is light sensitive

Inner segment

Inner segment

membrane carrying pigment: rhodopsin

connecting cilia

mitochondria

nuclei

end bulbs: these meet bipolar cells at synapses

The synaptic ending links the rod or cone to a network of nerve cells and then to the optic nerve.

cell absorbs light from one tiny point of the image. It then generates an impulse which carries information through a complex network of nerves and junctions to the **optic nerve** and then to the brain.

There are two types of light sensitive cells in the retina. These are known as **rods** and **cones** (Fig. 22). Rods are very sensitive to light and can respond to low levels of illumination but they give no information about colour. Cones are less sensitive, but they respond to a narrower range of wavelengths; the overall response pattern gives us colour vision. Under normal, daylight conditions our vision relies on cone cells.

This false-colour scanning electron micrograph of the retina shows rod cells (blue) and cone cells (green).

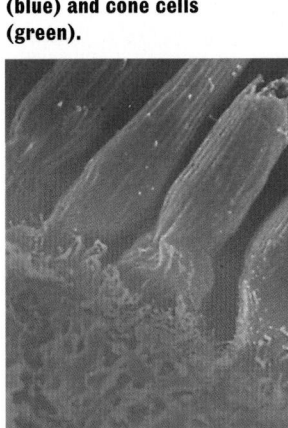

Colour vision

All rod and cone cells contain a specialised chemical known as a photopigment. The molecules of a photopigment can absorb light and stimulate the cell. There are about six million cone cells in a human retina and it is these that provide us with colour vision. Cones can contain any one of three different photopigments – erytholabe, chlorolabe and cyanolabe – each of which responds to a different range of wavelengths (Fig. 23).

When a photon of light strikes the retina, it may be absorbed by one of these photopigments in a cone cell. This produces a change in the electrical potential of the cell of between 20 mV and 30 mV. Different wavelengths of light produce the same change in potential but the probability that a certain photopigment will absorb a photon does depend on the wavelength of the light. A given wavelength of light will stimulate a certain ratio of the three different types of cone cell. This enables the brain to identify wavelengths and produce the sensation of colour.

The yellow on a TV screen is caused by the red and green light emitted by phosphors, which trigger the 'red' and 'green' cones in the right proportion to give the sensation of yellow.

Fig. 23 Graph showing spectral sensitivity of different photopigments

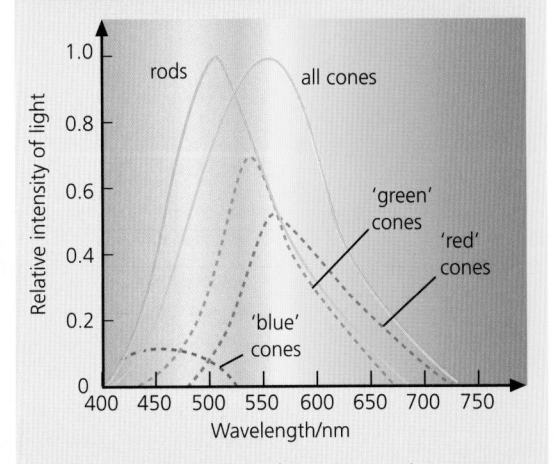

The eye can respond to electromagnetic waves over a range of wavelengths from about 380 nm to 750 nm. Each photopigment responds to a different range of wavelengths.

13 Why do objects lose their colour in moonlight?

14 At school, students are often shown that they can 'create' yellow light by overlapping red and green spotlights. Explain what is really happening.

Seeing in the dark

We rely on cones for colour vision, but they only work well in bright light, or *photopic* conditions. It is the rod cells which are important in low-light, or *scotopic*, conditions (Fig. 24).

In rods, the photopigment is **rhodopsin**, sometimes called visual purple, consisting of two joined molecules, opsin and retinal. Retinal is a derivative of vitamin A. When the retinal molecule absorbs a photon it changes configuration and is detached from the opsin. Opsin then begins to act as an **enzyme**. In this 'active' condition the opsin causes a chain reaction in the cell that leads to a tiny pulse of current lasting roughly 300 milliseconds. During this time the rhodopsin is said to be 'bleached' and the rod cannot detect any other photons that arrive. In normal daylight, much of the rhodopsin is bleached by light, so the rods function only at a low level.

When you step from bright sunlight into a darkened room, you cannot see clearly at first. There is not enough light to stimulate the cones, and the rods are still inactive. However, as soon as the retina is in darker conditions, the rhodopsin begins to be regenerated as retinal rejoins opsin. After some time has passed, your eyes become sensitive to low levels of

The eyes of a Tawny Owl are more than 450 times as responsive in dim light than a human's. The eyes of nocturnal animals, such as owls and cats, only contain rod cells. These cells are both more sensitive and more numerous than the rod cells in human eyes.

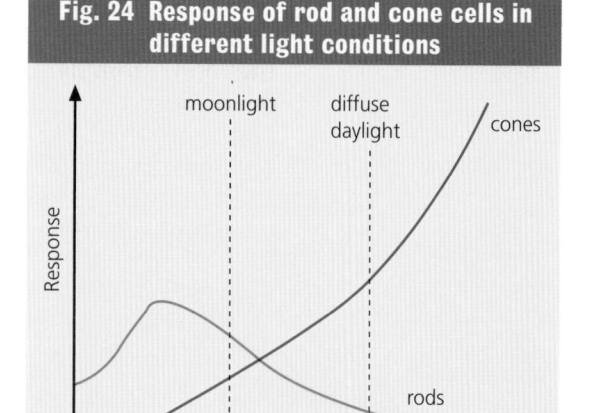

Fig. 24 Response of rod and cone cells in different light conditions

Rod cells become important in low light conditions.

illumination and are said to be **dark adapted**. It takes about half an hour to become fully dark adapted, when rod cells are up to 100 000 times more sensitive than in bright light (Fig. 25). After this time, a rod cell can contain about 100 million regenerated rhodopsin molecules, each capable of absorbing a photon. A single photon of light can cause a current of about one picoampere to flow from the cell. This may not be enough to trigger a nerve impulse, but in the human retina several rod cells are connected to the same nerve fibre, so that the combined effect of several rods can stimulate a signal. This increases the sensitivity, but at the cost of losing some detail in the image.

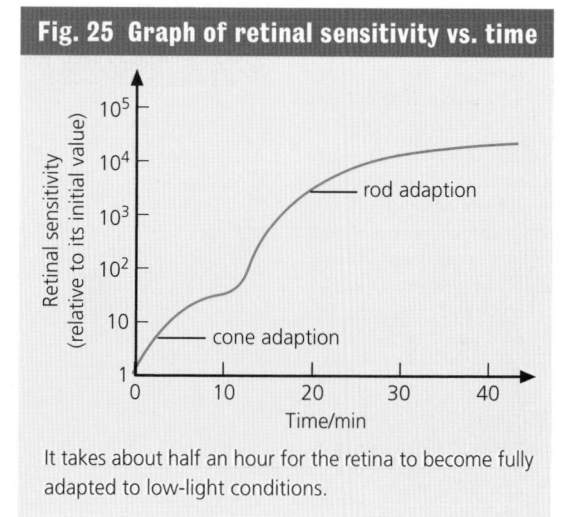

Fig. 25 Graph of retinal sensitivity vs. time

It takes about half an hour for the retina to become fully adapted to low-light conditions.

95

There is also a mechanism known as **light adaption** which protects the cells in the retina from damage due to overexposure to light. Just beneath the rods and cones there is a layer of brown pigment. In bright light, granules of this pigment migrate to the spaces around the cone cells screening them from the light.

Seeing in detail

The eye's ability to see detail, its visual acuity, depends crucially on the spacing of rod and cone cells in the retina. We can only tell that two objects are separate if there is at least one unstimulated cell lying between stimulated cells (Fig. 26). The average separation of light sensitive cells on the retina is 0.003 mm. The distance from the retina to the optical centre of the eye is about 15 mm which gives a minimum angle that can be resolved of:

$$2 \times \frac{0.003}{15} = 0.0004 \text{ rad}$$

or 1.4 minutes, a visual acuity of 0.72 min^{-1}. Our eyes can actually do better than this because rods and cones are not uniformly distributed across the retina. At the edge of our field of view there are more rods than cones, but towards the centre of the field of view cones dominate. One area, known as the **fovea**, has no rod cells at all and the cones are packed to a density of 150 000 cones per mm^2. This area, which is directly in the centre of our field of view, has no large blood vessels near it and the nerve fibres run radially from it, giving an

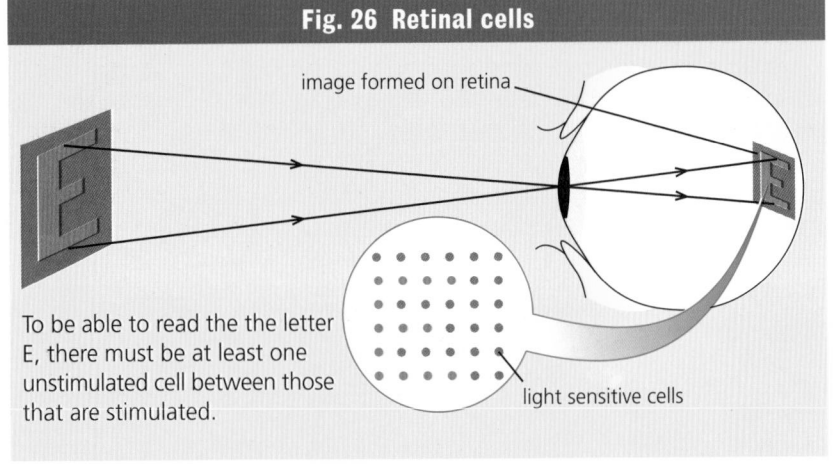

Fig. 26 Retinal cells

image formed on retina

To be able to read the the letter E, there must be at least one unstimulated cell between those that are stimulated.

light sensitive cells

To be able to read the the letter E, there must be at least one unstimulated cell between those that are stimulated.

The eyes of a buzzard are adapted for hunting. The pupils are large, which reduces the amount of diffraction, and each retina has two fovea, each with over one million cones per mm^2. Their eyes are elongated from front to back, which means that larger images of distant objects are formed on the retina.

Fig. 27 The blind spot

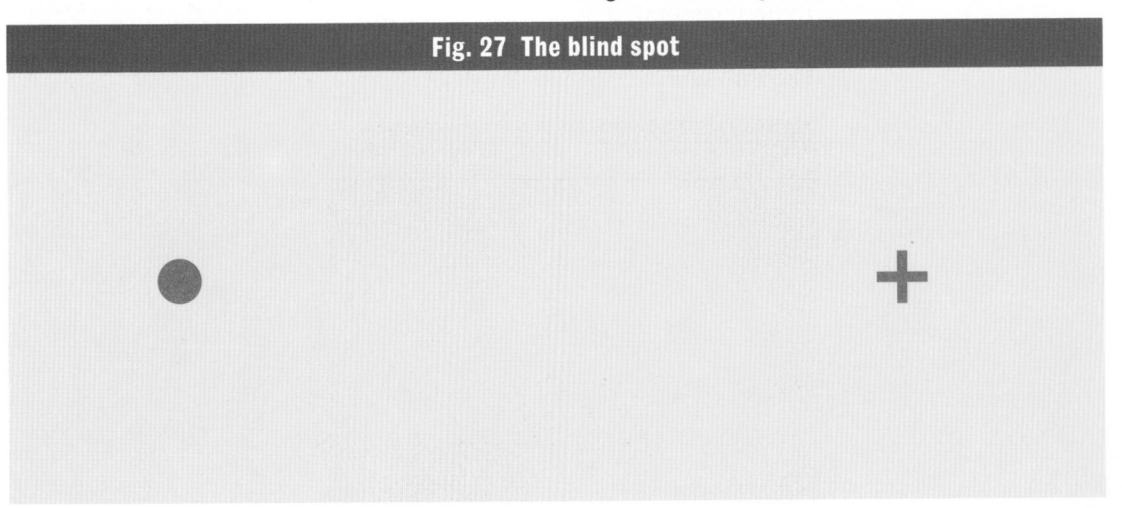

Close your left eye and stare at the dot. Gradually bring your eye closer to the page. When you are about 25–30 cm away, the cross should disappear. At this distance, the image of the cross falls on your blind spot, a part of the retina where there are no rod or cone cells. In fact, this is the point where the optic nerve leaves the eye.

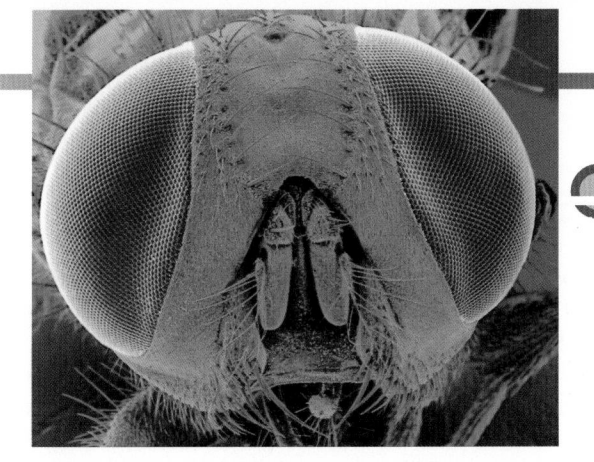

A fly can detect flicker at rates up to 200 Hz.

unobstructed passage for light. This part of the retina gives the maximum visual acuity, about 2 min^{-1}, a visual angle of 0.5 minutes. This is a very close match with the limit due to diffraction (see Fig. 14).

15 Astronomers can often see a very faint star by looking away from it by about 10–15°. Why does this work?

Persistence of vision

When a cone cell detects a flash of light, the whole signalling process takes between 50 and 80 milliseconds, depending on the intensity of light. A rod cell is about four times slower, taking up to 300 milliseconds to finish its signal. If another stimulus arrives at the end of this process the eye cannot tell that the signals are separate flashes, they simply merge together as one continuous light. This is known as **flicker fusion** and is an example of persistence of vision. Humans can detect flashing of up to 60 Hz in very bright lights, but at low intensities flashes of only 5 or 6 Hz can appear continuous.

Cinema projectors rely on persistence of vision. They show only 24 frames per second but we get the impression of a steady picture.

16 Why is it particularly difficult to play ball games, such as tennis, in bad light?

17 a How does the way that rods are connected together make them more sensitive?
b How does this affect the resolution of the image?

Video vision?

When the retina becomes detached or damaged, blindness can result. A major cause of blindness in old age is a condition known as macular degeneration. As the light-sensitive cells in the eye deteriorate, cell debris can accumulate in clumps. New blood vessels may grow and there may be bleeding and scarring. This damages the retina and people begin to have difficulty in recognising faces or reading. Laser treatment can help to remove new blood vessels but no-one has yet been able to transplant a human retina successfully. However, even when the light-sensitive cells are destroyed, the underlying nerve cells that carry the message to the brain remain intact. That is why researchers at the Massachusetts Institute of Technology are working on a new technique in which the damaged retina is replaced with a small video camera placed in spectacles. The camera is linked by a small infrared laser to a microchip implanted in the eye. The microchip stimulates the retinal nerve endings in the same way that healthy retina cells do. The technique has not yet been tested on humans, and there are many problems to overcome, but early experiments have yielded promising results.

Key ideas

- The retina contains two types of light-sensitive cells known as rods and cones.

- Cones enable us to create highly detailed colour images. They work well in daylight.

- Rods are more sensitive and provide us with vision in low-light conditions. They do not provide colour vision and the image is less detailed.

- Visual acuity depends on the spacing of the cone cells and is at its optimum when the image falls on the fovea.

- Rod and cone cells take time to signal the arrival of light. This leads to persistence of vision.

9 Sound thinking

Continual exposure to loud sound has the same effect on your ears as growing old; some teenagers have the same hearing loss as a typical 50 year old. Recent studies on personal stereos have shown that the output can peak at 127 decibels. The sound is generated very close to the ear and the time of exposure can be lengthy.

Experts suggest that to avoid risk the output should be below 90 decibels and exposure should be kept below two hours per day.

In 1996, the French government passed a law limiting the maximum output of personal stereos to 100 decibels, though in the UK there is no such legislation. The French government are also considering limiting the sound level at concerts and clubs. In France, at least, the days of ear-splitting music may be numbered.

The sound level that a rock concert audience is exposed to would be illegal in a factory.

9.1 Learning objectives

After working through this chapter, you should be able to:

- **describe** the structure of the ear;

- **define** sensitivity, frequency response and intensity of sound;

- **calculate** the sound level in decibels from the intensity of sound;

- **explain** how the ear responds to sound;

- **describe** the effects on hearing of exposure to excessive noise and of ageing.

9.2 Hearing performance

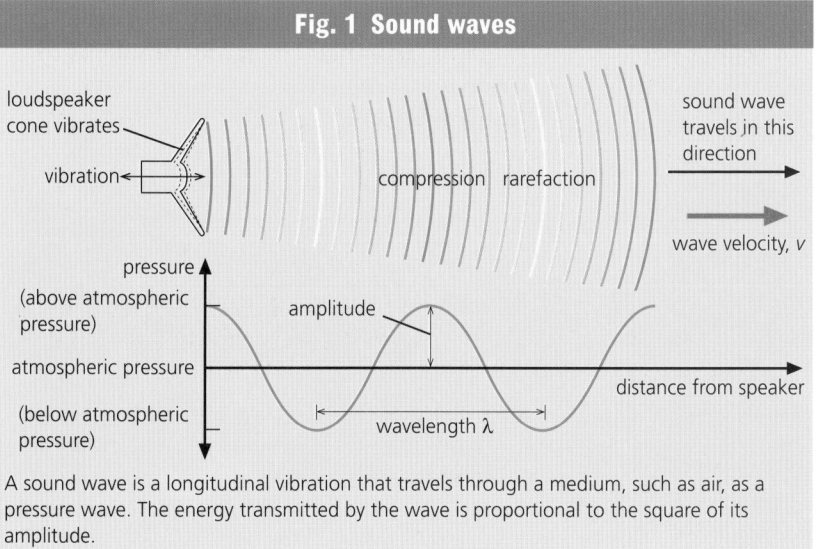

Fig. 1 Sound waves

loudspeaker cone vibrates

vibration

sound wave travels in this direction

compression rarefaction

wave velocity, v

pressure (above atmospheric pressure)

amplitude

atmospheric pressure

(below atmospheric pressure)

distance from speaker

wavelength λ

A sound wave is a longitudinal vibration that travels through a medium, such as air, as a pressure wave. The energy transmitted by the wave is proportional to the square of its amplitude.

Loudness and intensity

The **loudness** of a sound is a difficult thing to measure because it depends on the listener as well as on the sound. What is loud for one person may be barely audible for another. The loudness we perceive also depends on the frequency of the sound because our ears are more sensitive at some frequencies than others. However, for a given person the loudness of a sound of a certain frequency will depend on the rate at which energy is transferred by the sound wave (Fig. 1). This is an objective quantity known as **sound intensity**.

Sound intensity is the energy transferred every second through an area of one square metre held perpendicular to the direction of propagation (travel) of the

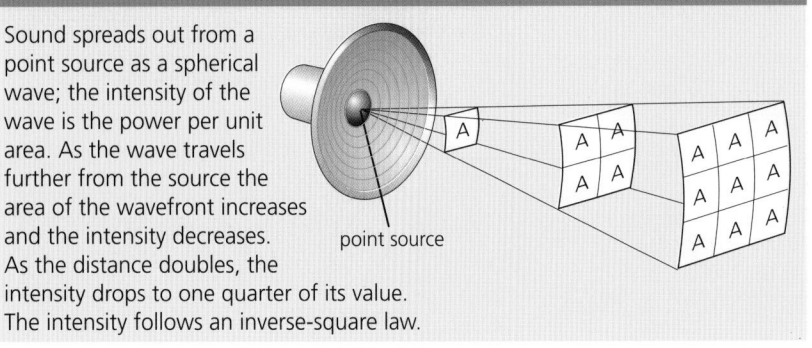
wave (Fig. 2). The unit of intensity is the watt per square metre.

The loudness of a sound is the sensation that we actually experience. That depends on the frequency of the sound and the performance of our ears, as well as the intensity of the sound. At a frequency of 1 kHz, the quietest sound that a healthy human ear can detect corresponds to an intensity of around 1×10^{-12} W m^{-2}. This intensity is defined as the **threshold of hearing**, I_0. The loudest sound that we can detect without severe discomfort corresponds to an intensity of about 100 W m^{-2}. This is known as the **threshold of pain**.

Between these very quiet and very loud sounds the intensity changes by a factor of 10^{14}. However, the sensation of loudness that we experience does not vary by this much. Our ears have an 'automatic volume control' that turns down the amplification when we are exposed to high intensity sounds. The ear is not a *linear* device, so turning up the intensity of a sound wave in equal steps does not make the loudness go up by equal amounts. When it is quiet, a small increase in the sound intensity, such as someone coughing in a library, would

Sound levels near a motorway are higher than you might expect because the motorway acts as a line source of sound, rather than as a point. The sound waves spread out in the shape of a cylinder, not as a sphere, so the inverse-square law does not apply. The sound level is inversely proportional to distance, not distance squared.

seem loud. The same increase in sound intensity at a rock concert would go unnoticed.

In fact, the change in the loudness we hear is proportional to the fractional change in intensity:

$$\text{change in loudness} \propto \frac{\text{change in intensity}}{\text{initial intensity}}$$

We hear the same change in loudness when the sound intensity increase from 1×10^{-12} W m^{-2} to 2×10^{-12} W m^{-2} as from 1 W m^{-2} to 2 W m^{-2}. This means that the loudness, L, that we experience is proportional to the logarithm of the intensity, rather than to the intensity itself:

$$L \propto \log\left(\frac{I}{I_0}\right)$$

where I_0 is the threshold of hearing.

This logarithmic response gives the human ear an enormous **dynamic range**. Under the right conditions, a healthy ear can respond to noises as loud as a jet aircraft taking off and detect sounds as quiet as a pin dropping, a ratio of sound intensities of about 10^{14}.

1 **Sounds of equal intensities do not always seem equally loud. Explain why this is so.**

2 **The dynamic range of the ear is about 10^{14}. If the threshold of hearing is 1×10^{-12} W m^{-2}, what is the highest intensity of sound that the ear can cope with?**

3 **If you are 100 m from a large jet aircraft taking off, the intensity at your ears is likely to be about 10 W m^{-2}. What would the sound level be if you were 10 m away?**

4 **Explain why buying a stereo with twice the output power will not produce music that sounds twice as loud.**

The decibel scale

Because the ear has a logarithmic response to intensity, we use a logarithmic scale to measure sound intensity. **Sound intensity**

level is measured on the decibel (dB) scale, which is defined as:

$$\text{sound intensity level (in dB)} = 10 \log_{10}\left(\frac{I}{I_0}\right)$$

equation 1

On the decibel scale (Fig. 3), all sound levels are related to the threshold of hearing, I_0. A sound that has twice the intensity of the threshold will have a sound intensity level given by:

$$\text{sound intensity level} = 10 \log_{10}\left(\frac{2 \times 10^{-12}}{1 \times 10^{-12}}\right)$$
$$= 10 \log_{10} 2$$
$$= 3 \text{ dB}$$

Doubling the sound intensity always corresponds to a change of 3 dB in the sound intensity level.

Box 1. 'So quiet that you could hear a pin drop ...'

Is this really possible? How far away could you hear it? Suppose that a pin has a mass of 0.1 g and is dropped from a height of about 10 cm onto a hard, metal surface. We could calculate the change in potential energy, $\Delta(mgh)$, of the pin:

$$\Delta(mgh) = 0.1 \times 10^{-3} \text{ kg} \times 10 \text{ m s}^{-2} \times 0.1 \text{ m}$$
$$= 1 \times 10^{-4} \text{ J}$$

A reasonable assumption is that only 0.1% of this energy would be transferred as a sound wave. If we assume that the sound lasts for about 0.1 s, we can calculate the sound power emitted by the pin:

$$\text{power} = \frac{\text{energy transferred}}{\text{time taken}} = \frac{1 \times 10^{-7} \text{ J}}{0.1 \text{ s}} = 1 \times 10^{-6} \text{ W}$$

If we further assume that the sound is radiated equally in all directions, at a distance r away this sound wave now covers a sphere of area $4\pi r^2$, so:

$$\text{intensity} = \frac{1 \times 10^{-6} \text{ W}}{4\pi r^2}$$

Rearranging gives:

$$r^2 = \frac{1 \times 10^{-6}}{4\pi \times \text{intensity}}$$

If the threshold intensity of hearing is 1×10^{-12} W m^{-2}:

$$r^2 = \frac{1 \times 10^{-6} \text{ W}}{4\pi \times 1 \times 10^{-12} \text{ W m}^{-2}}$$
$$r = 280 \text{ m}$$

Although we have made a number of assumptions, the calculation gives some idea of how responsive our ears can be. All you need now is a really quiet place to try it out!

Fig. 3 The decibel scale

dB	
130	Jet aircraft taking off
120	
110	Pneumatic drill one metre away
100	A discotheque
90	Symphony orchestra at a crescendo
80	A vacuum cleaner one metre away
70	Inside a moving bus
60	General classroom noise
50	A whisper one metre away
40	A quiet classroom
30	
20	
10	Quiet countryside
0	Threshold of hearing

The decibel scale is used to quantify everyday sounds. The scale takes its name from Alexander Graham Bell, inventor of the telephone. The decibel scale measures sound intensity level, not loudness. A sound intensity level of 20 dB would seem louder to some people than others, and it may not even be audible to an older person.

In a discotheque, the sound intensity level could be as high as 120 dB if you are unfortunate enough to be close to the speakers. We can rearrange equation 1 to calculate the sound intensity:

$$I = I_0 \log^{-1}\left(\frac{\text{sound intensity level (dB)}}{10}\right)$$
$$I = 1 \times 10^{-12} \log^{-1}\left(\frac{120}{10}\right)$$
$$I = 1 \text{ W m}^{-2}$$

5 At a rock concert, the sound intensity level 10 m from a bass speaker is 105 dB. Calculate how much sound power is emitted from the bass speaker. (If a loudspeaker is small compared with the wavelength of sound it can be treated as a point source, so you can apply the inverse-square law to this problem.)

6 If the 'safe' level of sound is around 90 dB, how far from the speakers do you need to be?

Sensitive ears

Our ability to detect small changes in intensity, ΔI, is known as the **sensitivity** of the ear. Sensitivity depends on the logarithm of the fractional change in intensity. It is defined as:

$$\text{sensitivity} = \log_{10}\left(\frac{I}{\Delta I}\right)$$

equation 2

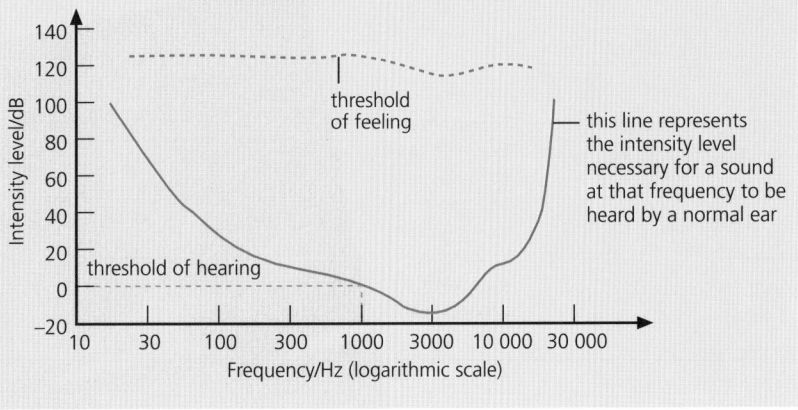

Some animals have a much larger frequency range than humans. Bats can detect sounds with frequencies as high as 115 kHz.

Sensitivity is affected by the frequency of the sound. Our ears are most sensitive at around 2 kHz. At this frequency, the ear can detect changes of intensity of about 12%. Compare this with the eye which can detect changes in the intensity of light of around 1%.

In a disco, it can be difficult to make yourself heard over the sound of the music. Even at a frequency of 2 kHz, a large change in sound intensity is needed to make anyone notice. Suppose that the sound intensity level is 95 dB. The intensity of sound at 95 dB is 0.0032 W m^{-2}. The maximum sensitivity of the ear is 12%; putting these two values into equation 2 gives the minimum change in intensity that will be noticed:

$$0.12 = \log_{10}\left(\frac{0.0032}{\Delta I}\right)$$

$$\Delta I = \frac{0.0032}{10^{0.12}} = 0.0024 \text{ W m}^{-2}$$

The total intensity is now:

0.0032 + 0.0024 = 5.6 × 10^{-3} W m^{-2}

This is a sound intensity level of:

$$10 \log_{10}\left(\frac{5.6 \times 10^{-3}}{1 \times 10^{-12}}\right) = 97.5 \text{ dB}$$

Q 7 The sound level in a disco is 95 dB and someone shouts at you at a sound level of 80 dB. What is the total sound level?

Frequency response

Our ears respond differently to different frequencies of sound. The actual range of frequencies that can be heard varies from person to person, but a young adult with healthy ears should be able to detect sounds from about 20 Hz to 20 000 Hz (Fig. 4). Sounds below 20 Hz can often be felt as vibrations, but cannot be heard. Sounds above 20 kHz are referred to as **ultrasonic**.

The loudness of a sound for a given person is measured by allowing them to compare it to the loudness of a standard source of sound (Fig. 5). A 1 kHz sound source is placed next to the source of unknown loudness. The 1 kHz source is adjusted until it sounds just as loud as the unknown source. If the 1 kHz source is then measured as 70 dB, the unknown source has a loudness of 70 phons.

It is possible to take into account the frequency dependence of our hearing when we are trying to specify sound intensity levels. Sound level meters can have their output electronically weighted so that they simulate the response of the human ear. This involves using electronic filters – similar to the bass and treble controls on a hi-fi – to suppress certain frequencies by specific amounts. The weighted sound intensities are a measure of the *effect* on the

Fig. 4 Graph showing the frequency range of a normal ear

The threshold of hearing is defined as 0 dB at 1 kHz, but our ears can detect 3 kHz sounds at even lower intensities than this. Very high frequency sounds can be detected, if the intensity is high enough.

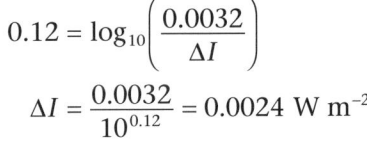

this line represents the intensity level necessary for a sound at that frequency to be heard by a normal ear

Fig. 5 Equal loudness curves for a normal ear

These equal loudness curves show the sound intensity level that is required to produce the same perception of loudness at different frequencies.

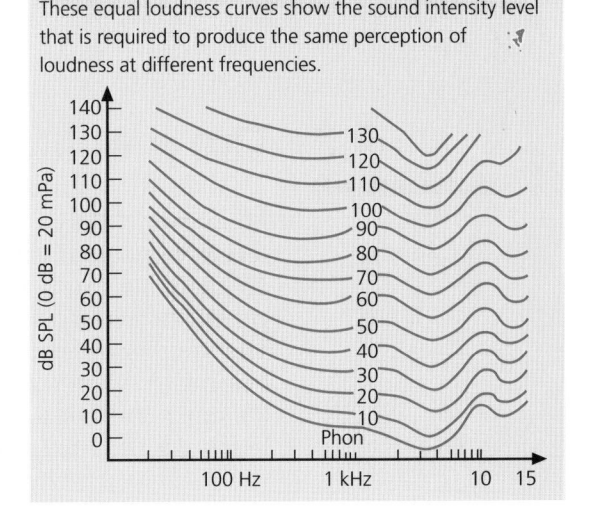

ear and are represented on the **dBA scale** (Fig. 6). Environmental monitoring uses the dBA scale.

Our ability to detect changes in frequency is not constant throughout the frequency range. Below 1 kHz we can discriminate between frequencies that are only 2 or 3 Hz apart. Above 1 kHz this deteriorates steadily and we find it very difficult to distinguish between notes that are above 10 kHz.

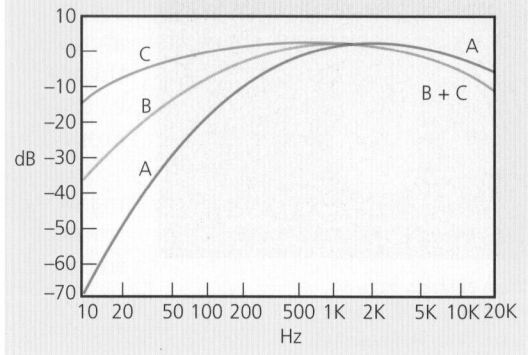

Fig. 6 The dBA scale

Other weighted scales are available (dBB, dBC, etc) which take into account the fact that our ears have different frequency response curves at different sound intensity levels

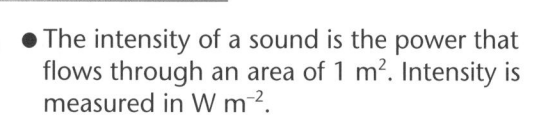

Q8 During a hearing test, a sound wave of frequency 3 kHz and intensity 8×10^{-7} W m^{-2} sounded just as loud as a 1 kHz wave of sound intensity level 60 dB.

a What is the sound intensity level of the 3 kHz sound?

b How loud is the 3 kHz sound?

c Why are the answers to parts a and b numerically different?

Key ideas

- The intensity of a sound is the power that flows through an area of 1 m^2. Intensity is measured in W m^{-2}.

- The ear has a large dynamic range, from the threshold of hearing, I_0 (1×10^{-12} W m^{-2}) to the threshold of pain (about 100 W m^{-2}).

- The loudness of a sound is a subjective quantity. It depends on the frequency of a sound as well as its intensity.

- Equal loudness curves plot the intensity of a sound needed to cause a given sensation of loudness against frequency.

- The sound intensity level is measured in decibels, dB.

$$dB = 10 \log_{10}\left(\frac{I}{I_0}\right)$$

- The sensitivity of the ear is its ability to detect small changes in intensity:

$$\text{sensitivity} = \log_{10}\left(\frac{I}{\Delta I}\right)$$

and is at its peak at 2 kHz.

- The dBA scale is a weighted scale that takes into account the frequency response of the human ear.

9.3 The mechanics of hearing

About two children in every thousand have severely impaired hearing. For those under 16, the main causes of deafness are a genetic defect or a severe childhood illness. The number of people who suffer from a hearing problem rises sharply with age. At 65, one person in three has a significant hearing loss; at 80, only one person in three can hear well without the assistance of a hearing aid.

Percussionist Evelyn Glennie has impaired hearing; she uses vibrations to keep in time with orchestras

Fig. 7 Cross-section through the ear

A sound wave passes through the three sections of the ear in about 20 milliseconds

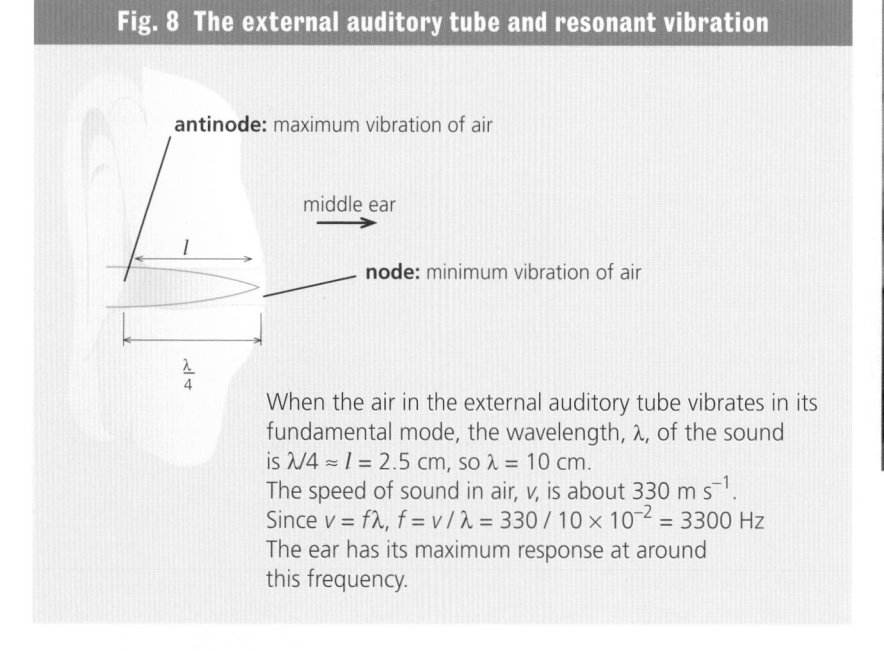

outer ear | middle ear | inner ear | brain | oval window
pinna
anvil
auditory nerves
eardrum | hammer
ear canal
cochlea
stirrup
round window
Eustachian tube

the outer ear collects sound waves and relays them to the eardrum

the middle ear transmits vibrations of the eardrum to the inner ear; amplifying or damping vibrations as necessary

the inner ear or cochlea converts vibrations to electrical signals which are transmitted to the brain via the auditory nerve

Extending the area of the pinna can help you to pick up more sounds. Just putting a cupped hand behind your ear can increase sound levels by 6 dB.

The outer ear

The visible part of the human ear is known as the pinna (Fig. 7). Its function is to collect sound waves and funnel them down the external auditory tube. The pinna is shaped so that sound sources in front of us are detected more easily than those behind. This helps us to determine the direction of a sound source.

The external auditory tube is about 2.5 cm long and 7 mm in diameter. Although it is not completely straight, it acts rather like a miniature organ pipe, closed at one end by the eardrum. The external auditory tube modifies the sound that we hear due to its resonant properties (Fig. 8).

The sound waves in the auditory tube cause the eardrum to vibrate. These vibrations have a remarkably small amplitude. For quiet sounds, your eardrum may move less than 10^{-11} m – less than the diameter of an atom! The eardrum can be damaged by very loud sounds of about 160 dB such as a rifle being fired next to the ear. Sudden pressure changes, perhaps caused by a blow to the ear, can also damage the eardrum.

Fig. 8 The external auditory tube and resonant vibration

antinode: maximum vibration of air

middle ear →

node: minimum vibration of air

l

$\frac{\lambda}{4}$

When the air in the external auditory tube vibrates in its fundamental mode, the wavelength, λ, of the sound is $\lambda/4 \approx l = 2.5$ cm, so $\lambda = 10$ cm.
The speed of sound in air, v, is about 330 m s^{-1}.
Since $v = f\lambda$, $f = v / \lambda = 330 / 10 \times 10^{-2} = 3300$ Hz
The ear has its maximum response at around this frequency.

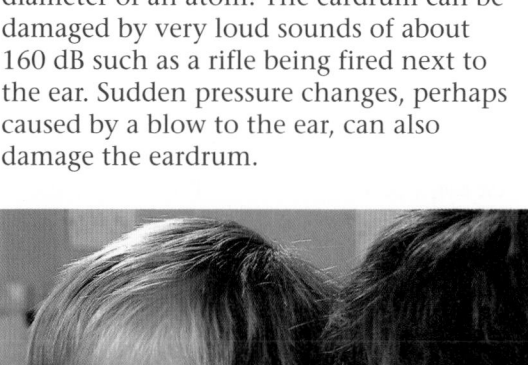

A doctor's otoscope gives a magnified view of the ear canal and ear drum. Any obstructions to the passage of sound through the outer ear may cause temporary deafness. Foreign bodies or too much wax are common problems.

The middle ear

The bones of the middle ear – or ossicles – are the malleus (hammer), incus (anvil) and stapes (stirrup). They pass the vibrations of the eardrum to the oval window which is the entrance to the cochlea (Fig. 9). They provide **acoustic matching** which enables vibrations in the air of the outer ear to be passed to vibrations in the liquid of the inner ear. The ossicles act as a lever, magnifying the force which acts on the oval window to 1.3 times larger than the force on the eardrum. The oval window has an area 20 times less than the eardrum. This serves to increase the pressure acting on the fluid of the inner ear by a factor of 20. The overall effect of the middle ear is to amplify the pressure changes by a factor of $20 \times 1.3 = 26$. Without this amplification there would be significant acoustic losses as the sound wave passed through different media.

The small muscles which are attached to the stapes and the malleus can protect our eardrums from loud noises to some extent. When the muscles contract they reduce the vibrations passed to the inner ear. This process takes about 50 ms and so cannot protect against sudden changes in volume. At 120 dB, the so-called threshold of feeling, the ossicles vibrate so hard they strike the walls of the middle ear and produce a tickling sensation.

The middle ear is connected to the throat by the Eustachian tube. This tube helps to make sure that the air pressure is the same in the outer and inner ear. Any pressure differences tend to reduce hearing sensitivity and can cause pain. The Eustachian tube is normally closed, but opens when we swallow or yawn. Some illnesses can cause the walls of the tube to swell and block the opening. This is common in children and can lead to hearing impairment as the middle ear fills with fluid. Small plastic tubes called grommets are inserted to allow the fluid to drain away.

Sound levels near to a one month old baby can be as high as 95 dBA. A reflex action causes the muscles in the baby's ear to contract as he begins to cry. This reduces sound transmission through the middle ear and prevents the baby from deafening himself.

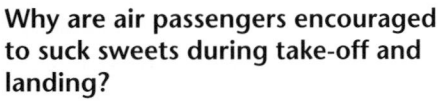

9 Why are air passengers encouraged to suck sweets during take-off and landing?

10 Explain why music with loud drum beats can damage your hearing?

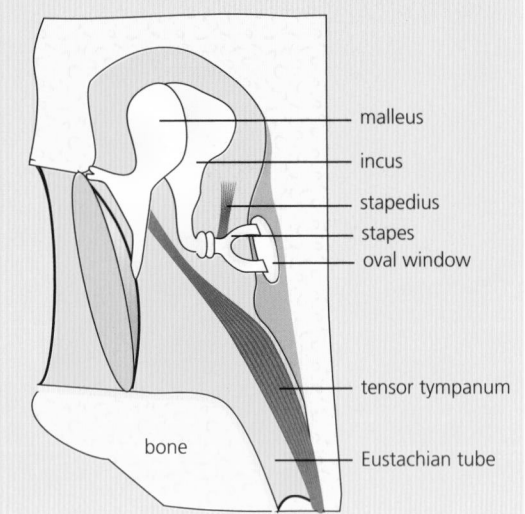

Fig. 9 The middle ear

The bones of the middle ear transmit the vibrations of the eardrum to the oval window.

Labels: malleus, incus, stapedius, stapes, oval window, tensor tympanum, bone, Eustachian tube

The inner ear

The vibrations of the oval window pass into the fluid of the inner ear. This is where the detection of the sound waves takes place, in a spiral tube known as the **cochlea** (Fig. 10). The cochlea is a cavity – about the size of a pea – in the bone of the thickest part of the skull.

The cochlea contains hair cells which convert vibrations to electrical impulses. There are about 30 000 sensory hair cells in each ear. They are amazingly sensitive; a distortion of 0.0003° can be detected. When the hairs vibrate they trigger a change in

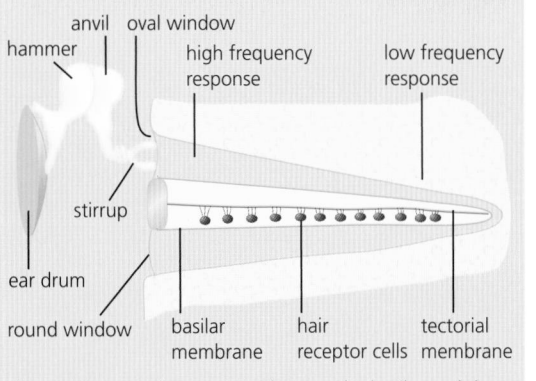

Fig. 10 The cochlea

Labels: anvil, oval window, hammer, high frequency response, low frequency response, stirrup, ear drum, round window, basilar membrane, hair receptor cells, tectorial membrane

The cochlea contains two membranes, the basilar and the tectorial. The basilar membrane holds a row of hair cells. These hairs project through the fluid of the inner ear to the tectorial membrane. When the stapes vibrates against the oval window, the basilar membrane vibrates and the hair cells are distorted.

electrical potential difference across the cell. A small current then flows in the auditory nerve, which leads to the sensation of sound in the brain.

Hair cells can fire quickly enough to detect low frequency waves of below 1 kHz. But nerve cells cannot carry impulses faster than 1 kHz, and another mechanism is needed to detect higher tones. Low-frequency sound waves cause the whole length of the basilar membrane to vibrate, whereas high-frequency sounds cause only the first part of the membrane to vibrate. So different frequencies cause different sections of hair cells to vibrate and the brain interprets this as pitch, signalling a high or a low note.

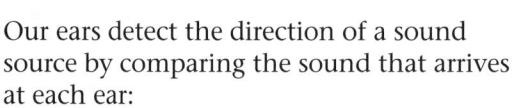 **11 Draw a the flow chart showing the stages involved when the human ear detects a sound.**

Our ears detect the direction of a sound source by comparing the sound that arrives at each ear:

- At low frequencies, the brain can detect phase differences in the sound wave arriving at each ear.
- A difference in intensity can help. The head tends to obstruct the sound to one ear. Diffraction makes this less important at low frequencies.
- The time delay between the two signals can give accurate direction information; remarkably, the brain can distinguish a time difference of 0.01 ms.

Hearing damage

One way of assessing hearing damage is to measure someone's response to sounds of different frequency. An **audiometer** is used to produce sounds at various frequencies and intensities in a pair of earphones. The audiometer is calibrated to read 0 dB for the level at which 'normal' hearing people can just detect the sound. If a patient can only detect sounds which are 50 dB louder than this, they are said to have a hearing loss of 50 dB. This test is usually carried out at eight frequencies between 125 Hz and 8 kHz. The plot of frequency against hearing loss is called an audiogram (Fig. 11).

There are maximum noise exposure levels and times laid down by the Health and Safety regulations. If the noise level gets to 99 dBA, workers are only allowed one hour's exposure. At 111 dBA, the maximum exposure time is under four minutes.

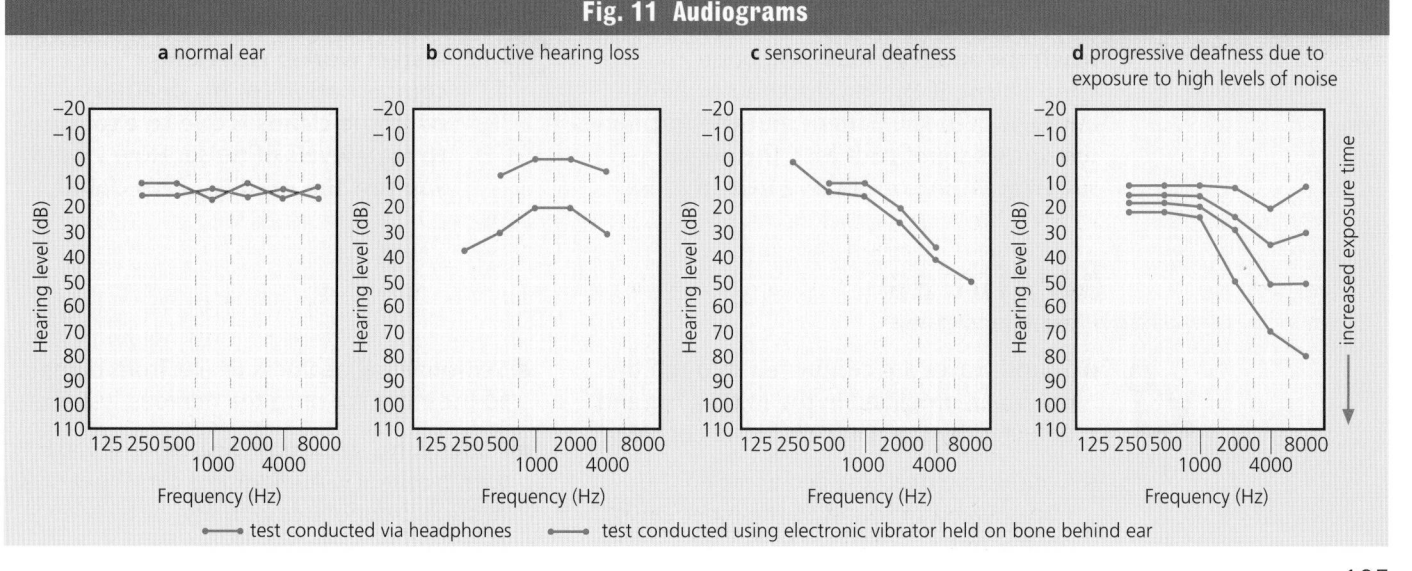

Fig. 11 Audiograms

a normal ear | b conductive hearing loss | c sensorineural deafness | d progressive deafness due to exposure to high levels of noise

test conducted via headphones   test conducted using electronic vibrator held on bone behind ear

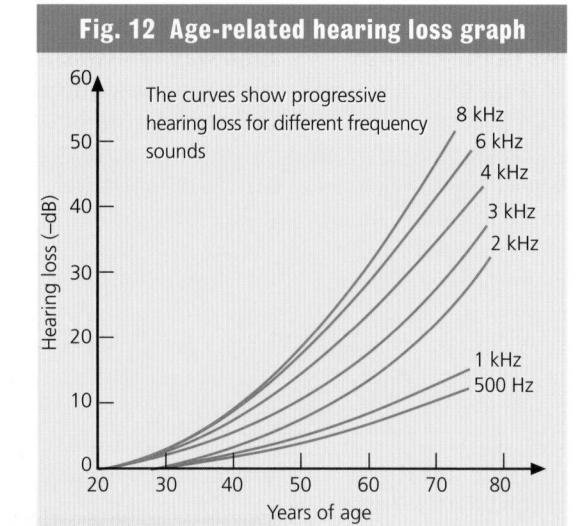

Fig. 12 Age-related hearing loss graph

The curves show progressive hearing loss for different frequency sounds

Hearing loss (–dB) vs Years of age. Curves labelled 8 kHz, 6 kHz, 4 kHz, 3 kHz, 2 kHz, 1 kHz, 500 Hz

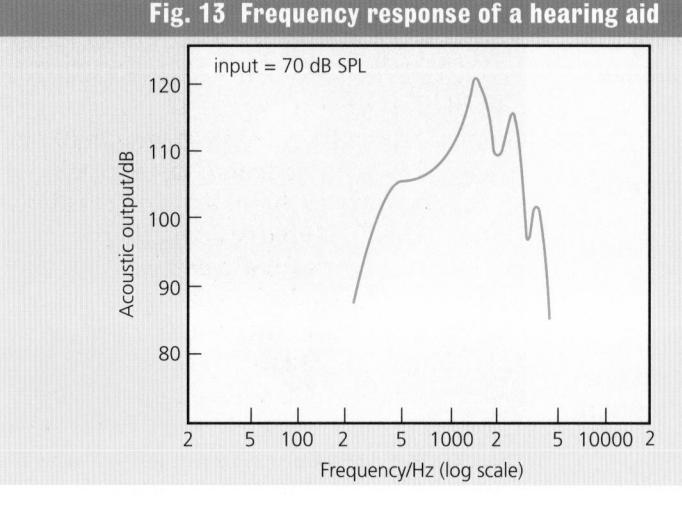

Fig. 13 Frequency response of a hearing aid

input = 70 dB SPL

Acoustic output/dB vs Frequency/Hz (log scale)

The audiometer can be used with an electronically calibrated mechanical vibrator, rather than earphones. The vibrating device is placed directly on the skull near the ear and produces sounds that reach the auditory nerve via bone conduction. If this produces a normal audiogram in the patient, but the earphones test shows significant loss, the person is suffering from **conductive hearing loss**.

There may be an obstruction in the outer ear or a middle ear infection. If both tests show hearing loss, the person is suffering from **sensorineural loss** and may have damage to the cochlea or the auditory nerve.

Our hearing gradually deteriorates with age (Fig. 12). Higher-frequency hearing deteriorates most; frequencies below about 500 Hz are barely affected. Although the main frequencies for the human voice are of the order of a few hundred Hz, there are higher-frequency harmonics present in sounds such as 's' and 't' which an elderly person finds it difficult to detect.

The audiogram of a person damaged by years of exposure to industrial noise or to loud music looks rather different (Fig. 11d). Hearing impairment is caused by damage to the delicate hair cells in the cochlea. High-frequency sound is particularly dangerous, though the audiogram shows damage around 4 kHz, whatever the frequency of the noise that caused the damage. Further exposure to loud sounds may cause damage down to 1 kHz.

For ears damaged through excessive noise, the only solution is to build in permanent sound amplification by fitting a hearing aid. A combination of microphone, amplifier and loudspeaker can boost sound levels by up to 90 dB. Boosting all frequencies by the same amount would cause uncomfortably loud low-frequency sounds for a person who is deaf only to higher frequencies, so modern hearing aids boost some frequencies more than others (Fig. 13).

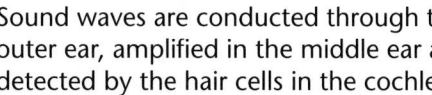

12 A steel worker is seeking compensation for his deafness which he claims is due to exposure to high levels of noise. How would you test the validity of his claim?

Key ideas

- Sound waves are conducted through the outer ear, amplified in the middle ear and detected by the hair cells in the cochlea.

- Conductive deafness occurs when the transmission of sound to the inner ear is obstructed.

- Sensorineural deafness results from damage to the inner ear or to the nervous system.

- Audiograms show how hearing loss varies with frequency. Audiograms can show how hearing deteriorates with age or by exposure to excessive noise.

Stay young and beautiful

Wrinkles are a visible sign of age. As we get older our skin loses its elasticity. This is partly due to cumulative damage to proteins, such as collagen, caused by UV radiation.
Americans spend $850 million a year on anti-wrinkle cream. However, it may be more effective to slap on some sun cream or to wear a hat.

People are living longer. A man born in Britain in 1900 had an average life expectancy of 46 years; a woman could expect to live to 49. One hundred years later, the life expectancy at birth is predicted to be 75 years for men and 80 for women. Modern medicine has allowed more people to reach old age, but that leads to other health problems.

As you age, your body changes in a number of predictable ways (Fig. 1). Sight and hearing deteriorate, bones weaken and tissue loses its elasticity. By the age of 50 your muscles will have about 80% of their youthful strength. Your heart, kidneys, liver and lungs also become less efficient. Blood pressure tends to rise as your arteries narrow and harden. Chronic illnesses such as diabetes, stroke, cancer and heart disease are also much more prevalent in old age.

The challenge facing scientists now is to make sure that we lead healthier lives, rather than just longer ones.

Fig. 1 Changes in effectiveness of body functions after age 38

Graph: % Property remaining (averaged) vs Age/years, showing lines for:
- nerve conduction velocity
- heart function
- kidney function
- maximal breathing capacity

10.1 Learning objectives

After working through this chapter, you should be able to:

- **calculate** the stresses acting on bones in the body;

- **describe** the propagation of nerve impulses;

- **apply** the principle of moments to joints in the body;

- **describe** the structure and action of the heart;

- **explain** the principles of ECG measurements;

- **explain** the principles of blood pressure measurement.

10.2 The human machine

The human body is an impressive machine (Fig. 2). The 206 bones of your skeleton are pulled around by over 600 muscles – via 187 joints – to allow you to run, swim, lift and bend. Bones need to be strong enough to support and protect the vital organs of the body, yet light enough to be lifted easily by the muscles that are attached to them.

Bone is formed mainly of the protein **collagen** impregnated with calcium phosphate which makes bone very hard. Bones need to withstand high compressive stresses. Compressive stress is the ratio of axial force acting on the bone to cross-sectional area and is measured in N m^{-2} or Pa (Fig. 3).

Bones often have to withstand forces many times greater than your body weight. For example, if your mass is 70 kg and you jump off a 1.8 m wall on to a hard surface, will you break your leg?

The speed, v, that you would reach just before you hit the ground is given by:

$$v^2 = u^2 + 2as$$
$$= 0 + 2 \times -9.8 \text{ m s}^{-2} \times -1.8 \text{ m}$$
$$= 35.3 \text{ m}^2 \text{ s}^{-2}$$
$$v = -5.94 \text{ m s}^{-1}$$

(taking up to be the positive direction).

Suppose that the collision with the ground takes 0.004 s to bring you entirely to rest. The deceleration, a, is given by:

$$a = \frac{v - u}{t}$$
$$= \frac{0 - (-5.94 \text{ m s}^{-1})}{0.004 \text{ s}}$$
$$= 1490 \text{ m s}^{-2}$$

The average force needed to decelerate a body of mass 70 kg is:

$$F = ma$$
$$= 70 \text{ kg} \times 1490 \text{ m s}^{-2}$$
$$= 104\,000 \text{ N}$$

Fig. 2 The musculo-skeletal system

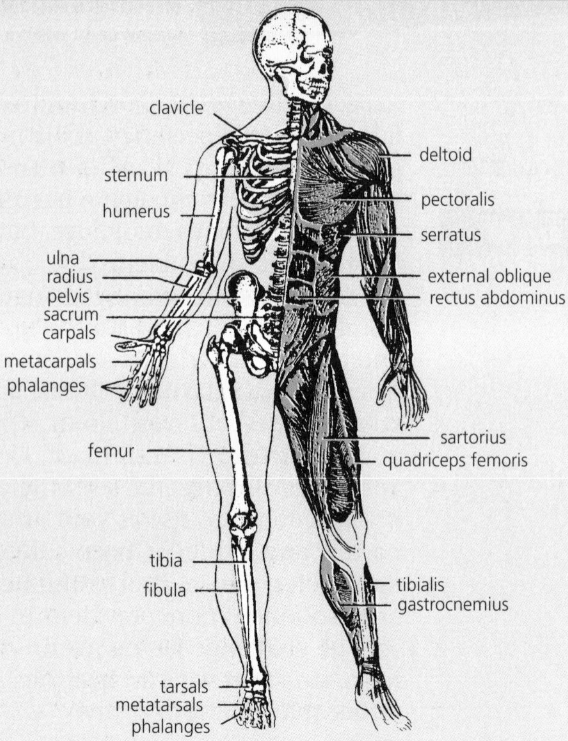

clavicle
sternum
humerus
ulna
radius
pelvis
sacrum
carpals
metacarpals
phalanges
femur
tibia
fibula
tarsals
metatarsals
phalanges

deltoid
pectoralis
serratus
external oblique
rectus abdominus
sartorius
quadriceps femoris
tibialis
gastrocnemius

In the science of biomechanics, the human body is viewed as a machine that can be analysed in terms of the forces, power and velocities of its components.

Table 1 The mechanical properties of bone and other materials

Material	Compressive breaking stress (MPa)	Ultimate tensile stress (MPa)	Young Modulus (GPa)	Density (Kg m^{-3})
bone	150	140	28	1850
concrete	≈ 40	≈ 4	14	2400
aluminium	–	80	71	2710
polypropylene	–	35	1.2	900

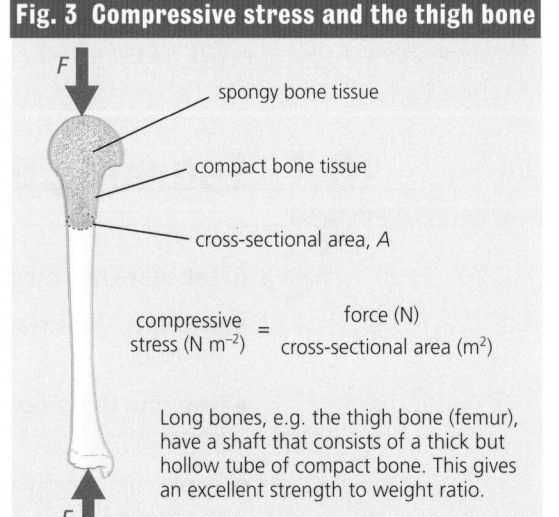

Fig. 3 Compressive stress and the thigh bone

F

spongy bone tissue

compact bone tissue

cross-sectional area, A

$$\text{compressive stress (N m}^{-2}) = \frac{\text{force (N)}}{\text{cross-sectional area (m}^2)}$$

Long bones, e.g. the thigh bone (femur), have a shaft that consists of a thick but hollow tube of compact bone. This gives an excellent strength to weight ratio.

F

Despite their strength, bones do fracture. A sideways impact causes the bones to bend and fractures often occur where the bone is in tension.

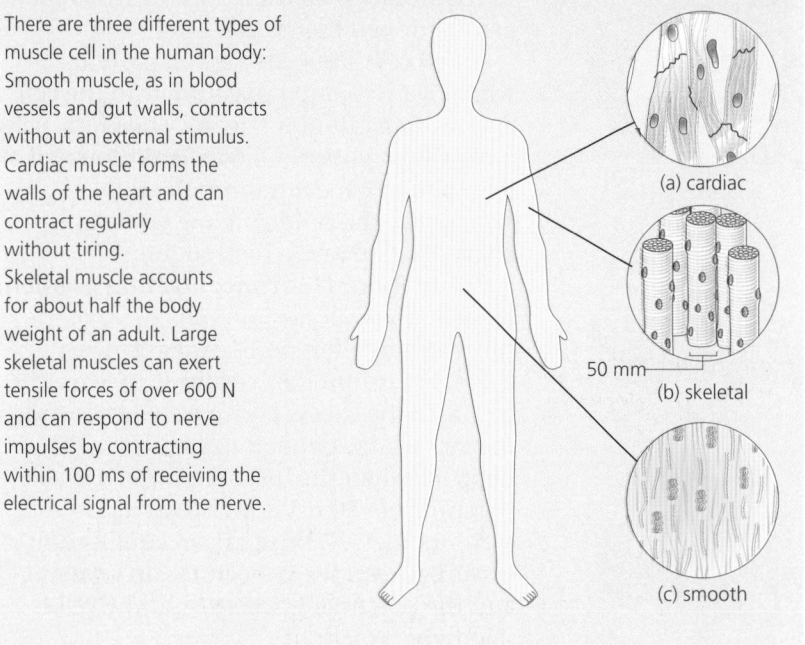

In space, astronauts are effectively 'weightless' and bone loss occurs up to ten times as fast as it does on Earth. Muscles also atrophy – after a few weeks in space, 40 per cent of muscle tissue may be lost.

If you land evenly on both legs, the force on each leg is half of this value, i.e. 52 000 N. The cross-sectional area of the bone in the lower leg is about 3.5×10^{-4} m². This gives a compressive stress on the bone of about 150 MPa, just about enough to break your legs.

In practice, you can reduce the size of the force by extending the time of the collision. Bending your knees at the moment of impact and cushioning from the soles of your shoes help to reduce the size of the force.

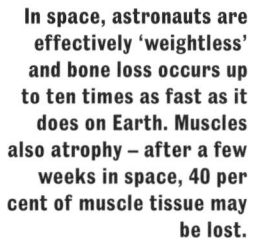

1　**About 70 per cent of body mass is in the torso and head. A thigh bone is typically 4 cm in diameter.**
　a　**Calculate the average compressive stress in a thigh bone when a person of mass 65 kg is standing.**
　b　**What is the value if the person lands from a height of 30 cm, stopping in 0.01 s?**

Bone is a living material. New bone is constantly being deposited and older bone is reabsorbed. Cells known as **osteoclasts** eat their way through about 0.05 mm of bone per day, which means that about 10% of the bone tissue in the body is replaced in a year. Many older people, particularly women, suffer from osteoporosis. This is a condition where bone is reabsorbed quicker than new bone is deposited. The bones become porous and prone to fracture. More than half of all women will suffer a fracture because of osteoporosis. Research suggests that a combination of a good diet, high in calcium and vitamin D, and plenty of exercise is the best way to combat bone loss.

Muscles

Muscles are the collections of fibres which pull on our skeleton, enabling us to stand up straight and to move around. In each muscle there are two types of fibre – thick and thin. When the muscle contracts, in response to an electrical impulse carried by the nervous system, the thin filaments slide between the thicker ones, shortening the overall length of the muscle.

The maximum force applied by a muscle is proportional to its cross-sectional area. Human muscles exert up to 300 kN m⁻².

Fig. 4　Muscle types

There are three different types of muscle cell in the human body:
Smooth muscle, as in blood vessels and gut walls, contracts without an external stimulus. Cardiac muscle forms the walls of the heart and can contract regularly without tiring.
Skeletal muscle accounts for about half the body weight of an adult. Large skeletal muscles can exert tensile forces of over 600 N and can respond to nerve impulses by contracting within 100 ms of receiving the electrical signal from the nerve.

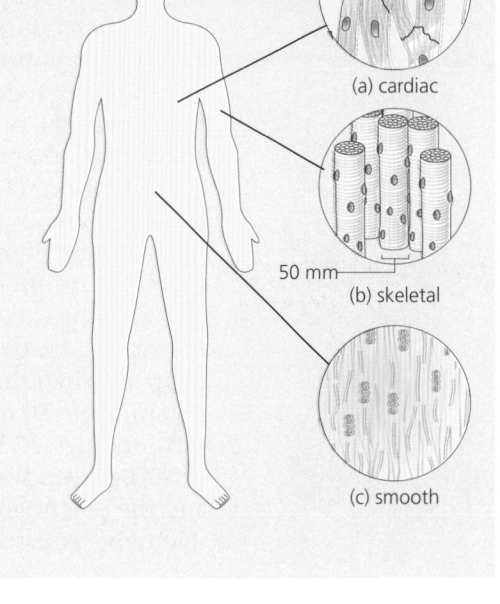

(a) cardiac

50 mm

(b) skeletal

(c) smooth

The work done by a muscle, W, is the average force it exerts, F, multiplied by the distance through which it shortens, x:

$$W = Fx$$

Power is the rate at which work is done, so the power developed by the muscle is:

$$P = \frac{Fx}{t} \quad \text{where } \frac{x}{t} \text{ is the rate at which muscle contracts}$$

As we age, we tend to lose muscle. In a young adult, almost half of the body's mass is muscle, but by age 70 this value falls to just over a quarter. Fortunately, muscle loss can be slowed if exercise is maintained.

Our nervous system allows us to interact with the outside world. Nerves have the task of carrying sensory information from the body to the brain, and of carrying motor signals back from the brain to the muscles.

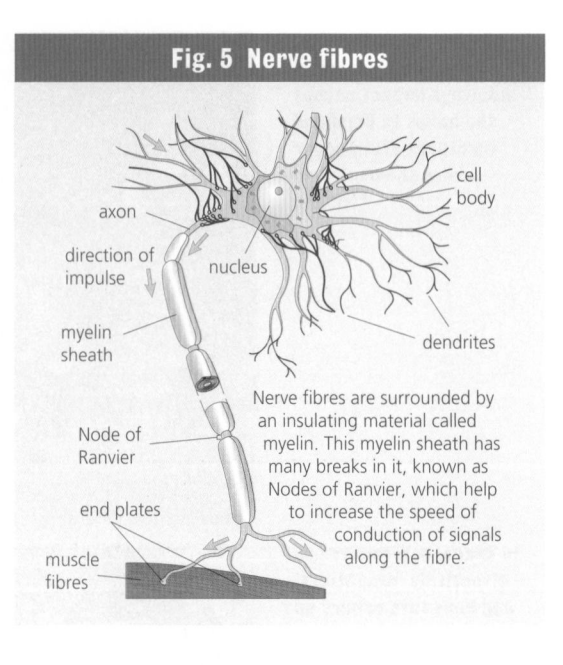

Fig. 5 Nerve fibres

Nerve fibres are surrounded by an insulating material called myelin. This myelin sheath has many breaks in it, known as Nodes of Ranvier, which help to increase the speed of conduction of signals along the fibre.

Sense and control

Nerves are made of fibres (Fig. 5). These fibres can be up to a metre long but are usually only a few micrometres in diameter. Signals travel along these fibres in the form of a changing potential difference (p.d.) known as the action potential.

The nerve fibre has a **cell membrane** which allows water to diffuse freely in or out of the cell. However, the membrane is much less permeable to the passage of sodium and potassium ions. An imbalance in the numbers of these ions causes a p.d. across the cell membrane.

In all cells there are certain proteins which act to pump potassium into the cell and sodium out of it (Fig. 6). Therefore, cells have a high potassium concentration and a low sodium concentration; the fluid *surrounding* the cell has a low potassium concentration and a high sodium concentration. This **concentration gradient** tends to cause potassium ions to leave the cell, carrying their positive charge with them. Potassium ions continue to leave the cell until the excess positive charge outside the cell is large enough to stop them. This happens when the inside of the cell is at a potential of −70 mV lower than its surroundings. At this p.d., an equilibrium exists between the concentration gradient and the potential gradient, and the cell is said to be 'polarised'.

Fig. 6 Ion channels, gates and pumps

(a) The nerve cell resting
In this state, there is an imbalance of ions (more potassium ions inside the cell and more sodium ions outside). This causes a potential across the membrane of −70 mV.
The cell membrane allows water to pass but blocks the movement of ions. However, the membrane has large protein molecules in it that act as channels, gates and pumps to transfer ions in and out of the cell.

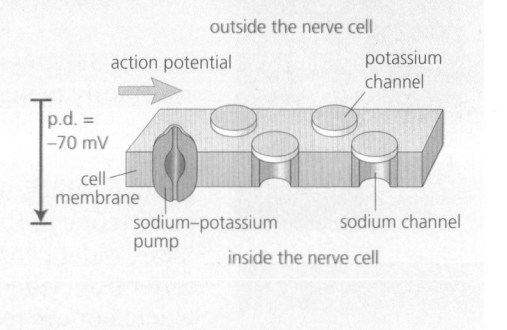

(b) An action potential is initiated
Gates of sodium channels open and sodium ions rush into the cell.
The inside of the membrane becomes positive with respect to the outside: the membrane is **depolarised**.

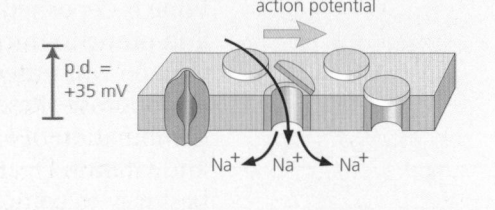

(c) Repolarisation
The increase in potential in the cell closes the sodium gate and opens the potassium gate. The potential drops again to −70 mV.

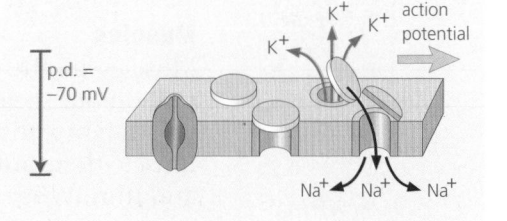

(d) Concentrations are restored
Both ion gates are closed and the sodium–potassium pump restores the original ion concentrations.

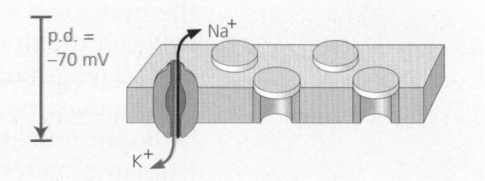

Fig. 7 The action potential of a nerve cell

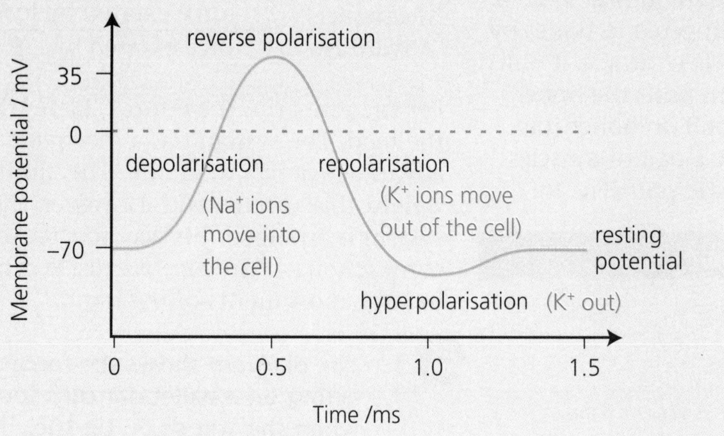

reverse polarisation

depolarisation

(Na⁺ ions move into the cell)

repolarisation

(K⁺ ions move out of the cell)

resting potential

hyperpolarisation (K⁺ out)

Membrane potential / mV: 35, 0, −70

Time /ms: 0, 0.5, 1.0, 1.5

Fig. 8 Propagation of potential

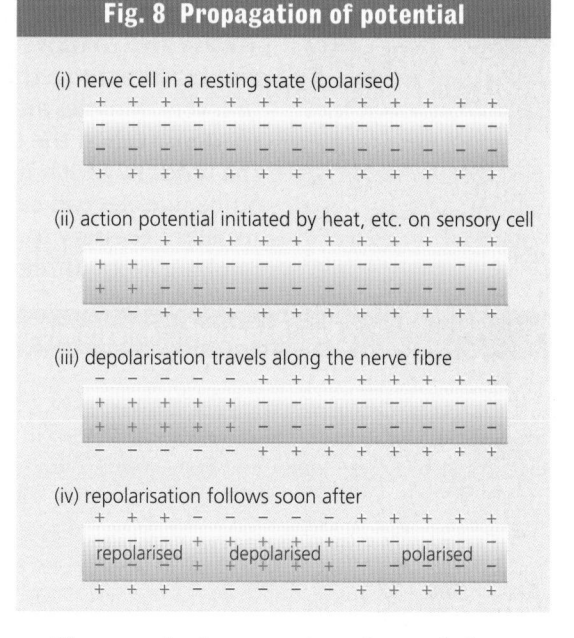

(i) nerve cell in a resting state (polarised)

(ii) action potential initiated by heat, etc. on sensory cell

(iii) depolarisation travels along the nerve fibre

(iv) repolarisation follows soon after

repolarised   depolarised   polarised

When a nerve impulse is initiated, a part of the cell membrane, known as a **voltage-gated channel**, suddenly becomes much more permeable to sodium ions. For a period of about 1 ms, sodium ions move into the cell. This causes the cell to become positively charged and the p.d. across the cell membrane rises to +35 mV before the sodium channels close. Reaching this positive potential then triggers another set of voltage-gated channels which permit potassium ions to leave the cell. The resting potential of –70 mV is then restored.

This pattern of changing voltage is known as the **action potential** (Fig. 7). A changing potential in one part of the nerve initiates a new action potential at an adjacent site (Fig. 8), and in this way the potential propagates along the fibre at a speeds of up to 100 m s⁻¹. The action potential can transfer to muscle cells where it travels more slowly – at about 4 m s⁻¹ – causing muscle cells to contract as it goes.

The speed of a nerve impulse and the size of the potential differences are not affected by the strength of the initial stimulus. A stronger sensation is conveyed by more nerve cells firing and by the frequency at which impulses propagate.

In western countries, about 10% of people over the age of 65 suffer from diabetes. One of the effects of the illness is to cause the myelin sheath around the nerve to degenerate. This slows down nerve impulses to speeds as low as 1 m s⁻¹ and may cause numbness.

2 A cell membrane is about 0.01 μm thick. Calculate the electric field strength across the membrane:
a when the cell is resting;
b when it is reverse polarised.
(In a uniform electrical field, the field strength $E = V/d$)

Key ideas

- When a nerve is activated, the potential difference across the cell membrane changes from –70 mV to +35 mV and back to –70 mV. The pattern of changing potential at any point on the cell membrane is known as the action potential.

- The action potential is caused by the transport of potassium and sodium ions across the nerve cell membrane. The action potential propagates along the nerve, carrying sensory information to the brain or motor signals to muscles.

Levers and joints

We are able to move because our muscles and bones act together as a complex system of levers. Muscles are connected to bones by tendons. When the muscle contracts it pulls the tendon, which in turn pulls the bone. Since muscles can only pull on bones it is usually necessary to have a pair of muscles working as an **antagonistic pair** (Fig. 9).

Fig. 9 An antagonistic muscle pair

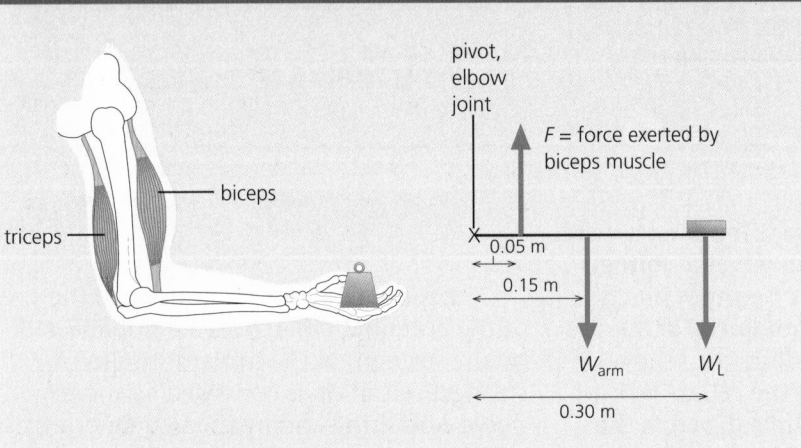

When the biceps muscle contracts, the forearm lifts.
When the triceps contracts, the forearm is extended.

The force due to the biceps muscle is closer to the fulcrum than the force due to the load carried in the hand. This means that the biceps muscle has to exert a force that is much larger than the weight held in the hand.

A muscle pulling on a bone can cause a turning effect, or **moment**, around the joint which acts as a pivot or **fulcrum**. When you lift your hand, your biceps muscle exerts a turning effect on your forearm, and your elbow acts as the fulcrum. We can use the principle of moments to calculate the force exerted by the biceps. The clockwise moment about the elbow is due to the weight of the arm and the load. This must be balanced by the anti-clockwise moment due to the biceps muscle:

$$F \times 0.05 = W_{arm} \times 0.15 + W_{load} \times 0.30$$

A typical value for the weight of the forearm is 20 N. To hold a 1 kg mass in your hand requires a force in the biceps of:

$$F = \frac{(20 \text{ N} \times 0.15 \text{ m} + 10 \text{ N} \times 0.30 \text{ m})}{0.05 \text{ m}} = 120 \text{ N}$$

The **mechanical advantage** of a lever is defined as:

$$\text{Mechanical Advantage} = \frac{\text{force exerted by load (N)}}{\text{force exerted by effort (N)}}$$

For the fore-arm, the effort is larger than the load. The system has a mechanical advantage of less than one. This limits the weight that can be held. However, the system is arranged this way so that small contractions of the biceps muscle can lead to large movements of the hand.

3 **The diagram shows the forces acting on a ballet dancer's foot when she stands on tip-toe.**

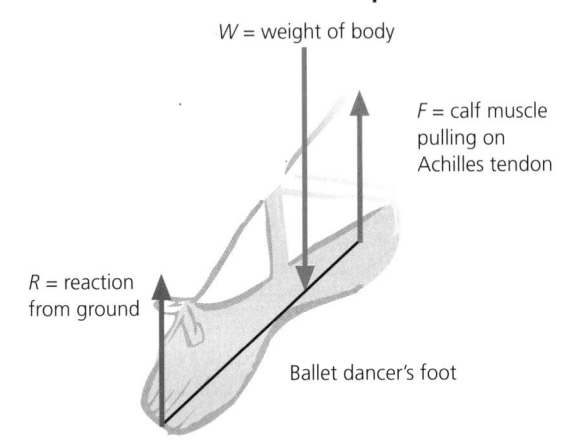

Ballet dancer's foot

a **Identify the load, effort and fulcrum.**
b **Explain whether the system has a mechanical advantage of less than or greater than 1.**

The hip joint is subject to surprisingly large forces. The joint itself is a cup-shaped socket which the top of the thigh bone (femur) fits into. When a person is standing on both feet, the hips share the weight of the top part of the body which is about 70% of the total body weight, W_B. The force on the head of each femur is therefore $0.35\ W_B$. For a man of mass 70 kg, this force would be around 250 N. The force can be separated into two components:

● a compressive force which acts along the bone;
● a shear force which acts at 90° to the compressive force (see Fig. 10).

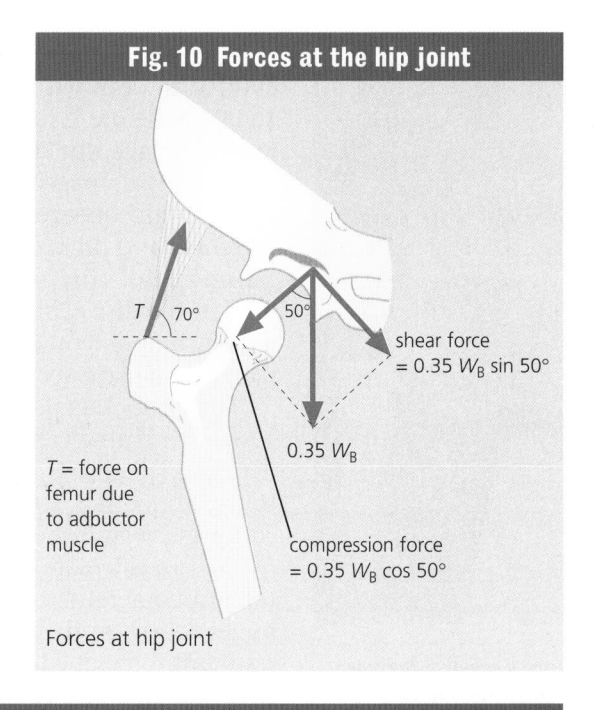

Fig. 10 Forces at the hip joint

T 70°   50°

shear force
= 0.35 W_B sin 50°

0.35 W_B

T = force on
femur due
to adbuctor
muscle

compression force
= 0.35 W_B cos 50°

Forces at hip joint

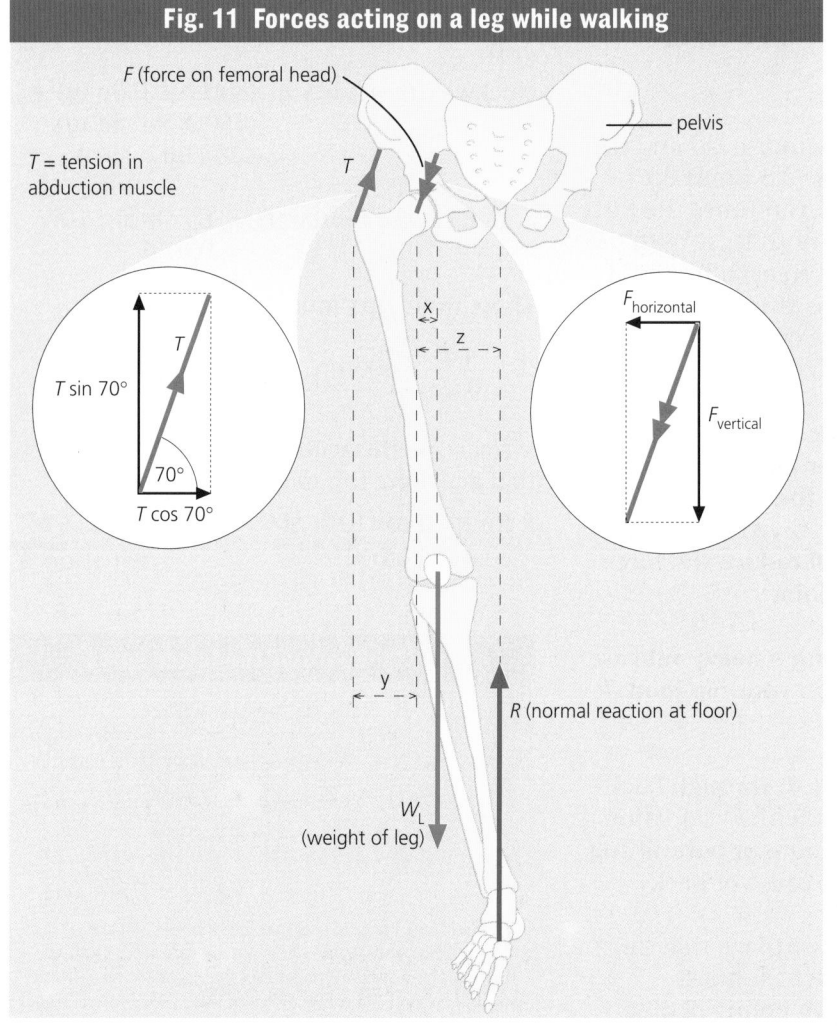

Fig. 11 Forces acting on a leg while walking

F (force on femoral head)

pelvis

T = tension in
abduction muscle

T

T sin 70°

T

70°

T cos 70°

$F_{horizontal}$

$F_{vertical}$

x

z

y

R (normal reaction at floor)

W_L
(weight of leg)

Since the neck of the femur is at an angle of about 50° to the vertical, the shear force would be 0.35 W_B sin 50°, around 190 N for an average man, and the compressive force on the bone would be 0.35 W_B cos 50°, typically 160 N.

When a person stands on one leg, all of the body's weight is supported through one hip joint. This happens briefly in every step during walking. In order to stay upright, it is necessary to lean to one side to keep the body's centre of gravity over the standing foot. The force exerted by the abductor muscle increases to provide a balancing moment. The total force at the femur head, F, is much larger when we walk than when we stand still (Fig. 11).

To find the new force at the femur head, F, we must first calculate the force, T, in the abductor muscle. Taking moments about the head of the femur gives:

$(W_L \times x) + (T \sin 70° \times y) = R \times z$
clockwise   anticlockwise

For the *whole body* to be in equilibrium, the reaction at the floor, R, must be equal and opposite to the body's weight, W_B. The weight of the leg, W_L, is about 0.15 of the total body weight. If $x = 0.025$ m, $y = 0.070$ m and $z = 0.10$ m, the equation becomes:

$(0.15 \ W_B \times 0.025) + (T \sin 70° \times 0.070) = W_B \times 0.10$

which gives $T = 1.5 \ W_B$.

We can use this value to find the force acting on the head of the femur.

For the *leg* to be in equilibrium, the sum of the vertical forces must be zero:

$R + T \sin 70° = F_{vertical} + W_L$

Substituting in values from earlier in the calculation gives:

$F_{vertical} = W_B + 1.5 \ W_B \sin 70° - 0.15 \ W_B$

$= 2.25 \ W_B$

The sum of the horizontal forces must also be zero:

$F_{horizontal} = T \cos 70° = 0.50 \ W_B$

The resultant force at the femur head is:

$F = \sqrt{(2.25 \ W_B)^2 + (0.50 \ W_B)^2}$

$= 2.3 \ W_B$

113

Total hip replacements are now a common operation. The socket is replaced by plastic and the femur is given a new metal head, bonded to the femur with bone cement.

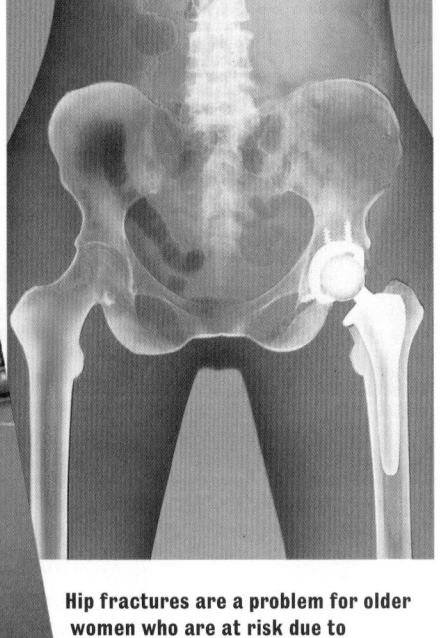

Hip fractures are a problem for older women who are at risk due to osteoporosis. Every year, 1.7 million people world-wide suffer hip fractures.

The force between the femur head and the hip socket is now almost 2.5 times the body weight (Fig. 11), seven times the force exerted by standing on both legs. With such large forces acting on each hip joint every time that you take a step, it is no wonder that hips often become worn or damaged by arthritis in old age.

4 After a hip replacement operation patients are often advised to use a walking stick on the side opposite the affected hip. Give two reasons why the stick will reduce the force on the new hip joint.

5 Why does carrying a heavy suitcase put extra force on your hip joints?

A pain in the back

More working days are lost through back pain than any other ailment. Occupational injuries due to poor posture or poor lifting technique are often the cause of back complaints.

The flexible discs of cartilage that lie between the vertebrae act as shock absorbers in the spine. In young people, the discs are very strong. A lumbar disc deforms *elastically* up to a load of around 1000 N and can withstand a force of 15 000 N before it ruptures. With increasing age, the discs deteriorate and are more easily damaged. The soft inner part of the disc can squeeze out from between the vertebrae and press on nerves in the spine, causing pain. This is known as a 'slipped disc'. If the disc ruptures, it releases fluid which can press on the spinal cord, causing pain and muscle spasm.

The lumbosacral disc (Fig. 12) at the base of the spine is particularly prone to damage. The disc is at an angle of about 40° to the horizontal, so it is subject to both compressive and shear (twisting) forces.

We can calculate the size of the force at the lumbosacral disc by considering the forces acting on the spine (see Fig. 13). The resultant force due to the erector muscles, E, acts at an angle of about 10° to the spine. Taking moments about the lumbosacral disc:

clockwise moments = (800 N × 0.36 m) + (250 N × 0.54 m)
= 420 Nm

anticlockwise moments = E × 40 sin 10°
= 0.07 E

These moments must be equal, so:

$$E = \frac{420}{0.07} = 6000 \text{ N}$$

We can use this value E to find R. The forces that act along the spine must balance, so:

$R \cos \theta = E \cos 10° + 800 \cos 65° + 250 \cos 65°$
= 6360 N   equation A

Fig. 12 Bones of the lower spine

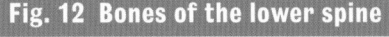
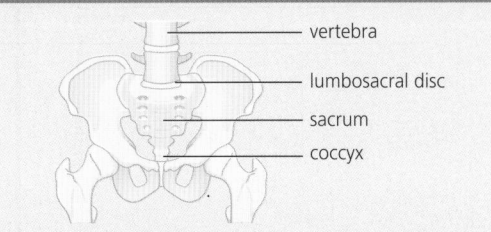

vertebra

lumbosacral disc

sacrum

coccyx

The backbone consists of 33 vertebral bones stacked on top of each other and separated by joints made from cartilage. The last nine bones are fused together to form the sacrum and the coccyx. The disc that lies between the lowest lumbar vertebra and the coccyx is called the lumbosacral disc.

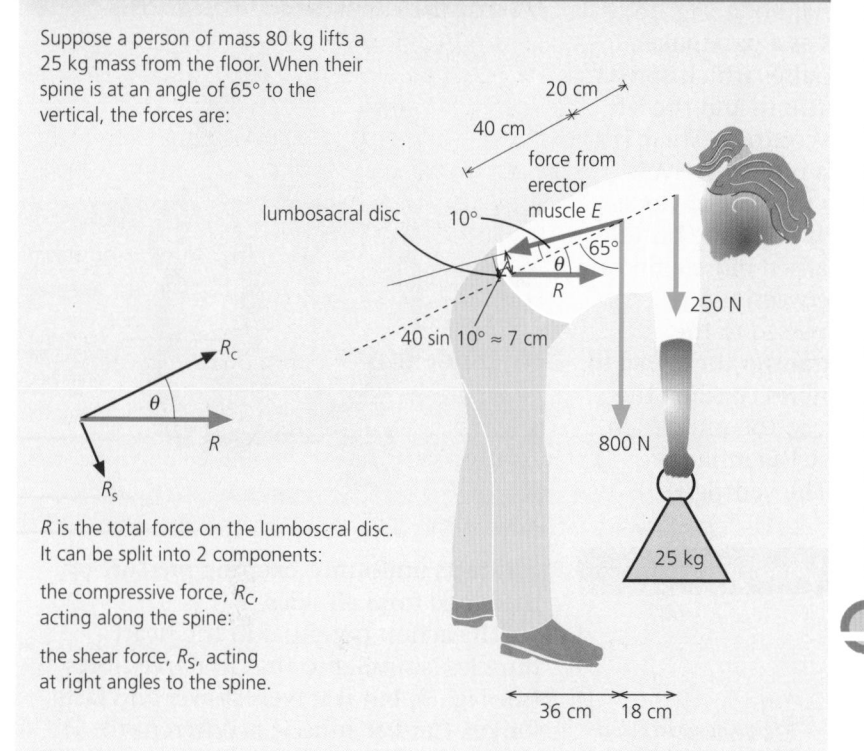

Suppose a person of mass 80 kg lifts a 25 kg mass from the floor. When their spine is at an angle of 65° to the vertical, the forces are:

20 cm

40 cm

force from erector muscle E

lumbosacral disc

10°

65°

R

250 N

40 sin 10° ≈ 7 cm

R_C

θ

R

R_S

800 N

25 kg

36 cm   18 cm

R is the total force on the lumboscral disc. It can be split into 2 components:

the compressive force, R_C, acting along the spine:

the shear force, R_S, acting at right angles to the spine.

When we bend and lift an object from the floor, the forces on the spine cause a turning moment about the lumbosacral disc. Erector muscles link the fixed bones of the pelvis with the vertebrae, enabling them to be moved. When the erector muscles contract, they provide a balancing moment to keep us upright.

The forces which act at 90° to the spine must also balance:

$R \sin \theta = E \sin 10° + 800 \sin 65° + 250 \sin 65°$
$\qquad\quad = 2000$ N   equation B

To find R we first need to find angle θ. This can be done by dividing equation B by equation A:

$$\frac{R \sin \theta}{R \cos \theta} = \frac{2000 \text{ N}}{6360 \text{ N}} = \tan \theta$$

so $\theta = \tan^{-1} 0.318 = 17.5°$.

This gives a value for R of 6670 N, about 8 times the body weight of the person. At forces like these, the disc has probably been compressed to about 75 per cent of its original thickness. Strain is compression divided by original length, so this is a strain of 0.25.

Q6 Olympic weightlifters can lift weights of over 250 kg. How can they do this without damaging their lumbosacral disc?

Key ideas

- Joints in the body act as levers. The principle of moments can be used to calculate the forces which act.
- The mechanical advantage of a lever $= \dfrac{\text{force exerted by load (N)}}{\text{force exerted by effort (N)}}$
- Large forces are exerted at the hip joint and on the inter-vertebral discs in the spine.

10.3 The heart of the matter

'I was out shopping when a old man nearby suddenly collapsed. He was sweating profusely and he looked grey. He didn't seem to be breathing and I couldn't feel a pulse in his neck. I was sure that he had suffered a heart attack, so I applied external cardiac massage until the ambulance arrived. Later they said that I had saved his life.'

The heart as a pump

The heart is a remarkably reliable pump. In an average lifetime it beats over 2.5 billion times, pumping between 5 and 20 litres of blood every minute. The chances of suffering from heart disease increase in old age. In the UK, one in five men will suffer a heart attack before they reach 65.

The four chambers of the heart contract

in a sequence (Fig. 14) that is controlled by signals from the sino-atrial node (Fig. 15). The sino-atrial node acts as a pacemaker, generating electrical impulses which spread rapidly across the right atrium and the left atrium, causing them to contract. There is a short delay as the signals travel relatively slowly through the atrio-ventricular node. The signal then travels through the **bundle of His**, a bunch of specialised muscle fibres which run in the wall between the ventricles. The signal is passed to the **Purkinje fibres**, which transfer the signal to the ventricles. Purkinje fibres conduct the impulse at about 3 m s^{-1}, so the muscles in the ventricle walls receive the impulse almost simultaneously. The ventricle

Fig. 15 The electrical pathways of the heart

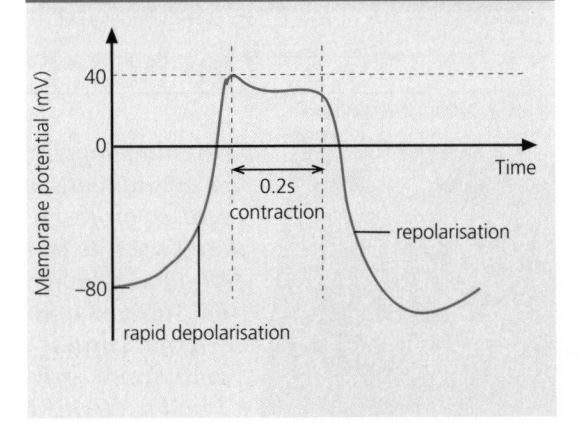

contracts uniformly, exerting pressure on the blood from all sides.

The action potential in the heart muscles is similar to that in nerve fibres (see Fig. 5), but it travels slower and lasts longer. Cardiac muscle is different to skeletal muscle in two main ways:

- It is self-excitatory – it does not need an external impulse from a nerve fibre to trigger a contraction.
- Cardiac muscle has an extra channel in its membrane which allows calcium ions to travel across the cell wall. This makes the depolarisation stage last longer (Fig. 16), about 0.25 s compared to 5 ms for skeletal muscle. Cardiac muscle cannot respond to other stimuli during this period and the delay allows the muscle to completely relax before the next cycle of contraction begins.

Fig. 14 The structure of the heart and blood flow

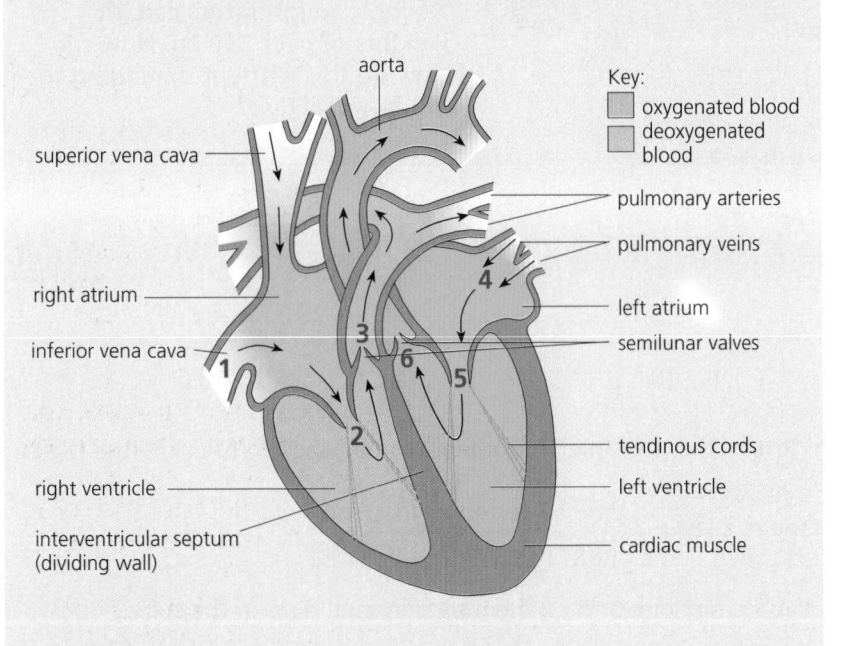

Key:
- oxygenated blood
- deoxygenated blood

1. Blood returning from the body enters the right atrium through the vena cavae.

2. Blood is pumped into the right ventricle.

3. When the right ventricle contracts, it pumps blood through the pulmonary artery to the lungs.

4. Oxygenated blood returns to the left atrium of the heart along the pulmonary veins.

5. Blood is pumped from the left atrium into the left ventricle.

6. The left ventricle contracts, pumping about 70 ml of blood into the aorta and around the body.

Fig. 16 The action potential of cardiac muscle

Membrane potential (mV)

40

0

−80

Time

0.2s contraction

repolarisation

rapid depolarisation

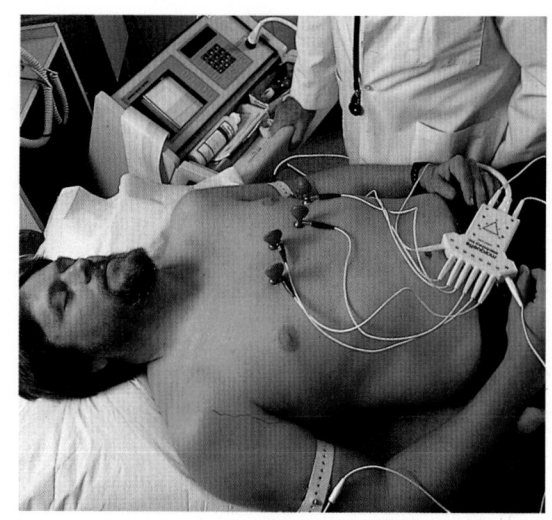

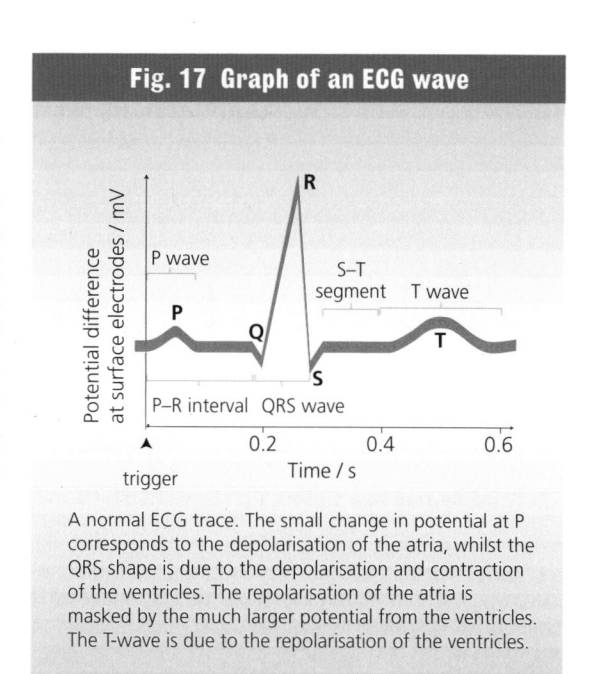

Fig. 17 Graph of an ECG wave

A normal ECG trace. The small change in potential at P corresponds to the depolarisation of the atria, whilst the QRS shape is due to the depolarisation and contraction of the ventricles. The repolarisation of the atria is masked by the much larger potential from the ventricles. The T-wave is due to the repolarisation of the ventricles.

The electrical signal from the heart spreads through the surrounding tissues and fluid and it can be detected by electrodes placed on the skin. The resulting voltage trace is known as an **electrocardiogram**, or ECG (Fig. 17). A good electrical contact with the skin is important, so hairs and dead cells are removed and a conducting gel is applied. Silver electrodes coated with silver chloride are taped to the patient's skin. These electrodes do not react with chemicals produced by the skin. Adhesive tape prevents voltage 'spikes' caused by electrostatic effects if the electrodes move across the patient's skin. The measured voltages are small so they need to be amplified with a high-gain amplifier. Unfortunately, unwanted electrical signals, i.e. **noise**, is also amplified. A particular problem comes from induced voltages due to nearby mains-operated equipment. Mains voltage alternates at 50 Hz, so small induced e.m.f.s occur in the ECG equipment. To combat this effect, leads are screened and the ECG apparatus is carefully shielded.

The exact shape of the voltage trace depends on the position of the electrodes. It is possible to site electrodes at several points on the chest, over the heart and on the limbs. A full 12-lead ECG gives a clear picture of the polarisation and depolarisation of the heart muscle, allowing doctors to detect any areas of damage in the cardiac muscle. Even a simple cardiac monitor checking the potential of one site above the heart can be used to diagnose some important defects (Fig. 18).

In an elderly person, the tissues in the heart become stiffer and the heart has to work harder to pump the same volume of blood. The heart valves may also stiffen so that they allow less blood through, or they may become **incompetent**, which means that they allow blood to flow back the wrong way. The number of pacemaker cells in the heart also decreases with age. A 75 year old may retain just 10 per cent of the cells they had as a young adult. A solution to these problems is to implant artificial replacements. Replacement valves can be taken from animals (pigs) or made from plastic and metal. An artificial pacemaker

Fig. 18 Abnormal ECG traces

(i) Ventricular standstill. Only the P-waves are recorded. There is no contraction of the ventricles; this is a cardiac arrest.

P waves only

(ii) Ventricular fibrillation. Electrical impulses originate from several places in the ventricles at a very high rate (up to 5 times per second). This causes the heart to contract in a random way, so that it shakes like a jelly or 'fibrillates'. This is also a cardiac arrest.

powered by long-life batteries can provide a steady 72 beats per minute to a heart that would otherwise have stopped.

7 The ECG traces in Fig. 19 are all abnormal. Match the trace to the correct description.

Fig. 19 ECG traces for Question 7

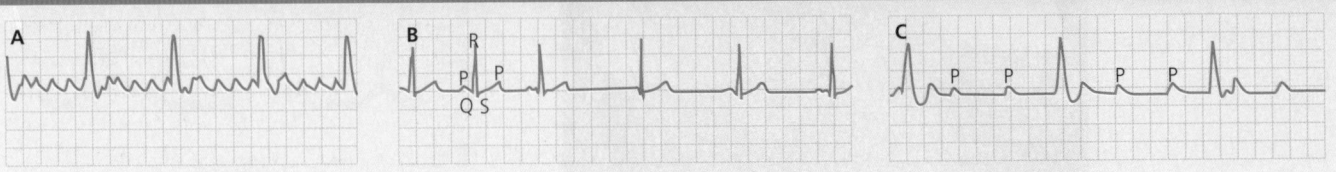

1 Sinus arrhythmia The impulse originates in the sino-atrial node but is irregular; P waves and the QRS complex should be normal.

2 Third degree heart block Can be caused by damage to the bundle of His. Atria and ventricles beat independently of each other. P waves are normal but QRS waves are abnormal because they can originate from anywhere. The P–Q interval is irregular.

3 Atrial flutter The atrial rhythm is fast, up to 300 min⁻¹. The ventricles cannot respond to such a rate and the atrio-ventricular node blocks most pulses. This means that the ventricles may contract normally. The P-wave is absent, but there is a rapidly changing atrial potential. The QRS wave is normal.

Key ideas

- The heart is a muscular pump which contracts in response to a stimulation produced within the heart.
- The changing electrical potential around the heart can be detected by electrodes attached to the skin, allowing an electrocardiogram (ECG) to be recorded.
- The form of an ECG can be used to diagnose heart disease.

10.4 Blood pressure

A bowl of medicine. New research has shown that eating about five pieces of fruit or vegetables a day will significantly reduce your chances of developing heart disease and cancer in later life.

Some people believe that the packaging of beefburgers and chips should carry a health warning in the same way as cigarettes. The warning might boast 'Products with a high sodium content can increase your risk of high blood pressure'. Conversely, some food manufacturers now claim that eating their product will make you healthier. The time may come when carrots carry a sticker saying 'Eating this product will reduce your risk of coronary heart disease and cancer'.

Fig. 20 Graph of average blood pressure vs. age

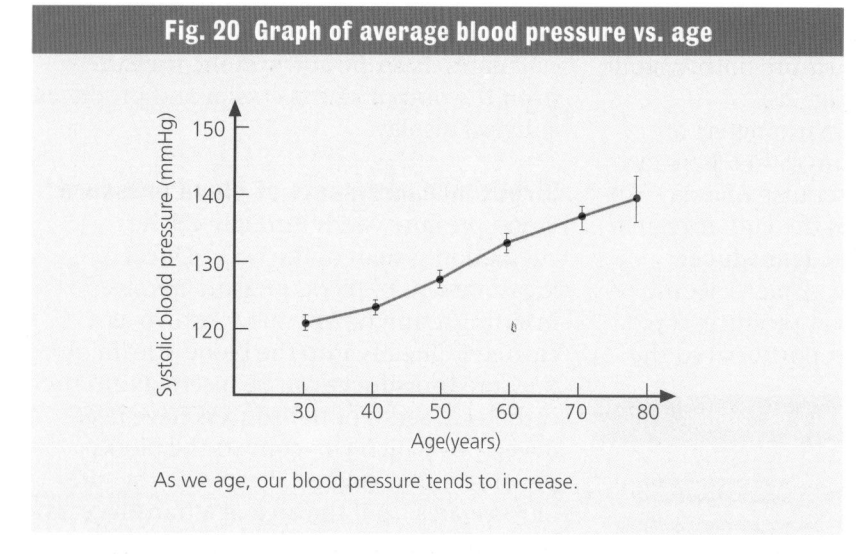

As we age, our blood pressure tends to increase.

Fig. 21 A sphygmomanometer

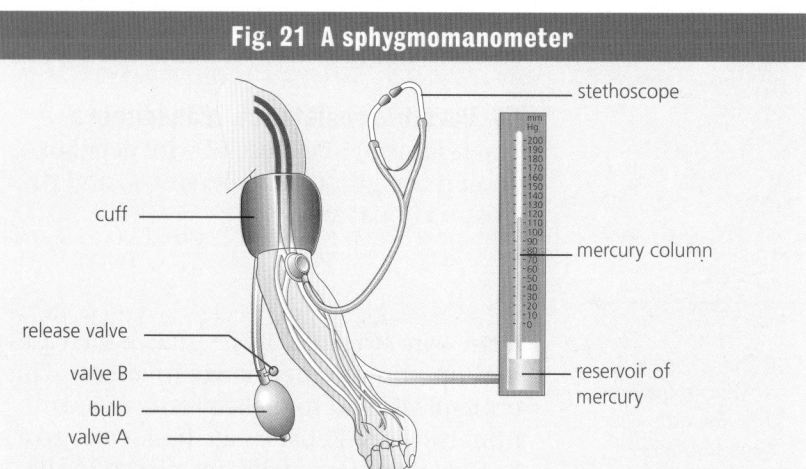

When the bulb is squeezed, valve A closes and B opens. Air is pushed into the rubber balloon. When the bulb is released valve A opens and B closes. Eventually, the air pressure in the balloon is equal to the blood pressure in the artery. When this happens, the blood flow in the artery below the cuff stops and the doctor no longer hears the pulse through her stethoscope. The blood pressure can then be measured by the height of the mercury column.

Fig. 22 Graph of pressure in the aorta during a heart beat

During the course of one heart beat the pressure in the aorta changes from 80 mmHg to almost 120 mmHg

High blood pressure, or hypertension, is a common problem in old age. As people grow older, the walls of their arteries become less elastic and fatty deposits such as cholesterol build up on the inside walls. This makes the arteries narrower, which increases the resistance to blood flow and raises blood pressure (Fig. 20). High blood pressure puts an extra burden on the heart and may cause heart failure. High blood pressure in arteries may burst the walls of a blood vessel. When this happens in the head, brain cells can be killed. This condition is known as a stroke. In some cases the victim is left with impaired speech and movement. This is one reason why monitoring blood pressure is important.

The most common way of measuring the pressure of blood in the arteries involves using a **sphygmomanometer** (Fig. 21). Blood pressure is usually measured in millimetres of mercury, mmHg. A blood pressure of 100 mmHg means that the same pressure would be exerted at a depth of 100 mm in mercury. The pressure, P, due to a column of liquid of height, h, and density, ρ, is given by:

$$P = h \times \rho \times g$$

where g is the gravitational field strength. Since the density of mercury is 13.6×10^3 kg m^{-3}, the pressure exerted by a 100 mm column is:

pressure $= 100 \times 10^{-3}$ m $\times 13.6 \times 10^3$ kg m^{-3}
$\times 9.81$ m s^{-2}

$= 13.3$ kPa above atmospheric pressure

The pressure in the blood rises and falls with every heart beat (Fig. 22). As the ventricles contract, the pressure in the aorta rises to its maximum value of between 110 mmHg and 120 mmHg. This is called the **systolic** blood pressure. When the ventricles relax, the blood pressure falls to its lowest value, the **diastolic** pressure, which is typically around 80 mmHg.

8 Copy the graph in Fig. 22 and sketch the voltage trace from a normal ECG below it on the same time scale. Explain the relationship between the two graphs.

The sphygmomanometer can be used with a stethoscope to measure both systolic and diastolic pressure (Fig. 23).

Automatic sphygmomanometers are used to monitor the changes in a person's blood pressure over the course of a day. An automatic pump inflates the cuff at regular intervals. A **piezoelectric transducer** replaces the stethoscope. A piezoelectric transducer is a crystal that produces a p.d. across its faces that is proportional to the

pressure applied to it. A microcomputer calculates diastolic and systolic pressure from the output of the crystal and produces a digital display.

Direct measurements of blood pressure

Blood pressure varies throughout the circulation system of the body. Direct measurement of blood pressure involves inserting a tiny hollow tube, known as a **catheter**, directly into the blood stream. A pressure **transducer** can be inserted into the catheter. A series of transducers have been developed which will convert the blood pressure into a voltage. Pressure is the ratio of force/area, so if the area of a transducer is constant we only need to measure force to know the pressure. Three different electrical methods can be used to monitor the force:

(i) Variable resistance transducers

The resistance of a piece of wire depends upon its length, l, its resistivity, ρ, and its cross-sectional area, A:

$$R = \frac{\rho l}{A}$$

If the wire stretches, its resistance increases in proportion to the change in length. This principle is used to make pressure gauges from resistors. Resistors are bonded onto a flexible diaphragm which is placed in the blood stream (Fig. 24). Temperature changes could affect the readings, so the resistors are arranged in a 'bridge'. Two of the resistors are extended by the pressure and two of them are compressed. The pressure is measured by the p.d. across the bridge. All resistors have been exposed to the same temperature changes, so the output depends solely on the length changes due to the pressure. Each of the arms in Fig. 24 acts as a potential divider across the supply voltage of 12 V.

$$V \text{ at A} = \frac{R + \Delta R}{(R + \Delta R) + (R - \Delta R)} \times 12$$
$$= \frac{(R + \Delta R)}{2R} \times 12$$

$$V \text{ at B} = \frac{R - \Delta R}{(R + \Delta R) + (R - \Delta R)} \times 12$$
$$= \frac{(R - \Delta R)}{2R} \times 12$$

Fig. 23 Graph of blood pressure in an artery vs. time

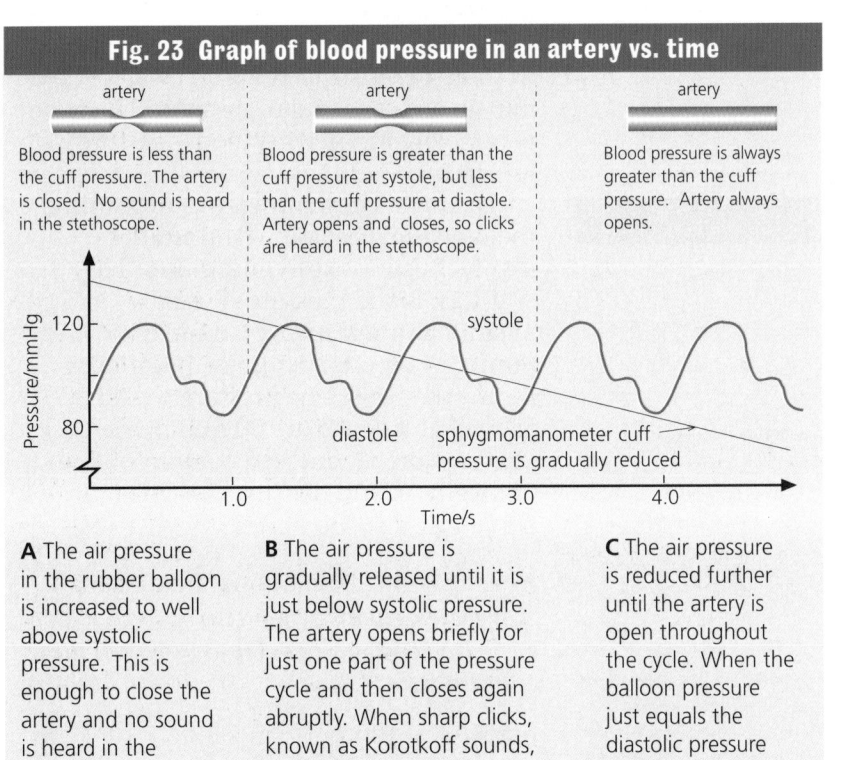

artery

Blood pressure is less than the cuff pressure. The artery is closed. No sound is heard in the stethoscope.

artery

Blood pressure is greater than the cuff pressure at systole, but less than the cuff pressure at diastole. Artery opens and closes, so clicks are heard in the stethoscope.

artery

Blood pressure is always greater than the cuff pressure. Artery always opens.

Pressure/mmHg

120 — systole

80 — diastole   sphygmomanometer cuff pressure is gradually reduced

1.0   2.0   3.0   4.0
Time/s

A The air pressure in the rubber balloon is increased to well above systolic pressure. This is enough to close the artery and no sound is heard in the stethoscope.

B The air pressure is gradually released until it is just below systolic pressure. The artery opens briefly for just one part of the pressure cycle and then closes again abruptly. When sharp clicks, known as Korotkoff sounds, are heard the systolic pressure is recorded.

C The air pressure is reduced further until the artery is open throughout the cycle. When the balloon pressure just equals the diastolic pressure a clear pulse is heard.

Fig. 24 Diaphragm and bridge circuit arrangement

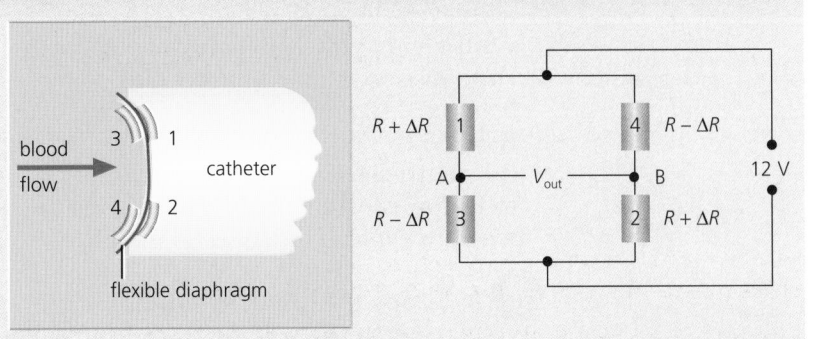

blood flow

catheter

flexible diaphragm

$R + \Delta R$ 1   4 $R - \Delta R$

A V_{out} B   12 V

$R - \Delta R$ 3   2 $R + \Delta R$

The total resistance of each arm of the bridge is the same, $2R$. Therefore the same current, I, flows in each arm.

The output voltage is the difference between the two voltages:

$$V_{out} = \frac{2\Delta R}{2R} \times 12 = 12\frac{\Delta R}{R}$$

A resistance change of 0.1% would give an output voltage of 12 mV.

Fig. 25 Possible designs for capacitance transducers

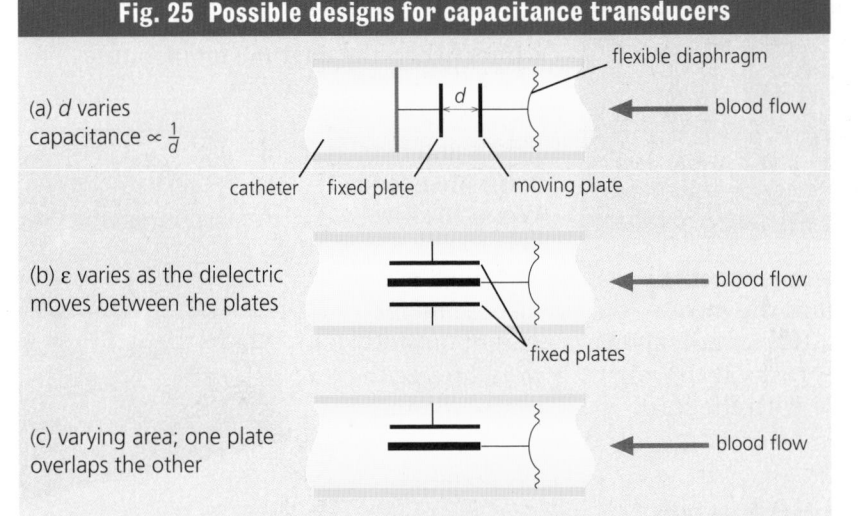

(a) d varies capacitance $\propto \frac{1}{d}$

catheter   fixed plate   moving plate

flexible diaphragm
blood flow
d

(b) ε varies as the dielectric moves between the plates

blood flow

fixed plates

(c) varying area; one plate overlaps the other

blood flow

Capacitance transducers can measure a large range of pressures; they respond quickly and can be very sensitive.

Fig. 26 A linear variable differential transformer

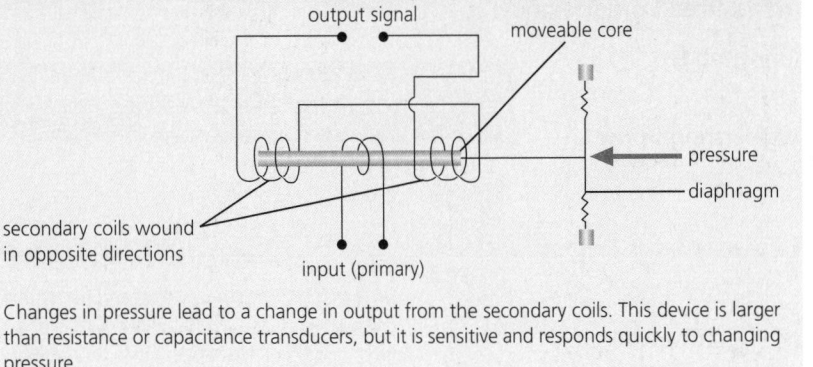

output signal

moveable core

pressure

diaphragm

secondary coils wound in opposite directions

input (primary)

Changes in pressure lead to a change in output from the secondary coils. This device is larger than resistance or capacitance transducers, but it is sensitive and responds quickly to changing pressure.

(ii) Variable capacitance transducers

The capacitance of a parallel plate capacitor is given by the formula:

$$C = \frac{\varepsilon A}{d}$$

where ε is a constant that depends on the material between the plates, A is the area of each of the plates and d is the distance between the plates.

The pressure can act in one of three ways (Fig. 25) to change the capacitance.

(iii) Variable inductance transducers

The mutual inductance of a pair of coils can be altered by sliding a core of magnetic material in or out of them (Fig. 26). One arrangement involves a transformer with two secondary coils that are wound in opposite directions to each other. The outputs of the coils cancel each other when the core is central, i.e. at zero pressure. Any movement of the core increases the induced voltage in one coil and decreases the induced voltage in the other. This produces a signal because the opposing signals are not equal. The measured output is the difference between the coils' outputs.

The core has a spring to return it to the zero position. This device is known as a **linear variable differential transformer**.

Pressure transducers can also measure pressure in the bladder, the uterus or inside the gastrointestinal tract.

9 a If you wanted to make a direct measurement of the blood pressure in an artery, what characteristics would you look for in a transducer?

b How would the characteristics differ if you wanted to measure pressure in a vein?

Key ideas

- A sphygmomanometer uses the height of a column of mercury to measure blood pressure.
- Transducers can convert pressure or force to a voltage to monitor blood pressure.
- Transducers can use changes in resistance, capacitance or inductance to measure pressure.

Going to extremes

Runners aged from 17 to 70 pay almost £2000 each for the privilege of running 230 km through one of the world's most inhospitable regions

Every year about 200 people enter the Sahara Marathon, perhaps the most gruelling race on Earth. It is so hot, about 40 °C in the shade, that rocks at the edge of the track can explode with the heat.

The fourth day of the race is the ultimate test, 80 km across open country with no shade from the scorching desert sun. Keeping your cool is vital.

Scientists working for the British Antarctic Survey have to cope with the other extreme of the world's climate. In the winter, when the daytime temperature drops below –30 °C, at least three layers of gloves and two layers of boots are needed. When the low temperatures combine with high wind speeds anyone caught outside would freeze to death in minutes.

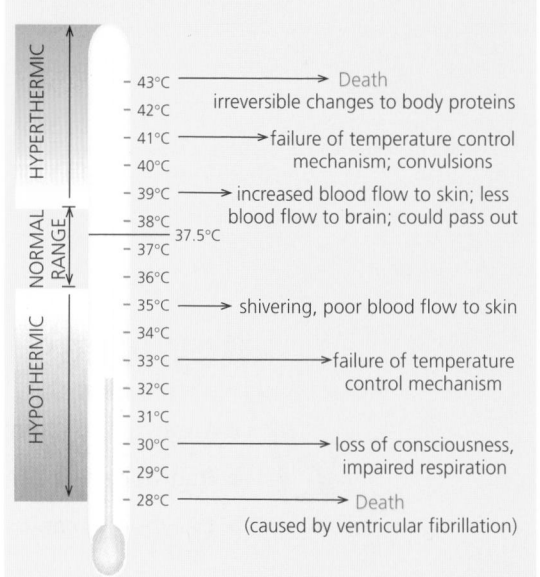

11.1 Learning objectives

After working through this chapter, you should be able to:

- **discuss** the body's energy requirements and **define** basal metabolic rate;
- **explain** how energy is transferred from the body;
- **describe** ways of measuring body temperature;
- **explain** the principles of thermography.

11.2 Keeping cool

Although people can survive climates as hot as in the desert or as cold as in polar regions, the temperature inside the body – the **core temperature** – has to be maintained within a few degrees of 37 °C (Fig. 1). Runners in the Sahara need to transfer energy out of their bodies to stay alive. In colder conditions, it is important to conserve heat generated by our bodies.

Basal metabolic rate
The human body needs a regular supply of energy to maintain breathing, its heartbeat

Fig. 1 The effects of changes to the body's core temperature

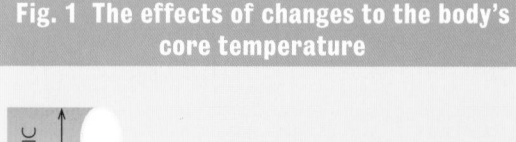

HYPERTHERMIC

- 43°C ⟶ Death
  irreversible changes to body proteins
- 42°C
- 41°C ⟶ failure of temperature control mechanism; convulsions
- 40°C
- 39°C ⟶ increased blood flow to skin; less blood flow to brain; could pass out
- 38°C — 37.5°C

NORMAL RANGE
- 37°C
- 36°C
- 35°C ⟶ shivering, poor blood flow to skin
- 34°C

HYPOTHERMIC
- 33°C ⟶ failure of temperature control mechanism
- 32°C
- 31°C
- 30°C ⟶ loss of consciousness, impaired respiration
- 29°C
- 28°C ⟶ Death (caused by ventricular fibrillation)

Hibernating animals take advantage of the fact that BMR falls at lower body temperatures. Their body temperature falls and this helps them to conserve food supplies during the winter.

and other vital functions. Cells need energy to power their activities, such as synthesising proteins for growth and repair or transmitting nerve impulses. The minimum rate of energy transfer required by a conscious person who is completely at rest in a comfortable environment is known as the **basal metabolic rate**, or BMR (Fig. 2). The S.I. unit of BMR is W m^{-2}, though the value is often given in units of kilojoules of energy transferred per square metre of body surface per hour, kJ h^{-1} m^{-2}. BMR depends on a person's age, sex and weight and is typically equivalent to a power of 85 W for a young man and slightly less for a woman (Fig. 3).

1 **Use data from Fig. 3 to show that the BMR for a 20-year-old woman results in a rate of energy transfer of about 75 W. (Assume that her surface area is 1.8 m^2)**

BMR is affected by the body's temperature. A dangerous **positive feedback** mechanism occurs when a person suffers from a fever. As their core temperature rises towards 40 °C, cell metabolism is stimulated and the BMR rises to about 30% above normal. This releases more energy as heat, and the body's temperature rises further. A patient with a fever may be treated by sponging them with tepid water or with drugs, such as aspirin, which help to restore the body's natural thermostatic control system.

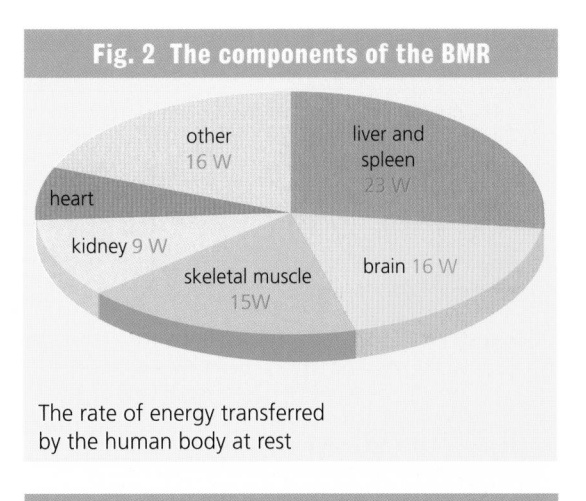

Fig. 2 The components of the BMR

The rate of energy transferred by the human body at rest

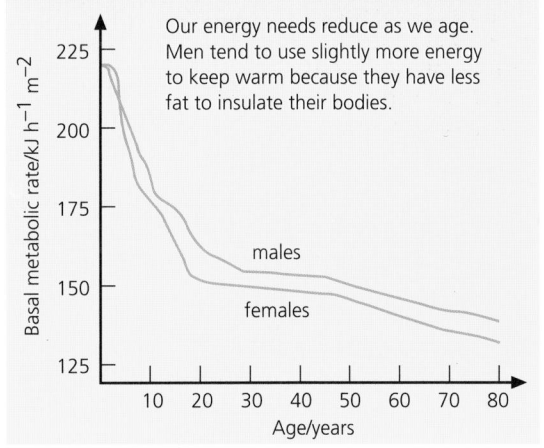

Fig. 3 Graph of BMR for men and women vs. age

Our energy needs reduce as we age. Men tend to use slightly more energy to keep warm because they have less fat to insulate their bodies.

Total energy requirement

The energy required to power our body is supplied by our intake of food. Our digestive system breaks down the complex chemicals in food into fuels, such as carbohydrates and fats, which are easily oxidised to release energy. A kilogram of glucose releases about 17 MJ of energy; a kilogram of fat releases over twice this amount.

The BMR is the rate of energy transfer needed to just keep the body 'ticking over'. Any activity, such as walking or climbing stairs, increases the energy demands. The additional energy transfer would cause the body's temperature to rise unless the extra energy is transferred away by means of cooling such as evaporation of sweat.

A person walking up stairs is increasing their potential energy as they do work against the gravitational attraction of the Earth. We can estimate the power

Fig. 4 Energy demands of everyday activities

The typical energy demands of everyday activities. The actual values for any person depends upon their mass and the external temperature.

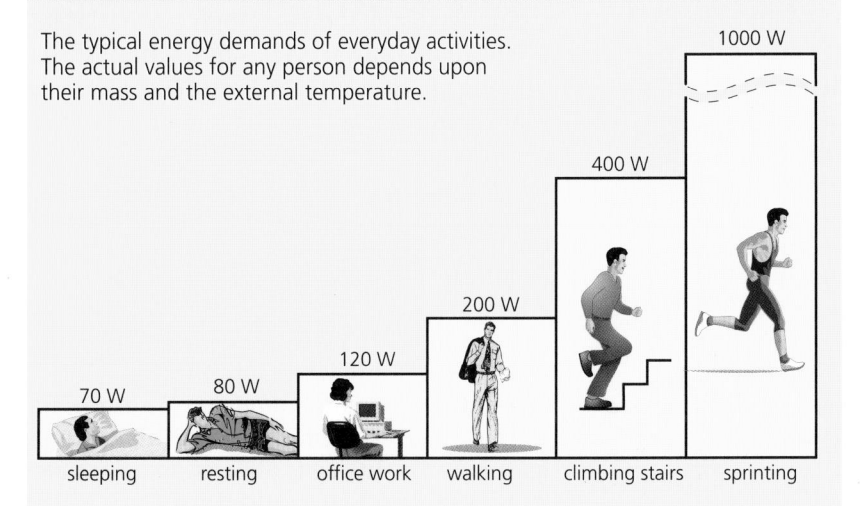

Fig. 5 Forces acting on the foot during walking

The resultant force, R, that the ground exerts on the foot is a combination of the normal contact force from the ground, N, and the friction, F.

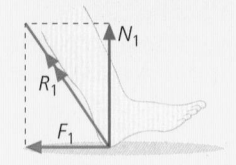

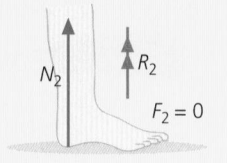

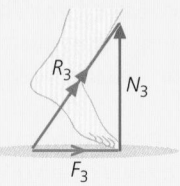

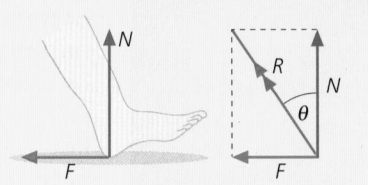

1 Heel-strike
Friction, F_1, prevents the foot slipping forward. N_1 supports the weight of the body and acts to decelerate the downward motion of the leg. The resultant force, R_1, is greater than the body weight, W.

2 Support
The normal contact force, N_2, is equal to the body weight.

3 Toe-off
The leg muscles push down on the ground and the resulting reaction, N_3, causes an upward acceleration in the leg. The frictional force, F_3, accelerates the body forward.

Resolving forces
The magnitude of the resultant force from the ground, R, is given by:
$$R^2 = N^2 + F^2$$

The force acts at an angle of θ to the vertical, where $\theta = \tan^{-1}\left(\frac{F}{N}\right)$.

---

developed by a person of mass 60 kg (weight ≈ 600 N) climbing two flights of stairs. Suppose that each flight of stairs is 5 m high and that it takes 20 seconds to reach the top. The power developed is:

$$\text{power} = \frac{\text{work done}}{\text{time taken}} = \frac{600\,\text{N} \times 2 \times 5\,\text{m}}{20\,\text{s}}$$

$$= \frac{6000\,\text{J}}{20\,\text{s}} = 300\,\text{W}$$

This is the power developed by the leg muscles in doing external work; it does not include energy used by other muscles or by the metabolic processes, which will have risen well above the BMR. Our estimate of 6000 J of work done in climbing the stairs is not a measure of the energy needs of the body to fulfil this task. Our skeletal muscle is between 25% and 30% efficient and extra energy is always needed to meet the requirements of the basic metabolism.

2a An athlete uses her arm muscles to lift a mass of 12 kg through 1 m. If she lifts the weight 30 times in a minute, calculate the power that her arm muscles produce.
b Explain why the rate at which energy is transferred by her body will be greater than this answer.
c The total power output of the athlete was measured as 500 W. How much glucose would she need to fuel this exercise?

Walking to victory

About half of the entrants in the desert marathon walk the entire distance of 230 km. Walking across the shifting sands is an energy sapping process and requires a new walking style, nicknamed the 'Saharan Shuffle'.

There are three phases to a normal walking action: heel-strike, support and toe-off. If we make the assumption that only one foot is in contact with the ground at any time, we can analyse the forces that act during walking (Fig. 5).

The maximum, or limiting, frictional force, F, that can be exerted by a surface depends on the normal contact force, N, and the coefficient of friction, μ, between the surfaces:

$$F = \mu N$$

If a walker is not to slip forward at heel-strike, F must be large enough to decelerate the leg. On a surface like sand, which shifts under foot, the value of μ is small. The walker slides forward at heel-strike. The foot also slips back at toe-off, reducing the efficiency of the step.

To prevent slipping, the angle between the leg and the vertical, θ, must be kept small. θ is related to μ because $\tan\theta = F/N$ and $F/N = \mu$. A small value of μ requires a small value of θ; the walker has to take shorter strides to avoid slipping.

One of the main energy expenditures in walking is in swinging the leg. This requires least effort if the leg is allowed to swing at its natural frequency. Adopting an

unnatural or variable pace is very taxing, as anyone who has tried to walk with young children will know.

Another source of energy loss during walking is the work done in lifting the centre of mass. With each stride, the centre of mass lifts and falls and we do work against gravity (Fig. 6). The energy needed for this part of walking is the increase in potential energy per stride:

$$mg\Delta h = 80 \times 10 \times 0.07 = 56 \text{ J}$$

Fig. 6 Walking and centre of mass

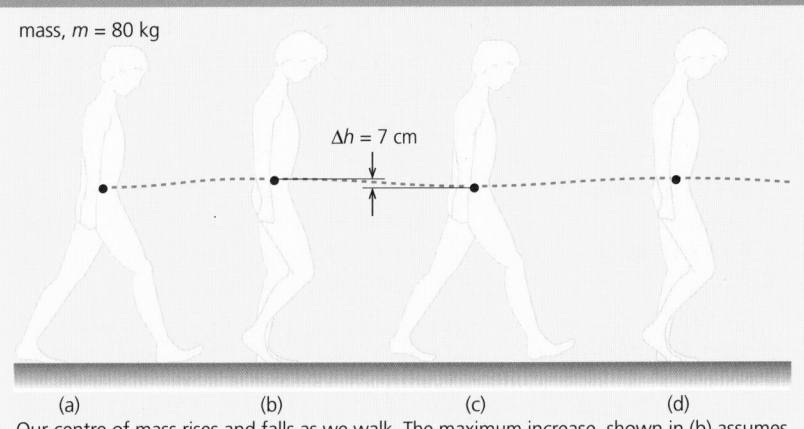

mass, $m = 80$ kg

$\Delta h = 7$ cm

(a)   (b)   (c)   (d)

Our centre of mass rises and falls as we walk. The maximum increase, shown in (b) assumes that we walk with rigid legs. Actually we bend our legs as we walk and the rise in the centre of mass is about half that shown, say about 7 cm.

Fig. 7 Conduction through skin

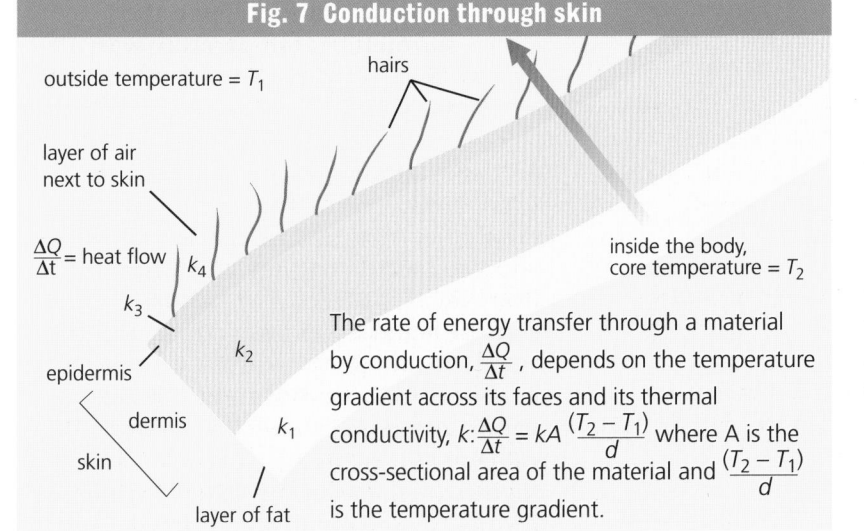

outside temperature = T_1

hairs

layer of air next to skin

$\frac{\Delta Q}{\Delta t}$ = heat flow

k_4

k_3

k_2

k_1

epidermis

dermis

skin

layer of fat

inside the body, core temperature = T_2

The rate of energy transfer through a material by conduction, $\frac{\Delta Q}{\Delta t}$, depends on the temperature gradient across its faces and its thermal conductivity, k: $\frac{\Delta Q}{\Delta t} = kA \frac{(T_2 - T_1)}{d}$ where A is the cross-sectional area of the material and $\frac{(T_2 - T_1)}{d}$ is the temperature gradient.

For a walker taking two strides per second, this is a power requirement of over 100 W.

A fast walking pace is only about 2 m s^{-1}, but top sprinters can run at over 10 m s^{-1}. This increase in speed is achieved by taking twice as many paces per second and by more than doubling the length of each stride. In fact, each stride becomes a jump, which demands greater forces from the leg muscles and increases the rate of energy transfer by the body. Every time the runner's feet hit the floor, all the vertical momentum is transferred to the ground. The leg muscles have to work to replace this, so an efficient running style has 'jumps' with a low trajectory.

3 a Why is it that you can walk safely across a slippery, muddy field, but you slip when you try to run?

b If the coefficient of friction between the mud and your shoes is 0.3, estimate the largest stride you can take without slipping.

Temperature control

The energy transferred by the body when we run or walk ends up as heat. This heat needs to be dissipated if the body's temperature is to remain steady. There are five processes by which the body transfers energy as heat to the surroundings:

1 Respiration and excretion

In cold, dry conditions there is a significant heat loss through respiration; it accounts for 30–40% of the total energy transfer. Cold air is breathed in, then warmed as it passes through the nose and respiratory tract, before it is exhaled.

Cold food or drink absorbs energy as it is brought to the temperature of the body. This energy is lost when the undigested food and drink is excreted.

2 Conduction

The rate of transfer of energy from the body due to conduction depends on the difference in temperature between the body and the surroundings. A greater surface area of exposed skin will increase the amount of energy transferred. Fat, skin and air are poor thermal conductors, and under normal conditions conduction

125

accounts for just 5% of the body's total energy loss (Fig. 7). The body can lose energy more quickly through contact with a cold stone floor or gain energy by walking on hot sand. Energy transfer is much greater when the body is in water. In water near 0 °C, hypothermia sets in within 15 minutes. Even in water at 16 °C, it only takes an hour for the body's core temperature to drop to around 34 °C.

3 Convection

The air next to the body is warmed by contact with skin and so expands, becoming less dense. This hot air rises, transferring energy. When the air is very cold and blows past the body at high speeds, as in the Antarctic winter, convection is the largest source of heat loss. Even in the UK, the effect of 'wind-chill' should not be underestimated; hill walkers have died from hypothermia at –10 °C, combined with a 20 m.p.h. wind.

4 Radiation

The rate at which energy radiates from the body is strongly dependent on its absolute temperature, T. The surface temperature of the body varies from about 25 °C (298 K) to 35 °C (308 K). An object at these temperatures emits radiation in the infrared region, with wavelengths between 2 μm and 50 μm. The total power, P, radiated from the body is given by the Stefan–Boltzmann law:

$$P_{rad} = \varepsilon\sigma AT^4$$

ε is a constant that depends on the nature of an object's surface. It is called the **emissivity** of the object. Its value varies from 1 for a perfect radiator (a 'black body'), to 0 for a perfect reflector. Human skin, whatever the colour, has a value of 0.98 at infrared wavelengths.

σ is the Stefan–Boltzmann constant, 5.7×10^{-8} W m^{-2} K^{-4}.

A is the effective radiating area of the body. It is less than the *actual* surface area of the body (about 1.8 m^2), and depends on the person's posture and on how much of the body is covered by clothing.

The body also absorbs radiation from its surroundings. The power absorbed is:

$$P_{abs} = \varepsilon\sigma AT_0^{\,4}$$

T_0 is the temperature of the surroundings. The transfer of energy per second to the surroundings is therefore:

$$P = \varepsilon\sigma A(T^4 - T_0^{\,4})$$

For a naked person, A is about 80% of the true surface area, so it is about 1.44 m^2. In a room at 22 °C, the rate of heat loss is:

$$
\begin{aligned}
P &= 0.98 \times 5.7 \times 10^{-8} \text{ W m}^{-2}\text{ K}^{-4} \times 1.44 \text{ m}^2 \times \\
&\quad (308^4 - 295^4) \text{ K}^4 \\
&= 115 \text{ W}
\end{aligned}
$$

Q 4 Estimate how much energy would be transferred every second by radiation for a person if the surrounding temperature was:
a 35 °C
b 40 °C?

5 Evaporation

Every day, about half a litre of water evaporates from the surface of your skin and you breathe out just under half a litre from your lungs. Energy is required to convert liquid water to a vapour. The energy required to vaporise 1 kg of liquid is known as the **specific latent heat of vaporisation**, l. At body temperature, the value of l for sweat is 2.425×10^6 J kg^{-1}, slightly higher than the value for water because sweat contains sodium salts and

This Schlieren photograph shows the column of rising, hot, turbulent air that surrounds the body. In still air at room temperature the body loses very little energy by convection

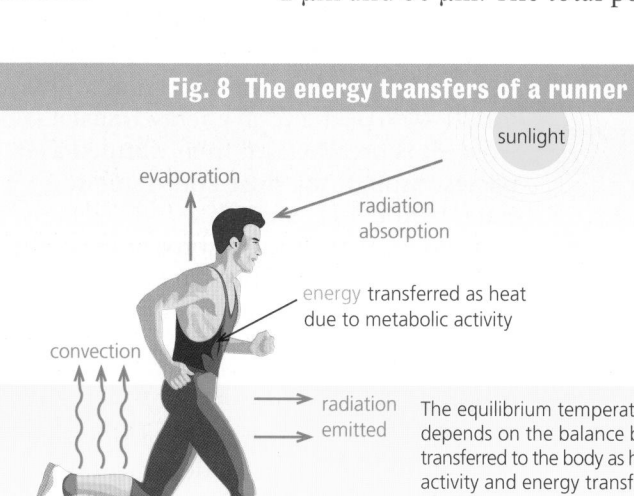

Fig. 8 The energy transfers of a runner

sunlight

evaporation

radiation absorption

energy transferred as heat due to metabolic activity

convection

radiation emitted

The equilibrium temperature of the body depends on the balance between energy transferred to the body as heat from metabolic activity and energy transfers from the environment. In the Sahara desert, marathon runners may absorb energy from their surroundings, rather than lose it, because the surrounding temperature is higher than body temperature.

conduction

Fig. 9 Modelling the surface area to volume ratio

If we model the human body as a sphere, we can see the effect that increasing size has on the surface : volume ratio

Person A has a radius, R.
Their volume is :
$$V = \frac{4}{3}\pi R^3$$
Their surface area is :
$$A = 4\pi R^2$$
The surface area to volume ratio is :
$$\frac{A}{V} = \frac{3}{R}$$

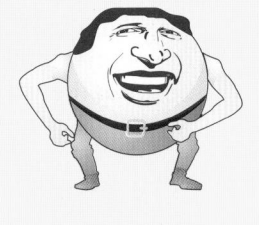
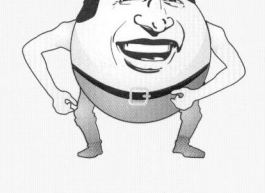
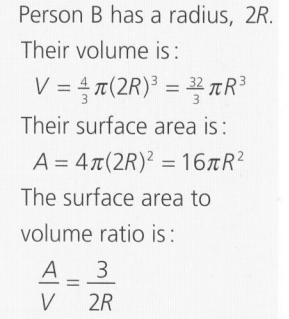

Person B has a radius, $2R$.
Their volume is :
$$V = \frac{4}{3}\pi(2R)^3 = \frac{32}{3}\pi R^3$$
Their surface area is :
$$A = 4\pi(2R)^2 = 16\pi R^2$$
The surface area to volume ratio is :
$$\frac{A}{V} = \frac{3}{2R}$$

The ratio of surface area : volume for the larger person is half that of the smaller person.

Small birds fluff up their feathers to trap air and reduce the rate of heat loss. They can also increase their cell metabolism to release more energy. This means that they need to consume a large amount of food relative to their body weight.

urea. We lose about 0.5 litre of sweat per day, an energy transfer of:

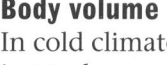

$$0.5 \text{ kg} \times 2.425 \times 10^6 \text{ J kg}^{-1} = 1.21 \times 10^6 \text{ J}$$

This is an average power of about 14 W. The actual rate at which we lose energy through evaporation depends on the temperature difference between us and the surroundings, as well as the area of skin that is exposed. The rate of evaporation is greater in high winds, and less in humid conditions.

Runners in the Sahara need to sweat to survive. When the external temperature is higher than body temperature, evaporation is the only energy transfer mechanism that is effective, because the body actually gains heat from conduction, convection and radiation. The body's sweat glands go into overdrive, producing up to 10 litres a day. If fluids are not replaced frequently, the runner will suffer from heat exhaustion.

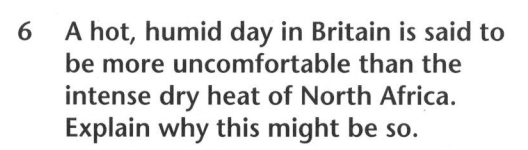 **5** Estimate the rate of energy transfer by evaporation for a runner in the Sahara.

6 A hot, humid day in Britain is said to be more uncomfortable than the intense dry heat of North Africa. Explain why this might be so.

7 If you are out in cold conditions in the mountains it is vital to keep dry. Give two reasons why this is so.

Body volume

In cold climates, the body has to work hard just to keep warm. The body's thermostat is the hypothalmus, which is located in the brain. The hypothalamus controls the core temperature of the body by directing blood to, or away from, blood vessels near the surface of the skin. When the core temperature drops too far, the hypothalamus secretes a hormone that promotes shivering. Shivering can increase the body's heat production to five times the resting level. Increased physical activity, such as stamping your feet, also helps.

The rate at which a body generates heat is proportional to its volume. However, the rate at which a body loses energy depends on its surface area. When it comes to keeping warm in cold conditions, larger people have an advantage, while babies are particularly at risk from hypothermia. This is because small bodies have a large surface area to volume ratio (Fig. 9).

8 Estimate the surface area to volume ratio for a baby of mass 5 kg and for an adult of mass 80 kg. Model the situation by treating the bodies as:
(i) spheres;
(ii) cylinders.
(Take the average density of a human to be about 1000 kg m⁻³)

9 Explain why emperor penguins often huddle together.

Key ideas

- Basal metabolic rate, BMR, is the minimum rate at which a conscious person at rest transfers energy.

- The body transfers energy to the surroundings – by conduction, radiation, evaporation, respiration and excretion – to maintain a constant temperature.

- Frictional forces on the foot provide the forward push and prevent us slipping when we walk. The coefficient of friction, μ, is given by $\mu = F / N = \tan \theta$. F is the maximum frictional force on the foot, N is the normal contact force and θ is the angle between the resultant force and the vertical. To prevent slipping, $F \leq \mu N$.

11.3 Taking the temperature

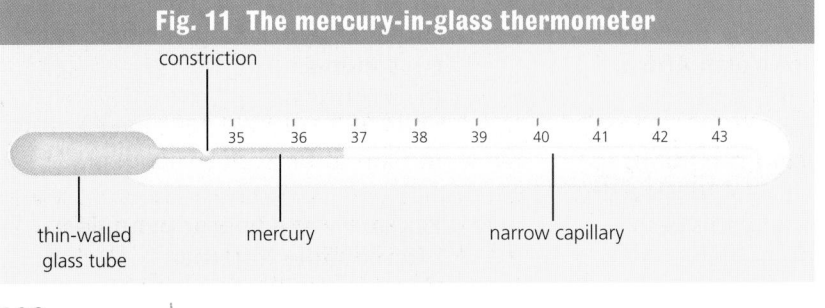

Sir Ranolph Fiennes lost a toe through frostbite during his Antarctic expedition in 1993. Frostbite usually occurs in the body's extremities – ears, fingers or toes – when localised freezing of the body tissues takes place. Prevention is far better than cure; the only treatment for severe frostbite is amputation.

The first visible sign of hypothermia is often a very pale complexion, as the body shuts down the blood supply to surface capillaries in an attempt to conserve energy and maintain the core temperature. The skin may look blue due to deoxygenated blood stagnating in the capillaries. This response leaves the extremities vulnerable to frostbite.

It is necessary to take the core temperature to assess the level of hypothermia in a victim. Under normal, warm conditions, the temperature recorded in the mouth, armpit or rectum is quite close to the body's core temperature. For a hypothermia victim, the mouth is probably the only reliable place (Fig. 10).

Body temperature is most commonly recorded by a mercury-in-glass thermometer (Fig. 11), which relies on the expansion of mercury to measure temperature. It is a reliable, sensitive thermometer which is relatively cheap to produce. The capillary tube is so thin that thickened, magnifying

Fig. 10 Body temperature distribution in warm or cold environments

The body restricts the blood supply to the periphery in cold conditions in order to maintain the temperature of the vital organs at 37 °C.

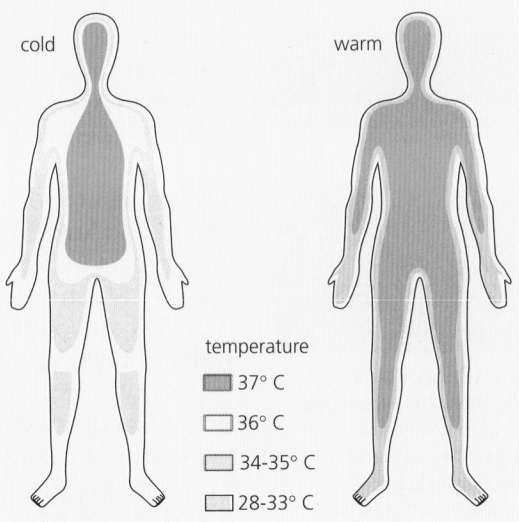

cold   warm

temperature

- 37° C
- 36° C
- 34-35° C
- 28-33° C

glass is used in front of the mercury thread so that it can be seen easily.

The thin capillary means that a small rise in temperature gives a detectable increase in the length of the mercury thread. The constriction in the capillary tube acts as a valve to prevent mercury returning to the bulb as soon as the thermometer is removed from the patient. The clinical thermometer has a large **thermal capacity**, which gives it a long response time. Nurses need to wait about four minutes before removing the thermometer, so it is not suitable for measuring temperatures that fluctuate rapidly.

Fig. 11 The mercury-in-glass thermometer

constriction

35 36 37 38 39 40 41 42 43

thin-walled glass tube   mercury   narrow capillary

Fig. 12 The Seebeck effect

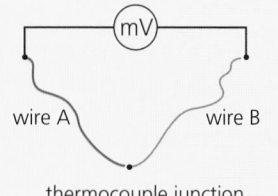

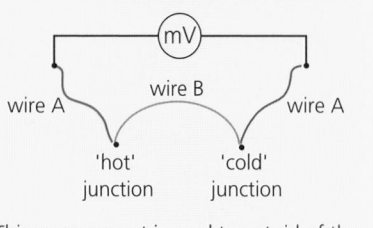

wire A   wire B

thermocouple junction

wire A   wire B   wire A

'hot'   'cold'
junction   junction

The e.m.f. generated, *E*, depends on the temperature of the junction. This is known as the thermoelectric effect or Seebeck effect. The situation is complicated by the connections to the millivoltmeter, which also introduce thermoelectric e.m.f.s into the circuit.

This arrangement is used to get rid of the e.m.f.s at the millivoltmeter connections. The junctions are now between the same metals and cancel out because they are equal and opposite. The cold junction is usually kept at 0 °C, and it acts as a reference level. In modern devices the 'cold' junction is simulated electronically.

Fig. 13 A thermopile

black shield to prevent radiation reaching cold junctions

radiation

highly polished surface

hot junctions   cold junctions

V

A thermopile measures surface temperature by detecting infrared radiation.

Thermistors

Sometimes it is useful to be able to measure temperature at a given point in the body, or to be able to record a rapidly fluctuating temperature. A **thermistor** is a small bead of semiconductor, about 0.1 mm across, whose electrical resistance changes with temperature. A thermistor has a low thermal capacity and has a precision of about 0.01 °C. It is an electrical method of measuring temperature, which allows continuous monitoring and recording, either by a computer or a chart recorder.

Thermocouples

A **thermocouple** is an alternative to the thermistor and has similar operational advantages. It relies on the fact that when two metals are joined together an e.m.f. is generated across the wires (Fig. 12). The size of the e.m.f. depends on the temperature of the junction.

The output of a thermocouple, typically only a few millivolts, can be increased by joining several thermocouples in series. The resulting device, known as a **thermopile**, can be used to detect infrared radiation. The radiation emitted from skin depends on skin temperature, so thermopiles can monitor skin temperature without any contact with the skin itself.

Thermography

Cameras that detect infrared radiation are now used to produce thermal images of the body. A germanium lens focuses the infrared radiation that is emitted by the body. A system of moving mirrors scans the infrared radiation across a detector. The detector is a semiconductor, such as

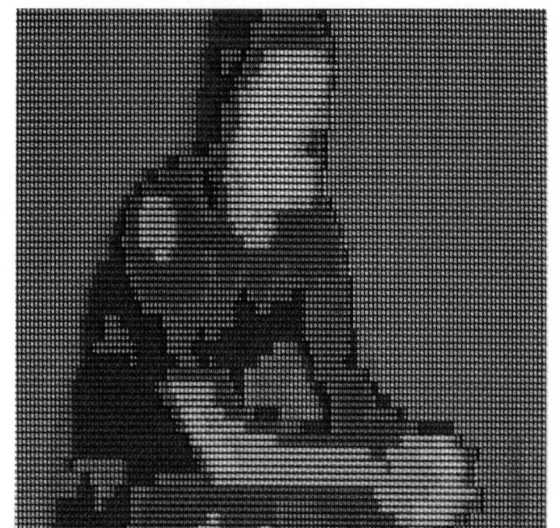

This thermogram reveals the differences in the surface temperatures of a squash player after a game. The hotter regions are white and yellow, and the cooler regions are red and blue.

This thermogram shows the temperature distribution in a pair of cold hands. Although the palms are still warm (yellow, red), the fingertips (green, purple) have dropped to a dangerously low temperature

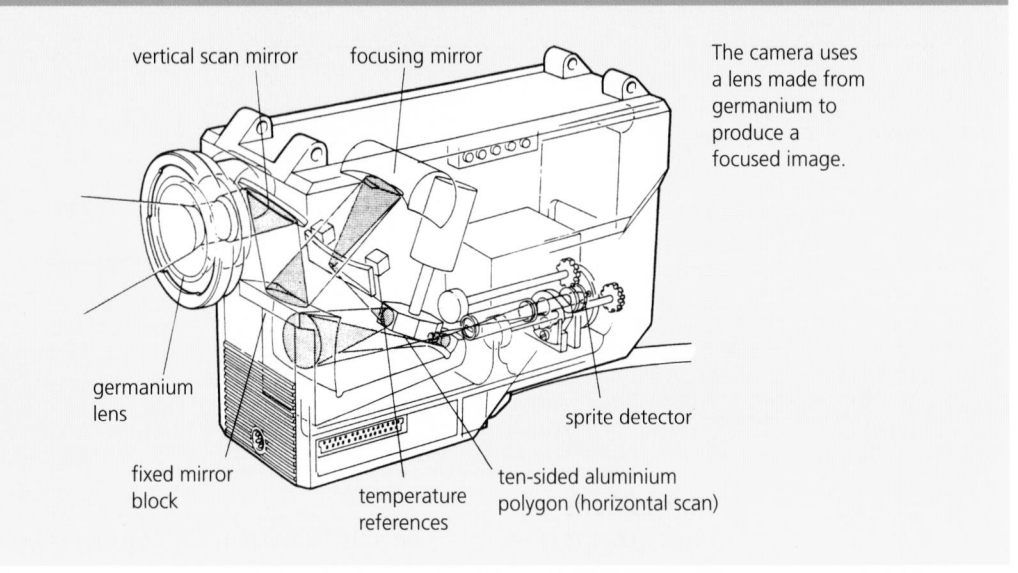

Fig. 14 An infrared camera

vertical scan mirror

focusing mirror

The camera uses a lens made from germanium to produce a focused image.

germanium lens

fixed mirror block

temperature references

ten-sided aluminium polygon (horizontal scan)

sprite detector

indium antimonide, which detects photons. Energy from the photons is absorbed by the semiconductor and causes electrons to become available for conduction. This leads to a change in voltage across the semiconductor which is used to control the output of a VDU. The intensity of infrared radiation emitted by a body depends strongly on its surface temperature, so the VDU can display a 'temperature map' of the body. Modern thermographic cameras produce images that display temperature differences of as little as 0.1 K in regions separated by an angle of only 0.5 mrad.

Thermography can be used to map the extent of a burn or frostbite. Changes to the surface temperature of the body may also indicate a malignant disease that has disrupted the blood flow.

Key ideas

- The core temperature of the body is maintained at 37 °C.

- The mercury-in-glass thermometer is simple and reliable, but has a long response time.

- Thermocouples and thermistors can be used to measure rapidly changing temperatures at a specific point in the body.

- Thermographs are images of the body showing differences in surface temperature.

12 Dangerous exposure

On April 26th, 1986, the nuclear reactor at Chernobyl in northern Ukraine went out of control. An explosion blew the 2000-tonne metal-and-concrete lid off the reactor. Rising smoke and hot gases carried radioactive isotopes high into the atmosphere where the wind scattered them over the northern hemisphere.

'Igor Pavlovets doesn't look like other children. He is only as tall as a toddler. He has no hips and where his thighs should be are two strange feet, bent back on themselves like flippers of muscle. Igor's left arm ... is perfectly formed, but he doesn't have a right arm at all. His left foot has only two extra-long toes ... his right foot is missing two toes. But his deformities are all on the outside. Igor is a sunny boy with a glorious smile. He is also extremely intelligent.'

Source: 'Igor. The Courage of Chernobyl's Child', *Jane Warren, Boxtree, 1996*

Igor Pavlovets was born 11 months after the disaster at Chernobyl. His parents lived just outside the evacuation zone. Igor's disabilities have been attributed to the effects of radiation on his parents, but no-one can be sure. How can we predict accurately the dangers of radiation to humans?

12.1 Learning objectives

After working through this chapter, you should be able to:

- **define** the units in which radioactivity and radiation are measured;

- **explain** the meaning of quality factor and relative biological effectiveness;

- **describe** the effects of ionising radiation on the body;

- **describe** the major sources of background radiation;

- **explain** the principles of radiation detection and monitoring.

12.2 A dose of radiation

Some of the effects of the Chernobyl radiation were immediate; thirty one people died of radiation sickness within a few weeks. Other effects of radiation may take thirty years to appear, and these long-term effects are harder to quantify. Estimates of the deaths from cancer and other diseases due to the Chernobyl disaster vary widely, from 5000 to 500 000.

How can we be sure whether people who suffer from a genetic disease, or an illness such as cancer, were actually affected by radiation or whether their disease was due to some other cause?

Radioactivity
Radioactive **nuclei** are unstable (see CAMS Physics Core, ch. 12 and 13). The nuclei of

Fig. 1 Alpha, beta and gamma radiations

Alpha (α), beta (β) and gamma (γ) rays are energetic enough to remove electrons from atoms that they collide with so they are termed ionising radiation.

An alpha particle is a tightly bound group of two protons and two neutrons that is emitted from the nucleus at high speed; is a charged particle of relatively high mass, so it is intensely ionising; can produce up to 10^5 ion pairs per cm in air; loses some energy with each ionisation; has a limited range of about 5 cm in air.

A beta particle is an electron emitted from the nucleus at around 95% of the speed of light; has a mass of 1/8000 that of an alpha particle and causes less ionisation, about 1000 ion pairs per cm in air; has a range of several metres in air.

A gamma ray is a very high frequency electromagnetic wave; is less densely ionising than an alpha or beta particle; is extremely penetrating.

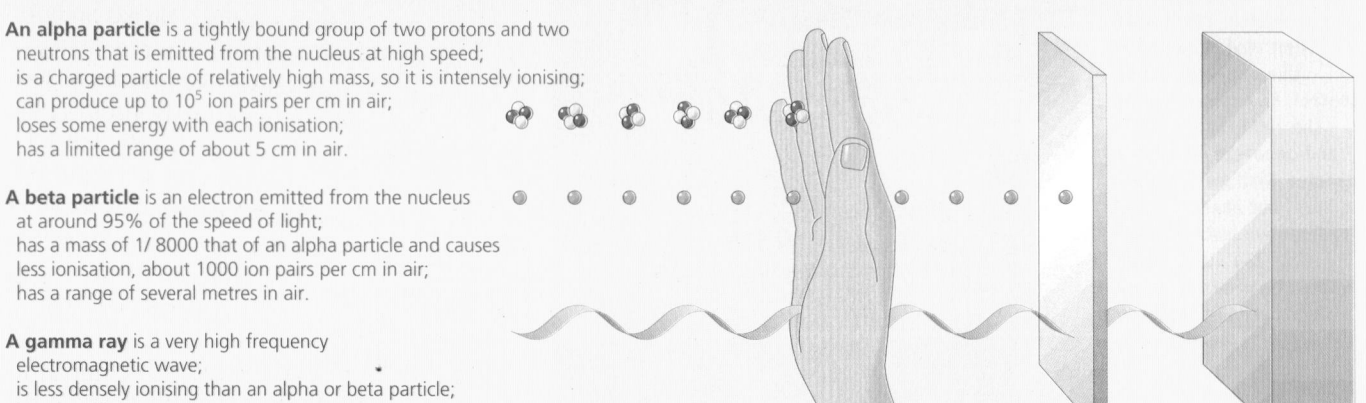

their atoms decay into new isotopes, emitting **ionising radiation** (Fig. 1) in the process. This decay is *spontaneous* and *random*. The rate of radioactive decay is not influenced by external factors, such as temperature or pressure. We cannot predict with any certainty when a given atom will decay. All we can say, for any specific isotope, is that there is a certain probability, λ, that a nucleus will decay in a given time. λ is known as the **decay constant**. Each radioactive isotope has a **half-life**, $T_{1/2}$, which is the time taken for half of the nuclei to decay (Fig. 2). The half-life is linked to the decay constant by the formula:

$$T_{\frac{1}{2}} = \frac{\ln 2}{\lambda}$$

The most common, 'ordinary' nuclei of elements are stable. However, natural or artificial **isotopes** exist with heavier or lighter nuclei. Some of these isotopes are radioactive and are known as **radioisotopes**.

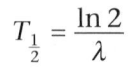 **1** The cloud chamber pictures below show the tracks left by ionising radiation. Explain which tracks were made by alpha particles and which by beta particles.

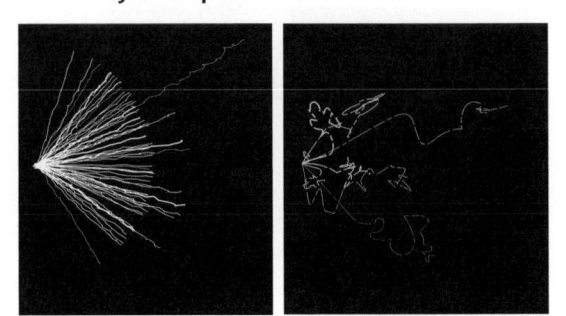

tracks A   tracks B

2 Calculate a value for the wavelength of a gamma ray emitted with an energy of 1 MeV. (Remember that the energy of a photon (in joules) = $h \times f$ and that 1 eV = 1.6×10^{-19} J)

3 Radioactive iodine–131 was a major risk to health following the Chernobyl accident. The decay constant of iodine–131 is 9.9×10^{-7} s^{-1}. Calculate its half-life.

Fig. 2 Graph of number of nuclei vs. time for a radioisotope

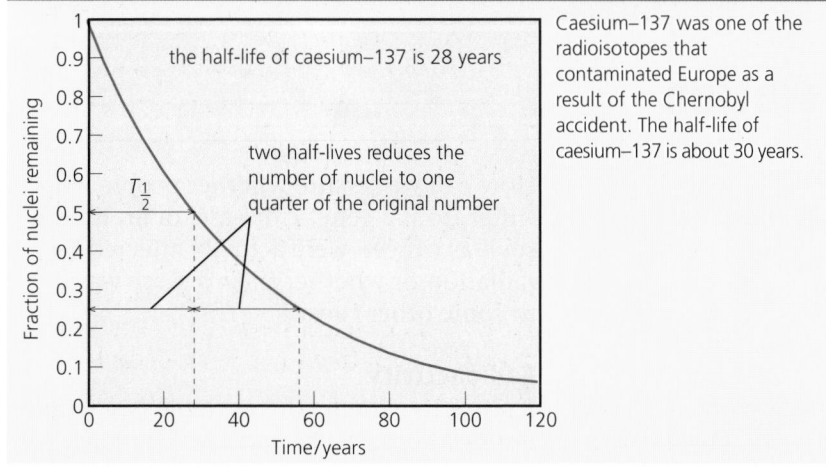

the half-life of caesium–137 is 28 years

two half-lives reduces the number of nuclei to one quarter of the original number

$T_{\frac{1}{2}}$

Caesium–137 was one of the radioisotopes that contaminated Europe as a result of the Chernobyl accident. The half-life of caesium–137 is about 30 years.

One way of defining the radioactivity of an isotope is by measuring its **activity**. The activity is the number of nuclei in the sample that decay in one second, i.e. the number of emissions per second. The S.I. unit of activity is the becquerel, Bq. If a source has an activity of 1 Bq then, on average, one of its nuclei decays every second. This is an extremely small unit and activities of kilobecquerel, kBq, or megabecquerel, Mbq, are often used. An older unit that is still used is the curie, Ci. One curie is the number of disintegrations per second in one gram of radium, equivalent to 3.7×10^{10} Bq.

Radioactive debris from Chernobyl's burning core travelled high into the atmosphere. Dangerous radioisotopes, such as iodine–131, strontium–90 and caesium–137, spread to Scandinavia, the UK and as far away as Japan. By May 2nd, 1986, the radioactive cloud was passing over the UK. It met rain over North Wales and the Lake District which washed radioactive materials to the ground. Grass, sheep and people were contaminated. **Specific activity** is used to measure contamination, that is the activity per kg. The government brought in regulations to prevent sheep with specific activity of more than 1 k Bq kg^{-1} being sold for slaughter.

4 **The total amount of radioactive material released by the Chernobyl reactor had an estimated activity of 100 million curie. Convert this figure to becquerel.**

Reindeer feed on lichens, which accumulate polonium–210. Laplanders who eat reindeer meat may experience thirty times the average radiation dose.

5 **On May 5, 1986, the activity level of iodine–131 in some fields in Cumbria was 40 kBq m^{-2}. Iodine–131 has a half-life of 8 days. Ignoring the effects of rain, how long would it take the activity levels to drop to the 'safe' level of 10 kBq on every square metre of ground?**

Setting the safety level

The UK government's 'safe' value for specific activity in meat was not universally accepted. The Swedish government set a level that was one third of the British safe level. One of the problems faced by those who set safety levels is to identify where the contaminants will end up.

Radioisotopes can become concentrated in certain areas or certain foods because of their chemical pathway through the environment. Radioactive lead and polonium are concentrated by shellfish. Caesium–137 from Chernobyl accumulated in sheep and radioactive iodine–131 became concentrated in cow's milk.

In the human body, iodine is concentrated by the thyroid gland. The thyroid gland makes no distinction between stable iodine–127 and the beta-emitting isotope, iodine–131. If iodine tablets are swallowed before any exposure, the thyroid becomes saturated with stable iodine and the radioactive isotope will not be absorbed. About 5 million people were given these 'radiation pills' about 4 days after the disaster, but this was far too late.

Biological half-life

Although some radioactive isotopes concentrate in parts of the body, most are excreted over a period of time. The time taken for half of the radioisotope to be removed from the body is known as the **biological half-life**, T_B. The radiation dose given by any radioisotope depends on its biological half-life as well as its **physical half-life**, T_P. If the fraction of the radionuclide that is excreted by the body every second is λ_B and the fraction of the radionuclide that decays every second is λ_P, then the total fraction removed each second is:

$$\lambda = \lambda_B + \lambda_P$$

Since $\lambda = \ln 2 / T_P$, the **effective half-life**, T, is a combination of the biological and physical half-lives:

$$\frac{1}{T} = \frac{1}{T_B} + \frac{1}{T_P}$$

The biological half-life of caesium–131 in sheep is 10–30 days and its physical half-life is thirty years. In this case, biological excretion is the more important factor. However, because sheep took in caesium from the grass and excreted it back onto the grass, the caesium was recycled. The Minister of Agriculture initially told parliament that restrictions on sheep would last for about three weeks, but 11 years on some sheep were still too radioactive to sell.

Q6 Iodine–131 has a biological half-life in humans of about 24 days. Its physical half-life is 8 days. Calculate its effective half-life.

Key ideas

- The activity of a radioisotope is the number of disintegrations per second. Activity is measured in becquerel, Bq.

- The physical half-life of a radioisotope, T_P, is the time taken for the activity of the source to reduce by half.

- Radioisotopes can concentrate in certain body organs or parts of the environment.

- The biological half-life of a radioisotope, T_B, is the time taken for the body to excrete half of the activity.

- The effective half-life, T, of a radioisotope absorbed by the body is given by:

$$\frac{1}{T} = \frac{1}{T_B} + \frac{1}{T_P}$$

Fig. 3 Radiation interacting with matter

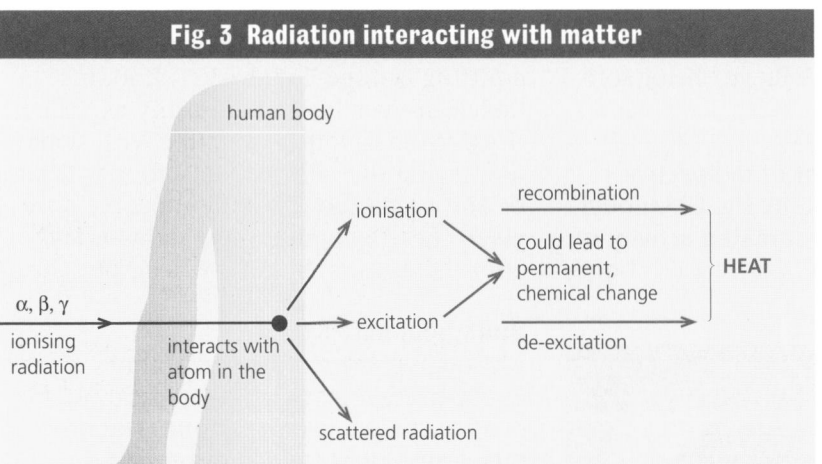

About 97% of the energy transferred to matter by radiation simply raises its temperature. 3% causes permanent changes to the matter.

Fig. 4 A simple ionisation chamber

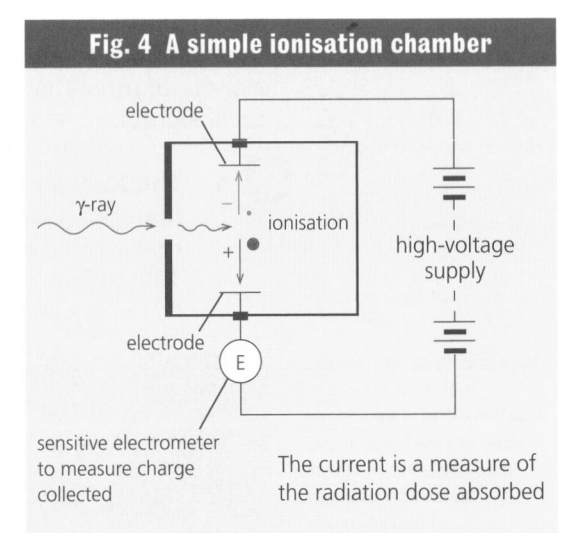

The current is a measure of the radiation dose absorbed

Measuring the effect of radiation

The activity of a radioisotope simply measures the number of disintegrations per second. No account is taken of the effect the radiation has on any material that it passes through. The **absorbed dose** is the amount of energy deposited in the material by the radiation. The unit of absorbed dose is the joule per kilogram, or gray (Gy):

$$\text{absorbed dose (Gy)} = \frac{\text{energy absorbed (J)}}{\text{mass of irradiated material (kg)}}$$

$$D = \frac{E}{m}$$

A radiation dose could be measured directly by the heating effect it causes (Fig 3). However, the temperature rise due to irradiation is usually extremely low, say

0.01 °C. An alternative is to measure the amount of ionisation that is caused by the radiation (Fig. 4). This is relatively easy in gases because the ions created are mobile and can be collected and counted. The ions are also further apart than in a liquid, which means that they are less likely to recombine before they can be detected.

Effects of X-rays and gamma rays

The energy deposited in a material by gamma rays, or by X-rays, depends on the atomic number of the material (see CAMS Physics Core, p.148). The effective atomic number of air is 7.64, similar to that of soft tissue, for which $Z = 7.42$. Therefore, equal masses of air and soft tissue absorb roughly the same dose when exposed to the same beam. The ionisation caused by gamma rays or X-rays in a specified mass of air is known as the **exposure**, measured in coulombs per kilogram.

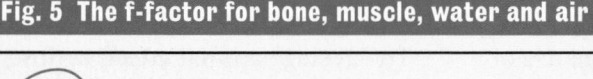

$$\text{exposure} = \frac{\text{total charge of ions of one sign}}{\text{mass of air}}$$

$$X \ (\text{C kg}^{-1}) = \frac{Q \ (\text{C})}{m \ (\text{kg})}$$

The charge measured is that of all positive ions *or* negative ions.

The exposure can be used to find the absorbed dose in air. On average, it takes 34 eV to create an ion pair in air. The charge on an electron is 1.6×10^{-19} C. If the total charge of all the ions created is Q, then the number of ion pairs liberated is:

$$\frac{Q}{1.6 \times 10^{-19}}$$

The total energy required will be:

$$E = \frac{Q}{1.6 \times 10^{-19}} \times 34 \ \text{eV}$$

In joules, this is: $E = Q \times 34 \ \text{J}$

Dividing by the mass of the irradiated material gives the absorbed dose *for air*:

$D \ (\text{Gy}) = \text{exposure} \ (\text{C kg}^{-1}) \times 34 \ (\text{J C}^{-1})$

Body tissue usually absorbs more energy. The energy required to cause ion pairs in other materials depends on the material and on the energy of gamma photons involved (Fig. 5):

$D \ (\text{Gy}) = $ f-factor (Gy C^{-1} kg) $\times$ exposure (C kg^{-1})

7 The old unit of exposure was the roentgen. An exposure of 1 roentgen would cause an ionisation of 2.58×10^{-4} C in 1 kg of dry air.
a What absorbed dose would this cause in air?
b If the exposure was due to 0.1 MeV gamma rays, what dose would this cause in bone?

Quality factor

The absorbed dose values do not give a true picture of radiation damage to human tissue. Alpha particles cause so much ionisation in a short distance that they kill more cells than beta or gamma rays at the same absorbed dose. To take account of this effect, different types of radiation are given a **quality factor**, Q (Table 1). The ability of radiation to cause biological damage is measured by a quantity called the **dose equivalent**, H, with units of sievert (Sv):

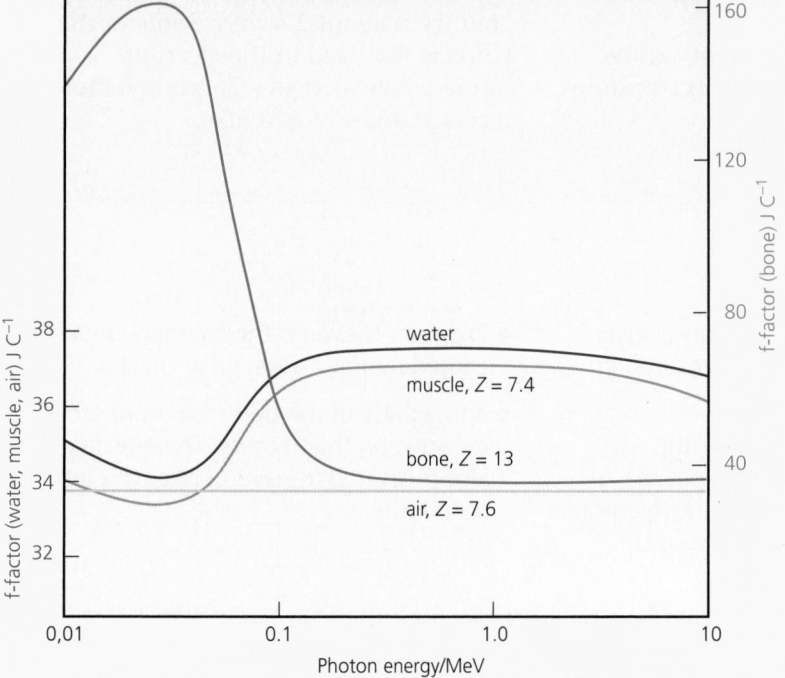

Fig. 5 The f-factor for bone, muscle, water and air

water

muscle, $Z = 7.4$

bone, $Z = 13$

air, $Z = 7.6$

f-factor (water, muscle, air) J C^{-1}

f-factor (bone) J C^{-1}

Photon energy/MeV

The f-factor is used to convert exposure to dose. Note the log scale on the x-axis.

135

dose equivalent (Sv) = absorbed dose (Gy)
$\times$ quality factor

$$H = D \times Q$$

Radiation that deposits its energy in a short distance is said to have a high **linear energy transfer**, LET. This gives an indication of the damage that the radiation will do to cells. α–particles have a high LET while γ–rays are low-LET radiation.

Another way of specifying the effect of a given radiation is to compare it with the effect of a standard radiation. The standard chosen is X-rays of energy 250 keV. The **relative biological effect**, RBE is:

$$RBE = \frac{\text{absorbed dose of 250 keV X-rays to produce a given effect}}{\text{absorbed dose of radiation to produce the same effect}}$$

 **8** **Would you expect alpha particles to have a higher relative biological effect than gamma rays? Explain your answer.**

The effective dose equivalent

Some cells in the body are more prone to damage than others. The effect on each type of cell can be assessed by the use of weighting factors, w (Table 2).

The effective dose equivalent can be calculated by adding up the effective doses to each part of the body:

Table 1 Quality factors of different types of radiation

Type of radiation	Quality factor, Q
β, γ and X-rays	1–2
slow neutrons	5
α-particles	10
protons, fast neutrons	10
heavy nuclei	20

Table 2 Weighting factors for different organs of the body

ovaries / testes	0.2
red bone marrow	0.12
colon	0.12
lung	0.12
stomach	0.12
bladder	0.05
breast	0.05
liver	0.05
oesophagus	0.05
skin	0.01
bone surface	0.01
other parts	0.05

effective dose (Sv) = $w_1 H_1 + w_2 H_2 + \ldots w_n H_n$

$$= \Sigma_i \, w_i H_i$$

The average annual effective dose in this country is about 2.4 mSv. Some of the workers involved in the clean-up immediately after the Chernobyl incident received doses of 600 mSv.

Key ideas

- The absorbed dose, D, measures energy deposited by radiation. It is measured in J kg^{-1} or gray, Gy.

- The quality factor, Q, measures the damaging effect of different types of radiation. The dose equivalent, H, measured in sievert, Sv, takes this into account: $H = QD$

- Exposure measures the ionisation in air caused by γ or X-rays. It has units of C kg^{-1}.

- Some parts of the body are more sensitive to radiation than others. The effective dose, also measured in sievert, takes this into account.

12.3 The human cost

The effect of radiation on cells

Radiation can kill or damage cells in a number of ways. The **nucleus** of the cell is particularly sensitive to radiation. There are 46 chromosomes in the nucleus of a human cell, each containing strands of DNA. Ionising radiation damages DNA directly by removing electrons from atoms and causing chemical changes. Radiation also damages the DNA indirectly by interacting with water in cells (Fig. 6).

Radiation-induced damage to DNA does not always cause the death of a cell. Human cells can repair the DNA; the DNA in a normal human cell is broken and restored about 10 000 times every hour. The ability of a cell to repair itself depends on the type of damage to the DNA helix (Fig. 7). A break in a single strand may be quite easy to repair, because the second strand of the helix acts as a template, but a double break may be irreparable. Radiation with a high linear energy transfer is more likely to cause double or compound breaks in DNA.

Permanent damage to DNA does not always result in cell death. A cell that has been irradiated may form a slow-growing colony, or it may divide abnormally and eventually result in a cancer. Non-fatal changes in the DNA may be passed on from irradiated parents to their children. Any increase in the number of these mutations is likely to increase the risk of genetic diseases in the next generation.

Fig. 6 Indirect radiation damage

A sequence of chemical changes can lead to changes in the DNA of a cell:

1. A gamma ray (or an alpha or beta particle) ejects an electron from a water molecule, leaving it ionised:

$$H_2O + hf \longrightarrow H_2O^+ + e^-$$

(hf = energy of gamma photon)

2. The H_2O^+ ion immediately dissociates into a hydrogen ion and an OH radical:

$$H_2O^+ \longrightarrow H^+ + OH^\bullet$$

while the electron joins up with a water molecule to form a negative ion, which quickly dissociates:

$$H_2O + e^- \longrightarrow H_2O^- \longrightarrow H^\bullet + OH^-$$

3. The ions, OH^- and H^+ are common to all body fluids, but the neutral $H^\bullet$ and $OH^\bullet$ radicals are very reactive, having a lifetime of about 10^{-5} seconds. These free radicals may react directly with an important molecule in the cell *or* react to form hydrogen peroxide:

$$OH^\bullet + OH^\bullet \longrightarrow H_2O_2$$

Hydrogen peroxide is a powerful oxidising agent, often used as a bleach, and it can break down proteins within the cell. Approximately 70% of the breaks in a DNA chain are due to the action of the $OH^\bullet$ radical.

Fig. 7 Possible effects of radiation on DNA

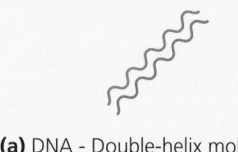

(a) DNA - Double-helix molecule

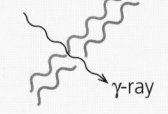

(b) Single breaks in the DNA are easy to repair

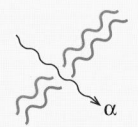

(c) densely ionising radiation can cause a break in both strands of the DNA molecule

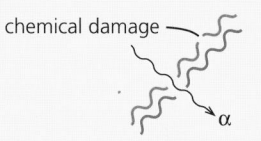

(d) compound breaks may be impossible to repair

Densely ionising radiation is more likely to cause a double break in DNA. Indirect action, such as the production of hydrogen peroxide, will also be greater in the region and the accumulated damage may be impossible to repair.

Table 3 Whole-body radiation syndromes		
Dose	Typical lifespan after irradiation	Syndrome
more than 100 Gy	minutes to 48 hours	central nervous system syndrome
between 10 and 100 Gy	between 5 and 14 days	gastro-intestinal syndrome
between 2 and 10 Gy	10 to 30 days	bone marrow death

Acute effects of radiation

Twenty eight of the Chernobyl firefighters died from radiation sickness within three months of the disaster. The symptoms of radiation sickness depends on which parts of the body are exposed. Some organs are more sensitive to radiation than others. Cells are at their most sensitive during cell division. Skin, bone marrow and testes contain cells that divide frequently so they are more **radiosensitive**. Liver, kidney, brain and bone cells rarely divide and are relatively **radioresistant**. A radiation dose to the whole body, or just the head, of more than 100 Gy is sufficient to kill the cells in the central nervous system (Table 3). The symptoms – epileptic fits, coma and respiratory failure – are irreversible and death occurs within hours.

At lower doses, between 10 and 100 Gy, cells in the gastro-intestinal tract are affected. The victim is unable to absorb essential nutrients and nausea, dehydration haemorrhagic diarrhoea and starvation result. Saline drips and antibiotics can delay death, but even continued intensive care is unlikely to be successful because at this dose level the cells in the bone marrow are also affected.

Doses of between 2 and 10 Gy inhibit cell division in the bone marrow where new blood cells are produced. Blood cells have a finite lifetime. As time passes after irradiation the numbers of red blood cells, white blood cells and platelets steadily decreases. As a consequence, victims suffer from anaemia and internal bleeding. The lack of white blood cells means that there is no resistance to infection. Death within a month is likely, though bone marrow transplants can be effective.

At doses lower than 1 to 2 Gy, most people survive the immediate effects of irradiation, but they may suffer from radiation sickness and skin burns. Although bone marrow cells are affected by these lower doses, they have a remarkable capacity for recovery. If as little as 10 per cent of bone marrow escapes damage from irradiation, it can regenerate and replace what has been lost. At Chernobyl many people escaped the acute effects of radiation, but many have since succumbed to the delayed effects.

Q9 An internal exposure to α-radiation may cause far more damage to cells than a larger dose of γ-rays. Explain why this is the case.

10 Strontium–90 is a β-emitting radioisotope with a half-life of 28 years. It is chemically similar to calcium which the body uses to make bone. Explain why ingesting strontium–90 is particularly dangerous.

Delayed effects of radiation

The most important delayed effect of radiation is cancer. Cancer is frequently caused by environmental factors, such as smoking, or exposure to carcinogens like asbestos, but there is often a delay between exposure and the onset of the disease. This latent period can be a few years for leukaemia or thyroid cancer, and over thirty years for lung cancer (Fig. 8).

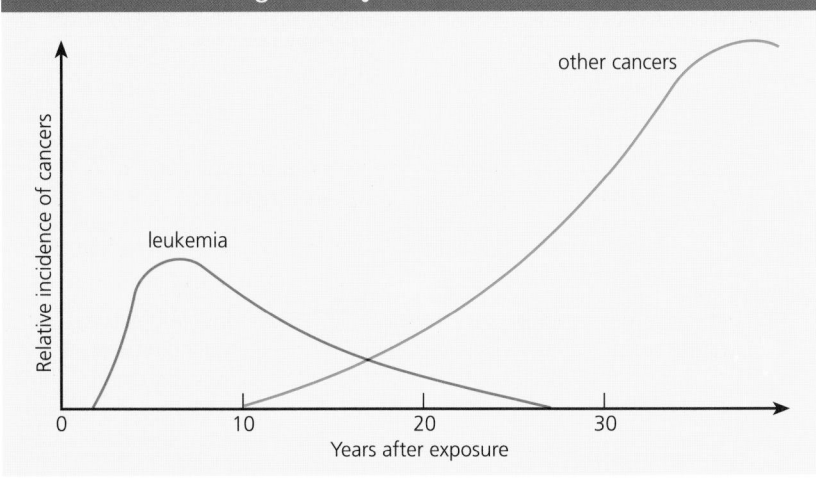

Fig. 8 Delayed onset of cancer

Relative incidence of cancers

leukemia

other cancers

Years after exposure

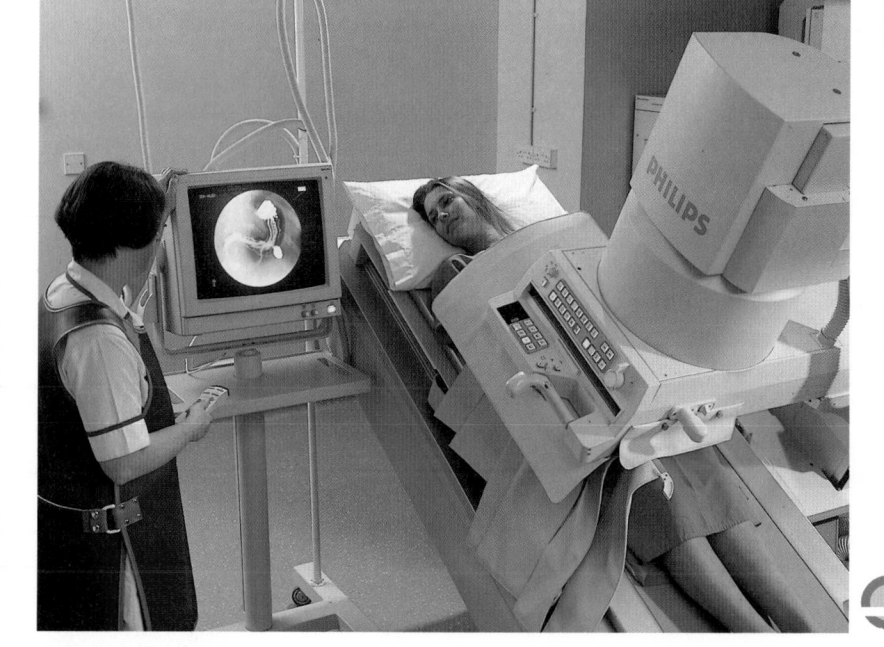

Radiation has a general life-shortening effect. A study of radiologists in the USA in the 1960s found that the mean lifespan of men exposed to radiation throughout their working lives was only 60.5 years, compared with a mean age of death at that time of 65.7 years.

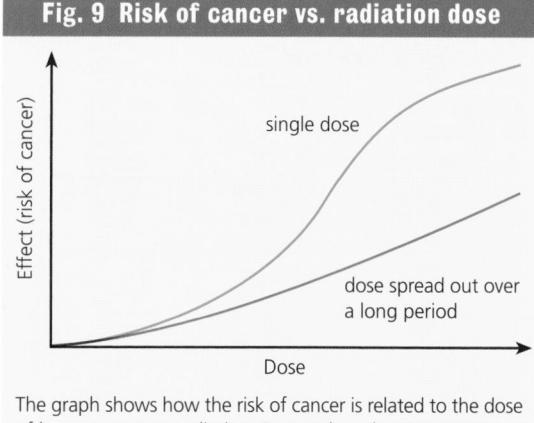

Fig. 9 Risk of cancer vs. radiation dose

single dose

dose spread out over a long period

Dose

Effect (risk of cancer)

The graph shows how the risk of cancer is related to the dose of beta or gamma radiation. Data at low doses is sparse. Scientists make the assumption that there is no 'safe' dose of radiation and then extrapolate from studies of people who have received high doses.

Being irradiated, rather like smoking, increases your risk of developing cancer, but it is not certain that exposure to radiation will lead to the disease.

Our best information on radiation-induced cancers comes from a study of the survivors from the Japanese cities Nagasaki and Hiroshima on which atom-bombs were dropped at the end of World War II. Recent calculations suggest that in a population of 1000 people who each receive a dose of 1 Gy, there will be an extra 70–110 deaths due to cancer. This is only an average picture; much will depend on the age and sex of those irradiated. Children are more vulnerable to radiation induced cancers than adults, and women are more at risk than men.

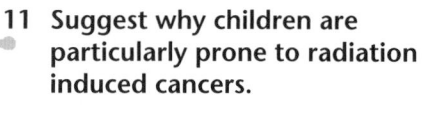

11 Suggest why children are particularly prone to radiation induced cancers.

12 a Fig. 9 shows that a given dose spread over a long period is less dangerous than the same dose given in a short time. Why do you think this is so?
b Explain why this effect does not apply to alpha radiation.

Radiation can lead to diseases other than cancer. About 38% of the 'liquidators' who fought the fires at Chernobyl are now suffering from diseases of the immune system, as well as cardiovascular and gastrointestinal complaints. There has been an increase in male infertility and in the number of pregnancies with complications.

Key ideas

● Radiation can kill or damage cells by directly changing DNA in the nucleus or by indirect chemical action.

● Cells that divide frequently, e.g. in skin or in bone marrow, are more radiosensitive than others.

● Large doses of radiation lead to acute effects that can be fatal.

● Lower doses of radiation lead to delayed effects, principally cancers and leukaemia.

139

12.4 Background radiation

Scientists make the assumption that there is no 'safe' level of radioactivity; even low doses carry some risk. One way of assessing when this risk has reached an acceptable level is to compare the radiation dose with that due to **background radiation**.

We live in a world which is radioactive. We are continually exposed to radiation from the air we breathe, the food we eat and from the ground we walk on. We also get ionising radiation from space in the form of cosmic rays. The total dose that we receive due to this background radiation varies from place to place, but the average dose in the UK is 2.5 mSv per year (Fig. 10).

Natural sources of radiation

1. Cosmic radiation

The Earth is constantly bombarded by a shower of high-energy particles and gamma rays from the Sun and from sources outside the solar system. The atmosphere acts as a shield and reduces the dose at sea level to about 0.3 mSv (Fig. 11). On average, just over 100 cosmic rays pass through you each second. The actual number varies from place to place; there is a larger dose at the poles than at the equator because the Earth's magnetic field diverts some of the radiation.

2. Radiation from rocks

Most of the radioactivity in rocks arises from the decay products of uranium–238 and thorium–232. These two radioisotopes have a very long half-life and have been present on Earth since it was formed. For

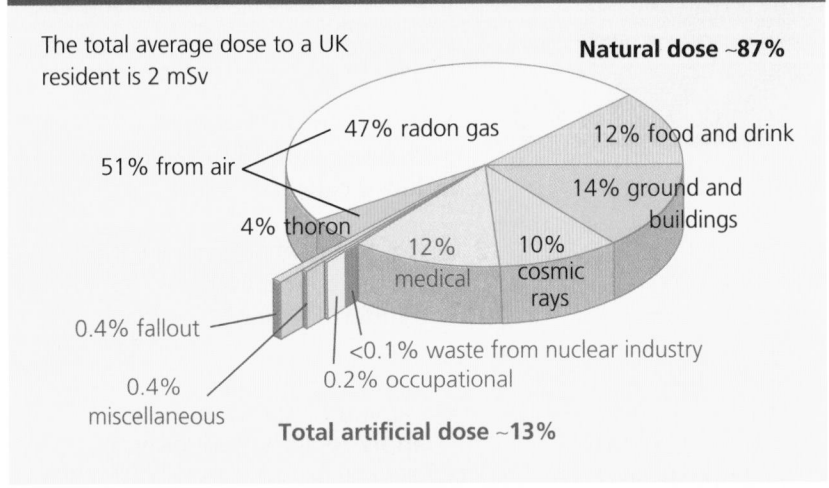

Fig. 10 Sources of background radiation

The total average dose to a UK resident is 2 mSv

Natural dose ~87%

47% radon gas
51% from air
4% thoron
0.4% fallout
0.4% miscellaneous

12% food and drink
14% ground and buildings
12% medical
10% cosmic rays
<0.1% waste from nuclear industry
0.2% occupational

Total artificial dose ~13%

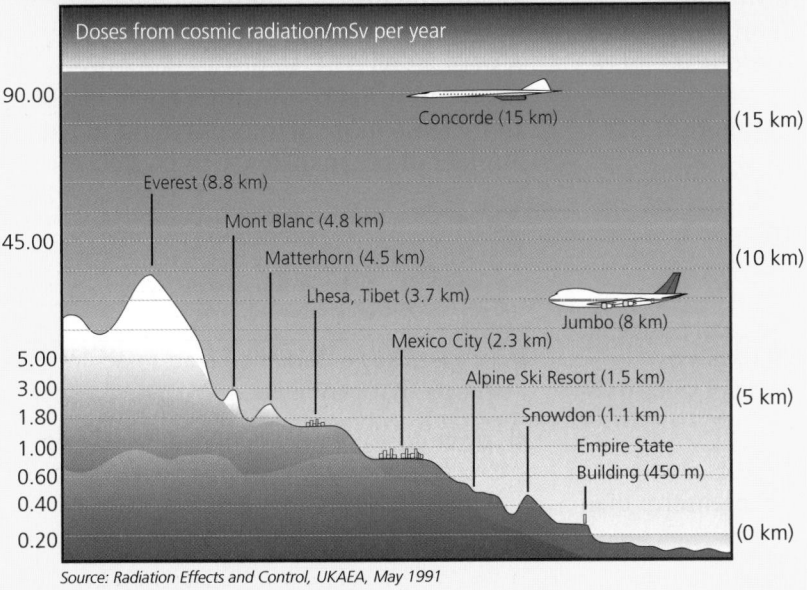

Fig. 11 Dose due to cosmic radiation at different altitudes

Doses from cosmic radiation/mSv per year

90.00 — Concorde (15 km) — (15 km)

Everest (8.8 km)

Mont Blanc (4.8 km)

45.00 — Matterhorn (4.5 km) — (10 km)

Lhesa, Tibet (3.7 km)

Jumbo (8 km)

Mexico City (2.3 km)

Alpine Ski Resort (1.5 km)

5.00
3.00
1.80 — Snowdon (1.1 km) — (5 km)
1.00
0.60 — Empire State Building (450 m)
0.40
0.20 — (0 km)

Source: Radiation Effects and Control, UKAEA, May 1991

Concorde flies at an altitude of about 15 km. A transatlantic trip in Concorde will add about 20 microsievert to your annual dose.

A week's holiday in Cornwall will add about 0.13 mSv to your radiation dose, slightly more than the dose from two chest X-rays. The dose is partly due to gamma radiation from the ground and buildings but mainly from radon in the air.

most people, this radiation adds about 0.5 mSv to their annual dose, but some places are much more radioactive.

3. Radiation from the air

Radon gas in the air is by far the most significant source of background radiation (Fig. 12). Radon gas forms as part of the decay series of uranium–238 and it seeps upwards through fissures in the rock. Our main exposure to radon gas is inside buildings, where it can accumulate (Fig. 13). Improvements in home insulation, such as double glazing and draught-proofing, have reduced the ventilation in houses so that very high levels of radon can build up. When we breathe in radon gas, our lungs are irradiated by radon and its daughter products, polonium–214 and polonium–218, all of which are alpha emitters.

4. Radiation from food and drink

Some radioactive materials dissolve in

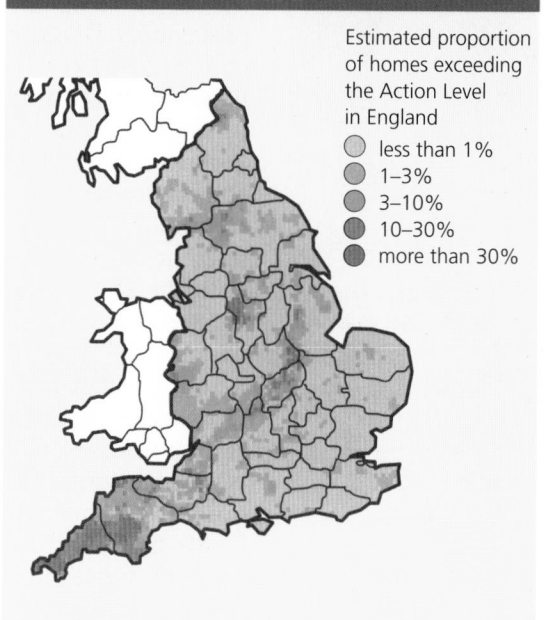

Fig. 12 Map of the UK showing high radon levels

Estimated proportion of homes exceeding the Action Level in England

- less than 1%
- 1–3%
- 3–10%
- 10–30%
- more than 30%

The average radon level in homes in the UK is about 20 Bq m^{-3}. 100 000 homes are thought to have radon levels above 200 Bq m^{-3}, the Action Level set by the government. At this level, the lifetime risk of lung cancer is estimated to be 10 cases per 1000 people. Smoking 15 cigarettes per day gives a lifetime risk of 100 cases of lung cancer per 1000 people.

water and are taken up by plants and animals. All food and drink is radioactive to some extent, but some foods – tea, coffee and brazil nuts – are more radioactive than others. Because we ingest radioactive materials, we are all radioactive at a level of about 50 Bq kg^{-1}.

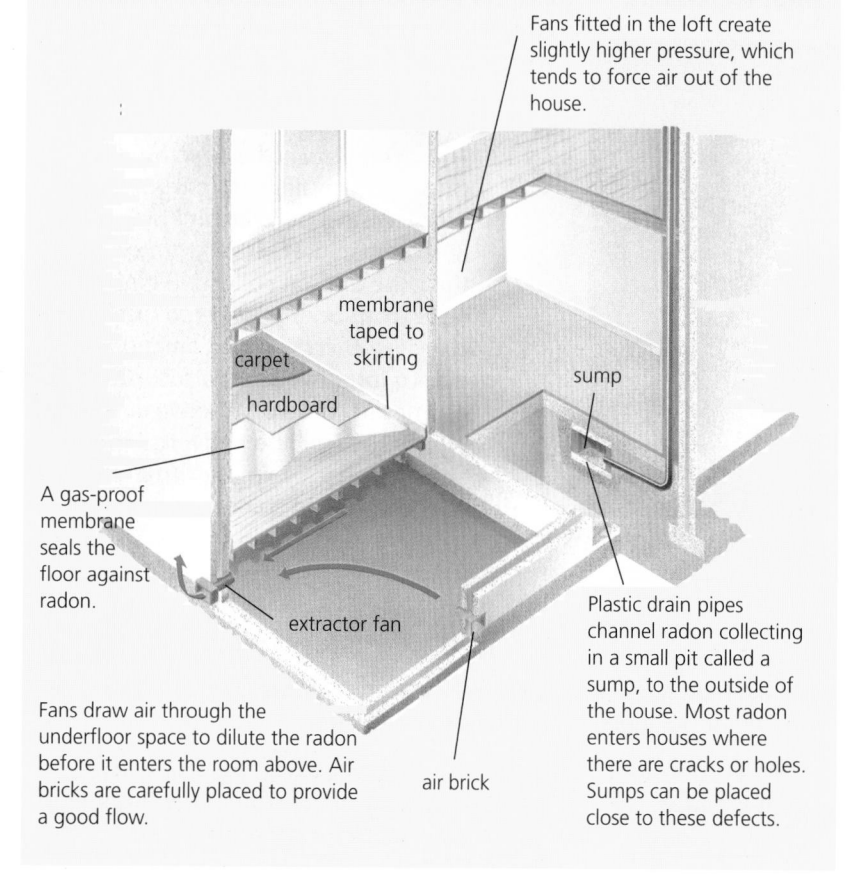

Fig. 13 Radon gas in buildings

Fans fitted in the loft create slightly higher pressure, which tends to force air out of the house.

membrane taped to skirting

carpet

hardboard

sump

A gas-proof membrane seals the floor against radon.

extractor fan

Plastic drain pipes channel radon collecting in a small pit called a sump, to the outside of the house. Most radon enters houses where there are cracks or holes. Sumps can be placed close to these defects.

Fans draw air through the underfloor space to dilute the radon before it enters the room above. Air bricks are carefully placed to provide a good flow.

air brick

Most of the radioactivity in our bodies is due to potassium–40, which tends to concentrate in muscle. Standing close to a body builder will increase your radiation dose!

Smoke detectors contain americium–241, an alpha emitter with a half-life of 432 years

5. Radiation from artificial sources

We get around 12% of our annual radiation dose from artificial sources, mainly medical procedures. Diagnostic X-rays are the most common source of medical radiation. Doses vary significantly, depending on the procedure. A chest X-ray gives a dose of around 0.05 mSv; an X-ray of the lower abdomen could give a dose of ten times this amount. Much larger doses are given to some cancer patients during their radiotherapy treatment. Patients typically receive doses of a few thousand mSv, spread over several sessions.

Nuclear medicine involves injecting a radioisotope into the body to diagnose certain diseases. The use of these techniques is now growing and we now get an average dose of 0.02 mSv per person each year.

Most of the radioisotopes created by the atmospheric testing of nuclear weapons were carried into the stratosphere, 10 to 50 km high, where they persisted for many months. Eventually these radioisotopes were distributed over a large area so that most of the Earth's population have had a small, but measurable, dose from nuclear explosions.

In 1954, the USA exploded its first full-scale hydrogen bomb near Bikini atoll. Four hours later fallout settled on nearby Marshall islands. The islanders suffered acute radiation sickness, skin burns and hair loss. They received a dose that was 25 times greater than the maximum lifetime dose. Two days later the US government evacuated the islanders.

Miscellaneous sources of radiation cover a wide range of consumer products. Radium was widely used in the paint of luminous watch faces until it was replaced by tritium, a beta emitter, in the 1960s. Tritium is now used in fluorescent exit signs. Thorium is used in the mantles of gas lamps used for camping. Industrial and research establishments contribute about 0.3% to the average annual dose.

Nuclear power contributes a small average dose per person of 0.001 mSv per year. However, the annual dose to workers in the nuclear industry is higher, about 2 mSv per year above the average annual dose of 2.5 mSv. This compares with an extra 0.2 mSv for medical radiographers. These occupations involve different numbers of people, so we use the term **collective effective dose**. It is the sum of the doses to all those affected, measured in **man-sievert**.

An estimate of the total dose that will be given to succeeding generations is known as the **collective effective dose commitment**, also measured in man-sievert. The accident at Chernobyl is thought to have added around 600 000 man-sievert to the collective effective dose commitment. Compare this with nuclear weapons tests, which have added 30 million man-sievert.

Q13 The *annual collective effective dose* caused by mining, refining and reprocessing nuclear fuel is about 800 man-sievert, 10 000 times less than the annual collective effective dose from *background radiation*. The *collective effective dose commitment* due to long lived radioisotopes is estimated to be 60 man-sievert, of which 10% will be delivered in the first 100 years. Explain the meaning of the terms in italics.

Key ideas

- Background radiation is the average level of radiation that affects the whole population.

- Natural background radiation accounts for about 88% of the total and it is caused by cosmic radiation and the decay of long-lived radionuclides on Earth.

- Artificial radiation comes largely from medical procedures.

- The collective effective dose from any source is the average dose × the number of people who are exposed to it. It is measured in man-sievert.

12.4 Detection and measurement

'I am responsible for the radiation safety of people who work on this site or live nearby. I need to monitor activity levels in the environment and the actual radiation doses that people receive.

My detectors rely on the ability of radiation to cause ionisation or excitation. I need to know the type of radiation, as well as the absorbed dose. Unfortunately, no single detector works well in all situations.'

Clive, a health physicist for the nuclear power industry

The scintillation counter

As radiation passes through matter it causes some of the atomic electrons to be raised to a higher energy level. Some materials, known as scintillators, emit tiny flashes of light as these excited electrons return to lower energy levels. The light output is approximately proportional to the energy lost by the radiation as it passes through the material. This effect is used to measuring radiation dose (Fig. 14).

Scintillators come in two main types:

- Organic scintillators, which contain chemicals such as anthracene or naphthalene, can be used in liquid form or they can be incorporated into a plastic and moulded into a required shape. Liquid scintillators are particularly useful

for measuring the radioactivity of a sample of material. The sample is dissolved in the liquid scintillator, which can detect very low energy β-radiation from sources such as carbon–14 or tritium.

- Inorganic scintillators are large crystals, up to 20 cm square, such as sodium iodide doped with thallium. Because of their high density and high atomic number, they are very sensitive to gamma radiation. One of their main applications is detecting gamma rays from the body as part of a gamma camera (see CAMS Physics Core, p.158).

The ionisation chamber

An ionisation chamber measures the ionisation of a gas due to radiation. It has a pair of parallel electrodes inside a gas-filled compartment (Fig. 15). When radiation

Fig. 15 Basic ion chamber in operation

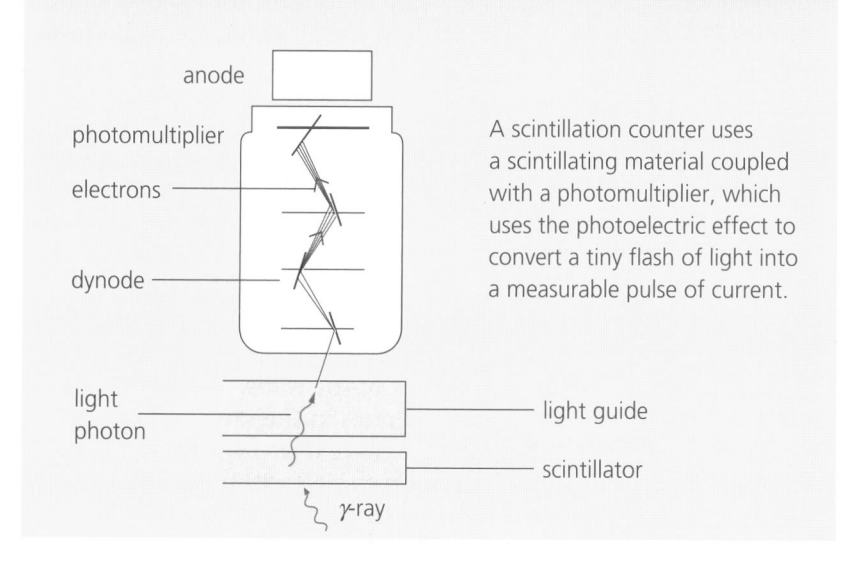

The ionisation chamber usually has air between the electrodes, though inert gases can be used. The guard electrodes are charged in such a way that they ensure that only ions from the uniform region of the electric field are collected. This allows an accurate measurement of the charge produced in a known volume of air. The gap between the plates can be adjusted for different energy radiation and can reach 1 m apart. The free-air ion chamber is not a practical monitoring device and is used to calibrate other detectors.

Fig. 14 The scintillation counter

A scintillation counter uses a scintillating material coupled with a photomultiplier, which uses the photoelectric effect to convert a tiny flash of light into a measurable pulse of current.

Fig. 16 Graph of applied field vs. output

week field (1) | ion saturation (2) | proportional (3) | Geiger-Müller (4) | (5)

Relative pulse height (log scale)

high-energy radiation

low-energy radiation

0   400   800   1200
Applied voltage/V

1. At low voltages many of the ions will recombine before they reach the electrodes and the output signal will be small. As the voltage increases the ions move more quickly to the electrodes, so less recombination occurs and the signal increases.
2. If the voltage is high enough, all the ions caused by the radiation reach the electrodes. This is known as ion saturation. Ionisation chambers operate in this region.
3. If the voltage is increased further, the electrons released by ionisation gain sufficient energy to cause secondary ionisation in collisions with other gas molecules. In this region output pulses are proportional to the energy of the ionising particle.
4. At even higher voltages, the avalanche of secondary ionisation is so great that the output pulse does not depend on the energy of the incident radiation. Geiger counters operate in this region.
5. Above a certain voltage, the insulation properties of the gas break down and continuous electrical discharges occur.

causes ionisation between the electrodes, any free electrons move rapidly to the positive plate and positive ions move more slowly towards the negative plate.

The operation of the ion chamber depends on the strength of the electric field between the electrodes. For a uniform field, the electric field strength is:

$E = V / d$

The performance of the ion chamber depends on the voltage applied to the electrodes (Fig. 16).

The thimble chamber

A small, practical version of the ionisation chamber is the thimble chamber (Fig. 17). The thimble chamber is used to measure total exposure or to monitor exposure rate.

The walls of the chamber are made from a material that absorbs radiation in a similar way to air, usually a mixture of plastic and graphite. The enclosed volume of air is only about 1 cm^3. The walls are designed to be thick enough to prevent entry by secondary particles caused by ionisation outside the chamber, but thin enough to allow radiation to pass through. The positive electrode is a thin wire at the centre of the chamber and the negative electrode is the inside surface of the walls. The thimble chamber operates in the saturated region of the response curve (Fig. 16), and it measures the ionisation caused within the wall and the small air space.

Fig. 17 Uses of a thimble chamber

A thimble chamber used as an exposure meter. The voltmeter measures the total charge which has accumulated on the capacitor during irradiation. The device gives a reading of exposure in C kg^{-1}.

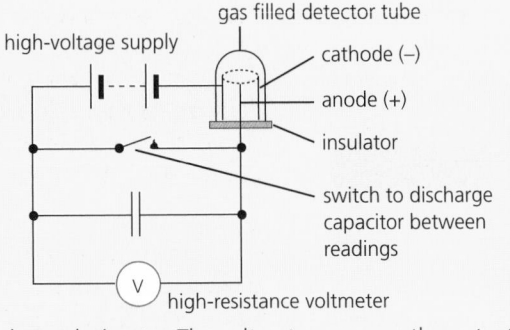

gas filled detector tube

high-voltage supply

cathode (–)
anode (+)
insulator
switch to discharge capacitor between readings

V high-resistance voltmeter

Thimble chamber used as a dosimeter. The voltmeter measure the potential difference across the high resistance, R ≈ 10^{12} Ω, as the ionisation current flows through it. The device measures exposure rate in C kg^{-1} s^{-1}.

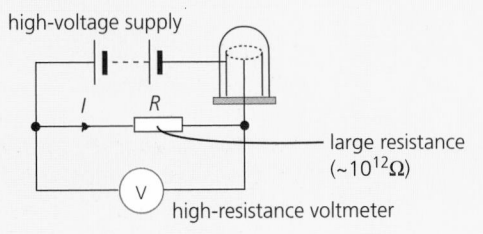

high-voltage supply

I   R

large resistance (~10^{12}Ω)

V high-resistance voltmeter

The thimble chamber has an air-equivalent wall and is small enough to be used in clinical situations, e.g. next to an X-ray set.

144

- window
- eye lens
- pocket clip
- field lens
- optical section
- objective lens
- quartz fibre
- scale
- insulator
- central electrode
- capacitor chamber
- charging unit

e pocket ionisation
amber gives a constant
adout and can be used to
onitor personal radiation
se where there is a risk
high exposures.

Pocket ionisation chamber

A drawback of the thimble chamber is that it needs a lead connecting it to the high voltage supply and voltmeter. The pocket ionisation chamber (Fig. 18), or condenser chamber, is truly portable. The detector consists of a large capacitor charged to a high voltage before use. During irradiation, charge leaks away from the capacitor. The total ionisation, and hence the radiation dose, can be calculated from the drop in charge on the capacitor. A tiny quartz fibre gives a constant readout, visible through an in-built microscope.

14 **What sort of radiation detector would you use for:**
a **measuring the activity of some contaminated food;**
b **detecting radiation from a person who has ingested a gamma emitter;**
c **monitoring the radiation dose received by a nuclear power worker in a high-risk area?**

The Geiger counter

The Geiger counter is a cheap, reliable detector which is sensitive enough to detect a single ionisation. A large potential difference across the tube creates a very strong electric field, particularly near the central anode. When radiation passes through the tube and causes ionisation, the liberated electrons accelerate towards the central anode. Soon the electrons gain enough energy to cause more ionisation in the gas atoms they collide with. These 'secondary' electrons go on to cause further ionisations, creating an avalanche of electrons. Within a microsecond, an electron shower of 10^8 electrons may reach the anode. This small pulse of current flows through the tube and causes a potential difference across a large resistor. Each voltage pulse indicates a single ionisation event.

The positive ions left behind by the liberated electrons are much less mobile and make their way towards the cathode relatively slowly. This means that a large positive 'space' charge tends to build up in the tube and this cancels out the electric field around the anode. No further electron avalanches can occur until these positive ions have moved away. This period, when Geiger counter cannot detect any ionisation, is known as the **dead time** of the tube.

If the positive ions were to accelerate towards the cathode with sufficient energy, their collisions with gas atoms would cause further ionisation and create more avalanches of electrons. To prevent this, the tube is **quenched** in two ways:
- electronically, by automatically reducing the tube voltage for about 300 µs after a voltage pulse;
- chemically, by adding a trace of bromine (or chlorine) gas to the tube. Positive ions lose energy as they collide with these quenching molecules and the collisions cause the bromine molecules to dissociate rather than ionise.

The time taken for positive ions to reach the cathode is the 'recovery time' of the tube. The device is less sensitive to radiation in this time. The tube can take up to 1 ms to return to full sensitivity and this limits the maximum count rate to about 1000 per second.

Any ionising event causes the same output, so the device does not provide information on radiation energy or type. The tube is relatively insensitive to gamma radiation, detecting only about 1% of those that pass through the tube. Despite this, the Geiger counter is widely used to monitor low rates of radiation, and it is especially sensitive to β-radiation.

Fig. 19 The Geiger–Müller tube

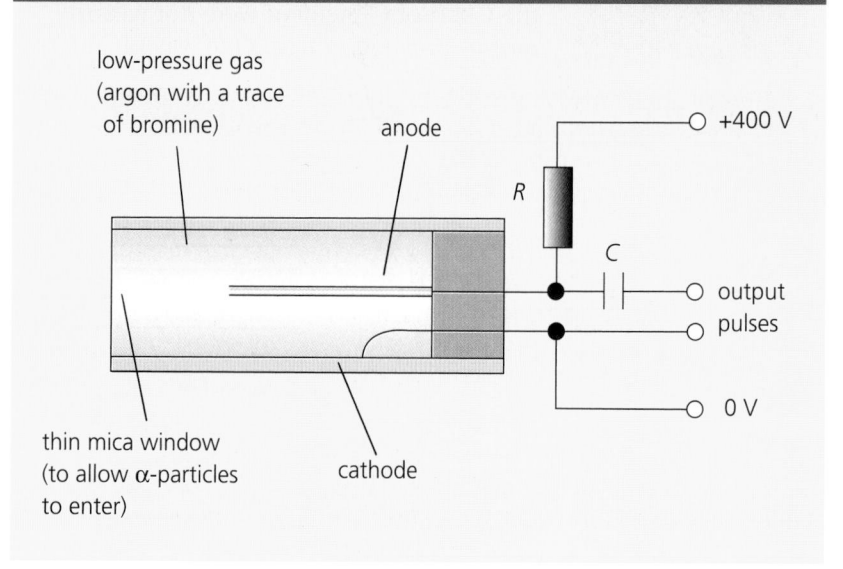

low-pressure gas (argon with a trace of bromine)

anode

R

C

+400 V

output pulses

0 V

thin mica window (to allow α-particles to enter)

cathode

15 Why is a Geiger counter not suitable for:
  a measuring the radiation from a high-activity source;
  b determining the radiation dose from a variety of different emitters?

The film badge

A film badge provides a cheap, reliable means of assessing radiation dose. Radiation causes ionisation of silver halide molecules in the photographic emulsion, which leads to a chemical change in the film. When the film is developed, the areas exposed to radiation turn black. The blackness, or density, of the film is a measure of the radiation dose. The film has a high atomic number, due to the presence of silver, so the response of the film is very dependent upon the energy of the incident radiation. It is difficult to distinguish between a high dose of low-energy radiation and a lower dose of high-energy radiation. To resolve this problem the film badge holder contains aluminium, lead and plastic filters (Fig. 20) which partially cover the film. The density of the film under the filters can be compared to the blackening of the film under the open window.

16 When a film badge is developed it is found to be almost equally dark under all the filters. What does this tell you about the radiation exposure to the wearer?

17 If the film under the plastic filters is much less dense than the film under the open window, what could you infer about the type of radiation that the wearer had been exposed to?

Thermoluminescent dosimetry

An alternative to the film badge is a thermoluminescent dosimeter, or TLD. Exposure to radiation can excite atomic electrons to higher energy levels. When this happens in some materials, such as lithium fluoride, the electrons can become 'trapped' in these energy levels. If these materials are heated the electrons are released from the traps and emit light as they fall back to lower energy levels. Photomultiplier tubes can detect and measure the light output, giving a good indication of the original radiation dose.

Measuring the dose after Chernobyl

Most of the people exposed accidentally by the Chernobyl incident were not wearing monitoring equipment. One way of

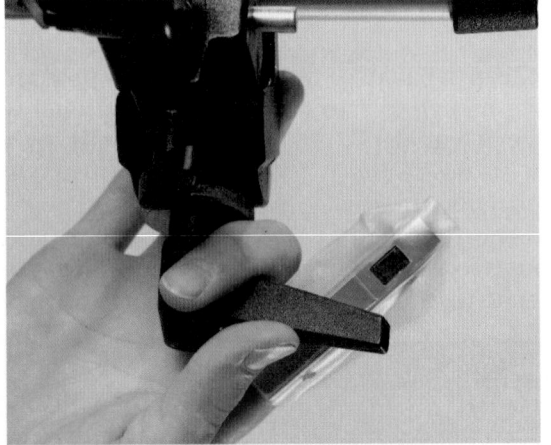

Thermoluminescent dosimeters are very rugged and can be made extremely small. They can assess the radiation dose to a surgeon's fingers during an operation that involves X-ray monitoring of the patient.

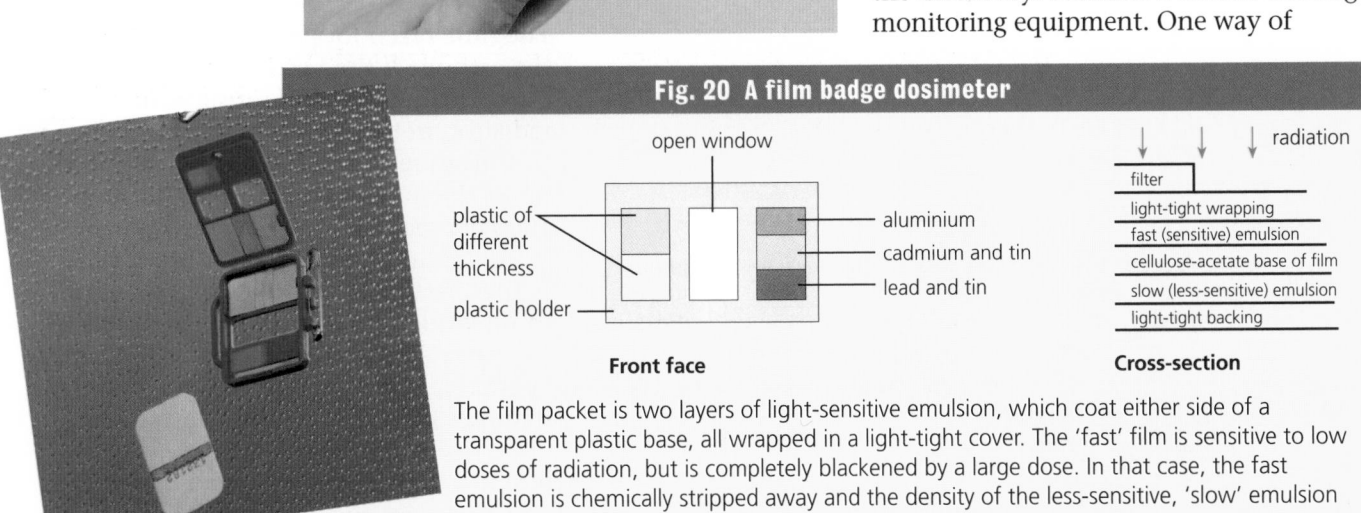

Fig. 20 A film badge dosimeter

Front face
open window
plastic of different thickness
plastic holder
aluminium
cadmium and tin
lead and tin

Cross-section
radiation
filter
light-tight wrapping
fast (sensitive) emulsion
cellulose-acetate base of film
slow (less-sensitive) emulsion
light-tight backing

The film packet is two layers of light-sensitive emulsion, which coat either side of a transparent plastic base, all wrapped in a light-tight cover. The 'fast' film is sensitive to low doses of radiation, but is completely blackened by a large dose. In that case, the fast emulsion is chemically stripped away and the density of the less-sensitive, 'slow' emulsion is measured.

Table 4 Comparison of radiation dosimeters			
Radiation detector	Typical application	Advantages	Disadvantages
thimble chamber	measuring output from X-ray set	accurate over a wide range of energies; small size	small output signal; needs amplification; at high energies, need to use 'build-up cap' 2–4 mm of Perspex
pocket ionisation chamber	personnel monitoring	accurate, direct reading of exposure; not dependent on energy of radiation; portable	relatively expensive; gives no information on type of radiation; some charge leakage with time
film badge	personnel monitoring	cheap, permanent dose record; can distinguish between α-, β-, γ-radiation	dose is only known after some delay; temperature and humidity can affect the film; limited accuracy, about 10%; critically dependent on developing conditions
thermoluminescent dosimeter	personnel monitoring	rugged; small size and weight	dose only known after some delay; bulky equipment needed for readout
scintillation counter	detecting γ- and β-radiation; monitoring low intensity radiation; measuring activity in liquid, e.g. blood	fast response means it can cope with a high dose rate; output can give information on the energy spectrum of the radiation; very sensitive to gamma radiation	expensive; relatively bulky
Geiger counter	measurement of β-radiation; contamination detection	high detection efficiency for β-radiation; reliable, stable and sensitive; output voltage is large, does not need amplification	low detection efficiency for γ- and α-radiation; dead time limits the maximum count rate

assessing their radiation dose is to measure the biological effects of radiation. A blood count to measure the numbers of red or white cells can give some indication of dose, but it isn't sensitive at low doses. Nor is it radiation-specific. New techniques measure radiation damage to the membranes of red blood cells. These seem to be permanent and are passed on to all subsequent 'daughter' cells when the cell divides.

Another possibility is to examine chromosome damage. Radiation-induced damage may be passed on to children who were not even born at the time of the radiation exposure.

Scientists have found that the mutation rate in the DNA of children near Chernobyl is double that in a similar population of British children. This has yet to be linked to a greater incidence of genetic disease, but it may be that the legacy of Chernobyl will be felt by many generations to come.

Key ideas

● Radiation detectors are used to monitor radiation doses to personnel and to measure the average dose in a given location.

● Different detectors are needed to operate in different circumstances and to respond to different types of radiation (see table 4).

An inside view

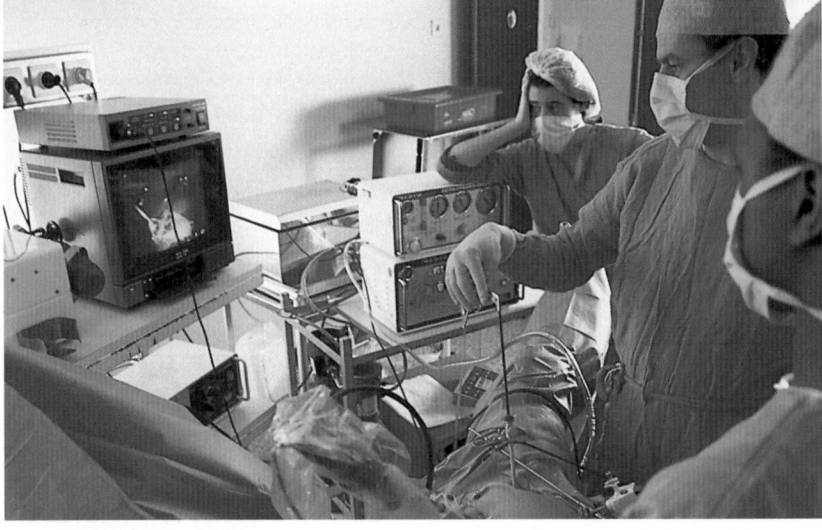

Keyhole surgery is carried out with the help of video cameras attached to fibre optic cables.

Every year in the UK, 100 000 people have their gallbladder removed. The gallbladder is a small organ near the liver which stores bile, an alkaline fluid used in digestion.

Sometimes the flow of bile becomes restricted and gallstones form. These are painful and can lead to serious liver damage. Traditional treatment involves a large incision, about 14 cm long, through the muscle of the abdominal wall.

New techniques such as keyhole surgery can reduce the trauma and disruption caused by an operation. Ultrasonic shock waves smash the gallstones into small pieces. If surgical removal is still necessary, four small 'keyholes' are made in the abdomen. One hole is for a laparoscope, a tube which holds a bundle of optical fibres. These carry light to a small video camera so that the surgeon can watch the operation. A laser cuts the gallbladder free before the surgeon removes it through another of the tiny holes. Recovery is much quicker; instead of a week in hospital, the patient can usually go home the next day.

13.1 Learning objectives

After working through this chapter, you should be able to:

- **describe** how fibre optics are used in medicine;

- **explain** the properties of laser radiation and explain how it interacts with tissue;

- **identify** some of the uses of lasers in medicine;

- **describe** how ultrasound can be generated and detected;

- **explain** how ultrasound is used in medicine.

13.2 Looking through the keyhole

Total internal reflection
During keyhole surgery, the surgeon watches the entire operation on a video screen. Light is carried into and out of the body by bundles of **optical fibres**. Optical fibres are very fine, flexible strands of glass that carry light on its twisting route into the body using **total internal reflection** (see CAMS Physics Core, p.131).

Rays of light that strike the inside surface of a glass fibre at less than the

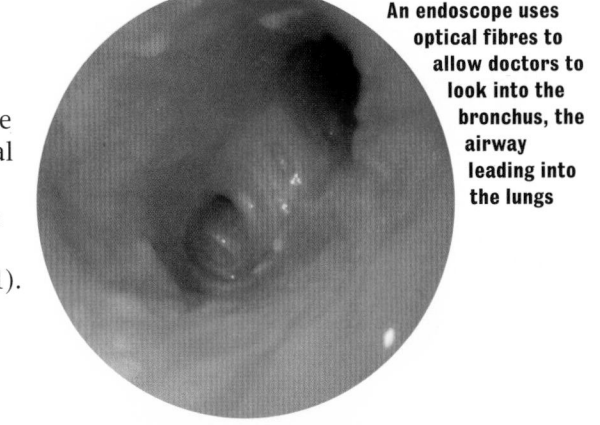

An endoscope uses optical fibres to allow doctors to look into the bronchus, the airway leading into the lungs

Fig. 1 Total internal reflection

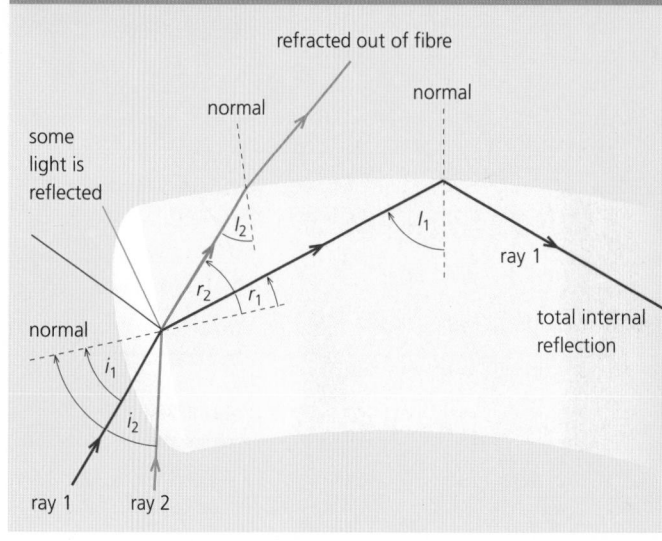

The path taken by a light ray through a glass fibre depends on the initial angle of incidence.

Ray 1 strikes the glass at an angle of i_1 and is refracted into the fibre. It hits the edge of the fibre at an angle of I_1. I_1 is greater than the critical angle for a glass–air interface and the ray is totally reflected inside the fibre.

Ray 2 strikes the glass at an angle of i_2 and is refracted so that it hits the edge of the fibre at an angle I_2. I_2 is less than the critical angle and so the ray is refracted out of the fibre. This effect is what limits the field of view of an endoscope, see Fig. 2.

critical angle are refracted out of the fibre, but any rays that are incident at greater angles are reflected along the fibre just as if it had mirrored walls (Fig. 1).

In an endoscope, thousands of fine optical fibres are packed together into bundles. If the fibres touch each other, light leaks from one fibre to the next. To prevent this, the fibres are coated with a second layer of glass of slightly lower refractive index than the core. However, this has another effect on the transmission of light along the fibre (Fig. 2).

The cladding increases the critical angle and therefore reduces the angle at which rays of light can enter the fibre and be totally internally reflected. Above the maximum angle of incidence for rays entering the fibre, i_{max}, light will not be transmitted down the fibre.

The field of view at the end of a fibre is defined by a quantity known as the **numerical aperture**. Increasing the numerical aperture would give a wider field

Fig. 2 The cone of vision

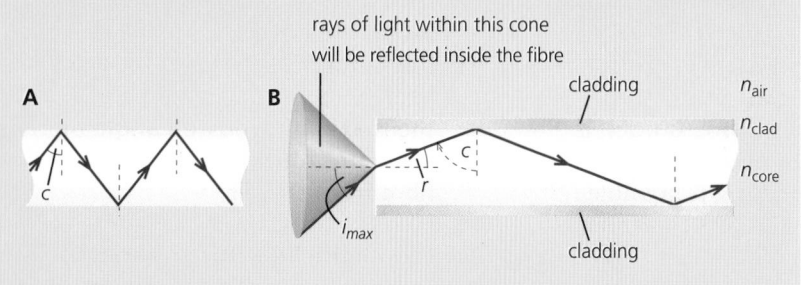

A For an unclad fibre, the critical angle, c, for a light ray travelling from glass to air is given by:

$\sin c = n_{air} / n_{glass}$

where n_{air} and n_{glass} are the refractive indices of air and glass. The refractive index of air is almost 1. If the refractive index of the glass is 1.6, then:

$\sin c = 1 / 1.6 = 0.625$

$c = 39°$

B For a fibre with cladding of refractive index 1.5, the critical angle is given by:

$\sin c = n_{cladding} / n_{core}$

$= 1.5 / 1.6 = 0.9375$

which gives a value for c of almost 70°.

There is a maximum angle of incidence, i_{max}, for light entering the fibre if it is to be internally reflected (using the equation from Fig. 3 you should see that, in this example, $i_{max} = 33°$). In three dimensions, this angle defines a cone of vision. Only light rays within this cone will be transmitted.

Optical fibres are coated with protective cladding. Contact with another object may prevent total internal reflection and light would escape from the fibre. Surface scratches also lead to loss of light.

149

Fig. 3 Deriving numerical aperture

Snells law gives:
$$\frac{\sin i_{max}}{\sin r} = \frac{n_{core}}{n_{air}}$$

so:
$$n_{air} \sin i_{max} = n_{core} \sin r$$

From Fig. 2,

$r + c = 90°$ so:
$$n_{air} \sin i_{max} = n_{core} \sin(90° - c)$$
$$= n_{core} \cos c$$

Squaring both sides: $n_{air}^2 \sin^2 i_{max} = n_{core}^2 \cos^2 c$

$\cos^2 c = 1 - \sin^2 c$, so: $n_{air}^2 \sin^2 i_{max} = n_{core}^2 (1 - \sin^2 c)$

But $\sin c = \dfrac{n_{clad}}{n_{core}}$, so: $n_{air}^2 \sin^2 i_{max} = n_{core}^2 \left(1 - \dfrac{n_{clad}^2}{n_{core}^2}\right)$

Rearranging gives: $n_{air}^2 \sin^2 i_{max} = n_{core}^2 - n_{clad}^2$

But $n_{air} \approx 1$, so: $\sin i_{max} = \sqrt{n_{core}^2 - n_{clad}^2}$

The quantity $\sqrt{n_{core}^2 - n_{clad}^2}$ is known as the **numerical aperture.**

Fig. 4 Light loss due to bending of the fibre an scattering

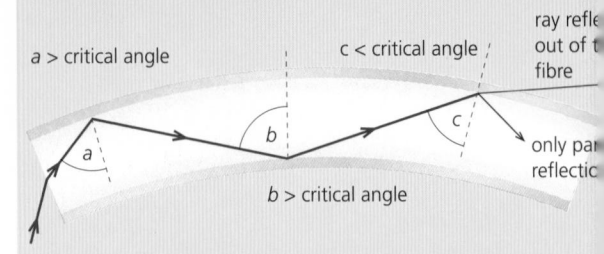

$a >$ critical angle

$c <$ critical angle

ray refle out of t fibre

b

c

a

only par reflectio

$b >$ critical angle

(a) Bending the glass fibre reduces the angle of incidence betw the core and the cladding and could lead to more light bein lost. In practice, as long as the bend has a radius of more th about 20× the core diameter, the amount of light lost will b minimal.

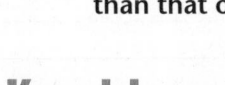

cladding

light scattered out of the fibre

impurity

(b) Some light is scattered by impurities in the glass and is t lost from the fibre because it strikes the cladding at less tha the critical angle.

of view (Fig. 3). This could be achieved by having a larger difference between the refractive indices of the cladding and the core. However, the value of the refractive index of the core is limited because a high refractive index tends to 'attenuate' (weaken) the light more. Light is also lost due to impurities in the glass and unevenness at the core–cladding border. If the fibre bends, the angle of incidence at the fibre wall changes, making it possible for light to strike the wall at less than the critical angle

1 Why are optical fibres clad with glass of a lower refractive index than that of the core?

2 An optical fibre has a core made from glass of refractive index 1.55 with a cladding of refractive index 1.45. For this fibre calculate:
   a the critical angle for reflections inside the fibre;
   b the numerical aperture for this fibre in air;
   c the maximum allowed angle of incidence for light rays entering the fibre from the air.

3 Not all the light that is incident upon a fibre will be transmitted along its length. Suggest three ways in which the light may be lost.

Key ideas

- Glass fibres can carry light into and out of otherwise inaccessible places, using the principle of total internal reflection.

- Cladding prevents the core coming into contact with other materials, which would prevent total internal reflection.

- The numerical aperture of a fibre defines its field of view. Numerical aperture depends on the refractive indices of the core and the cladding.

Fig. 5 The endoscope and its tools

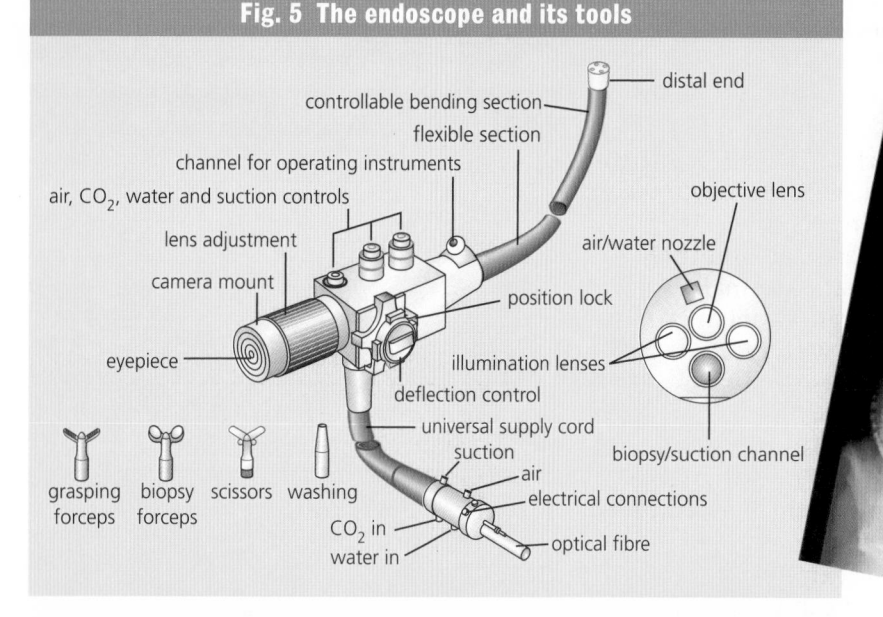

controllable bending section — distal end
flexible section
channel for operating instruments
air, CO₂, water and suction controls — objective lens
lens adjustment — air/water nozzle
camera mount — position lock
eyepiece — illumination lenses
deflection control
universal supply cord — biopsy/suction channel
suction — air
grasping forceps | biopsy forceps | scissors | washing — electrical connections
CO₂ in — optical fibre
water in

Fig. 6 Coherent and incoherent bundles

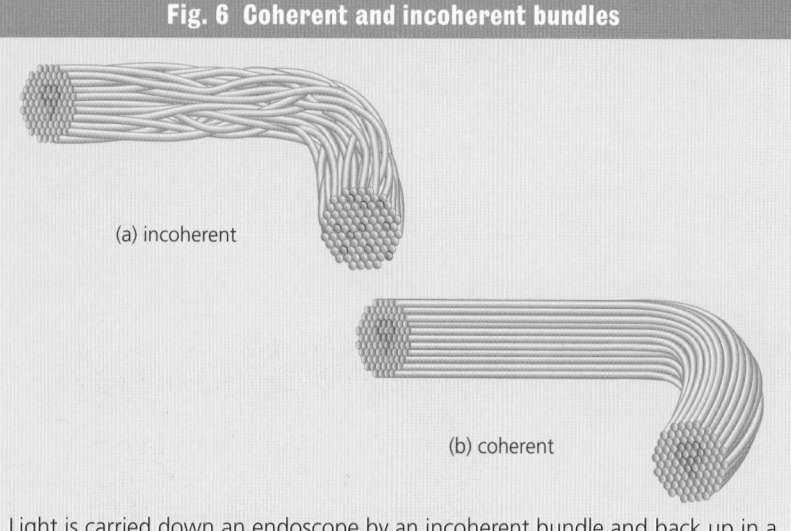

(a) incoherent

(b) coherent

Light is carried down an endoscope by an incoherent bundle and back up in a coherent bundle

Endoscopes

An endoscope is a sophisticated medical instrument. As well as being used to view the gastrointestinal tract, it carries air, water and suction channels and can carry tools with which to take samples of tissue for analysis (Fig. 5).

Key ideas

● Endoscopy is used to examine patients without the need for extensive surgery.

Endoscopes are commonly used to examine the upper digestive tract (gastroscopy) or the rectum and colon (colonoscopy).

This X-rays shows an endoscope winding through a patient's colon after being passed through the rectum.

Light is carried to the site of the examination through an **incoherent bundle** of glass fibres. As many as 30 000 individual fibres make up the bundle. An incoherent bundle cannot be used to form an image because the ends of the individual fibres are arranged randomly (Fig. 6a).

In a **coherent bundle**, the fibres have the same spatial position at each end of the bundle (Fig. 6b). The light emitted from the end of the bundle is an exact copy of the incident light and an image can be reproduced. Coherent bundles are expensive to manufacture, so incoherent bundles are used for illumination.

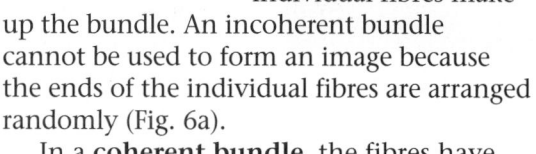 **4** **The diameter of each fibre in an incoherent bundle is about 50 μm. Fibres in a coherent bundle are much thinner, with a diameter of only 5 μm. Why do you think this is?**

The laparoscope, a rigid form of endoscope, is used for examining the body through the small incisions made in keyhole surgery. In addition to the usual channels, there is often an extra optical fibre used for transmitting laser light.

● Incoherent bundles of optical fibres carry light for illumination, and coherent bundles carry image information.

151

13.3 Making light work of surgery

Surgeons have used lasers for over thirty years. Carbon-dioxide lasers are often used in sensitive areas, such as the larynx, where bleeding is a problem. The laser beam seals blood vessels by heating them, i.e. it cauterises them. Dye lasers are routinely used to remove birthmarks. In many ways, the laser is a perfect surgical tool; it is clean, it can be wielded with great precision and it cauterises wounds.

The light from a laser is **monochromatic**; it consists of a single wavelength of light (Fig. 7). Furthermore, laser light is **coherent**; all the light waves it emits are **in phase**.

Laser beams can be extremely intense. The power of the beam can vary from milliwatts to hundreds of megawatts. Lasers can be based on solids, such as ruby rods, gases, such as carbon dioxide, or liquids, such as inorganic dyes. The material used determines the wavelength of the laser light. By careful choice of this wavelength, the surgeon can determine which tissues will absorb the laser's energy.

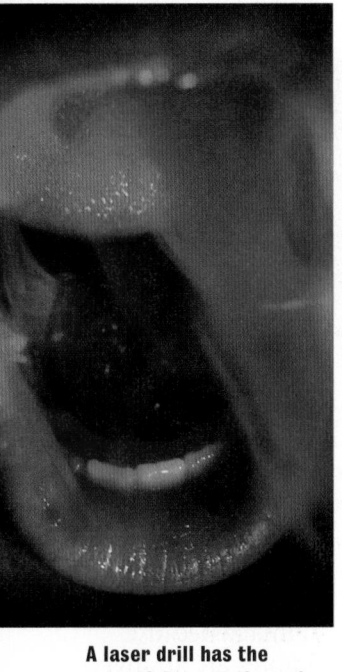

A laser drill has the potential to cut through all types of tissue and to desensitise nerves. A trip to the dentist may one day be pain-free.

Fig. 7 Comparing types of light

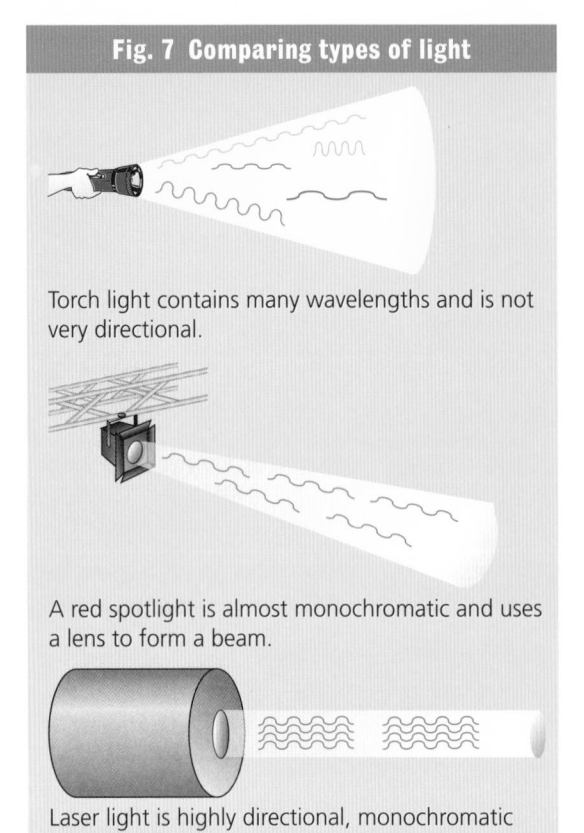

Torch light contains many wavelengths and is not very directional.

A red spotlight is almost monochromatic and uses a lens to form a beam.

Laser light is highly directional, monochromatic and coherent.

Fig. 8 Stimulated emission

The acronym **laser** stands for **l**ight **a**mplification by **s**timulated **e**mission of **r**adiation.

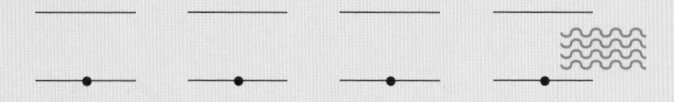

a Electrons in the atoms of the lasing material are excited to higher energy levels. This 'pumping' of the laser can be achieved by intense illumination from xenon flash tubes.

b Stimulated emission occurs when a photon from one atom causes an electron in another atom to return to the ground state, emitting another photon. The photons are identical in wavelength and phase.

c Emission from millions of atoms leads to a coherent beam, which is emitted from the laser through a partly silvered mirror.

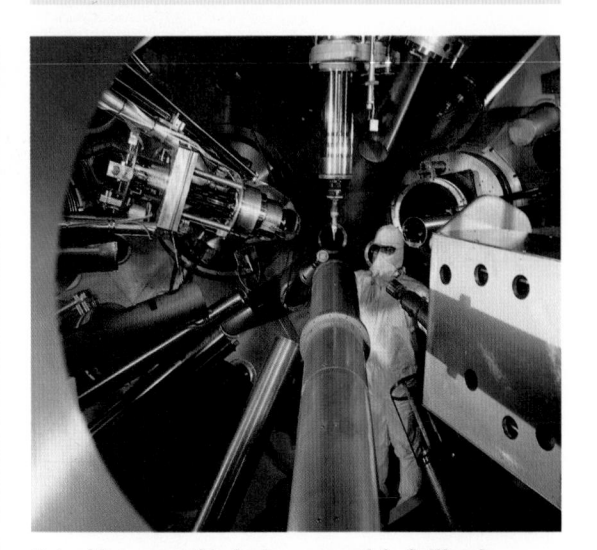

Pulsed lasers used in fusion research in California operate at powers of about 10^{14} W in a pulse lasting less than a nanosecond.
Much less powerful helium–neon (He–Ne) lasers are used to read bar codes at supermarket check-outs. He–Ne lasers of around 1 mW are used in school physics labs.

The laser scalpel

A laser can make an incision without distorting or damaging surrounding tissue. The way in which the beam interacts with tissue depends on the wavelength of laser light used. Photons of short wavelengths carry enough energy to break molecular bonds directly. Such lasers are known as photo-ablative or **excimer** lasers. Longer wavelength lasers rely on heating for their effect. As the light energy transfers to the material, molecular vibrations increase until interatomic bonds are broken. These lasers are known as **photo-thermal**.

Lasers in medicine

A neodymium–YAG laser is used to cut away the gallbladder in keyhole surgery. The laser's light, which passes down a laparoscope, is very localised and makes direct contact with the tissue through a sapphire tip.

Surgeons now combine laser treatment with ultrasonic imaging to destroy deep-seated tumours. The laser is directed to the tumour through an optical fibre and sophisticated ultrasonic imaging equipment monitors the laser's effect.

Another approach to killing tumour cells is to inject a photosensitive drug into the patient. Laser light of a specific wavelength activates the drug, killing the tumour but leaving nearby cells untouched.

Laser safety

Power levels of a few milliwatts are enough to cause permanent damage to an unprotected eye. Some of the higher powered lasers are known as 'eyeball poppers'. The victim hears a pop as the energy absorbed by the eye creates an audible shock wave, and the eye is instantly barbecued.

Tony Lang, New Scientist,
November 1996

The intensity of laser light enables it to kill cancer cells, but also makes it dangerous for healthy human tissues. The eyes are especially vulnerable. A laser concentrates light into a small area, and the lens of the eye can focus it still further, burning a part

Table 1 Lasing materials				
Lasing material	Wavelength	Typical power	Use	Comment
carbon dioxide	10.6 µm (far infrared)	up to 100 W	cutting skin, surgery on fallopian tubes	cannot be directed through optical fibres, as this wavelength is absorbed by glass; also strongly absorbed by water and human tissue
neodymium-YAG (neodymium atoms in a crystal of yttrium-aluminium-garnet)	1.06 µm	from 1 W to 100 W	stopping ulcers bleeding; removing fatty deposits from arteries; destroying cancerous tissue; dentistry	used through optical fibres; photo-thermal
argon-ion	blue-green	about 5 W	removing birthmarks; spot-welding detached retinas back into place	strongly absorbed by the red colour of blood
dye laser	tuneable; ultraviolet	up to 5 W	shaping the cornea; shattering kidney stones	an excimer laser

of the retina and creating a new blind spot. Visible-range lasers can be particularly hazardous, because the eye is designed to transmit these wavelengths. Goggles with the correct colour filter have to be worn to absorb light at the laser's wavelength, but unfortunately this means that you can't see the laser beam that you are working with. Doors are protected with cut-out locks that automatically shut off the laser, so that any surprise visitors are not greeted with a beam in the face. Laser rooms are painted black to avoid stray reflections. Things can be even worse with infrared lasers; they are invisible and they can cause intense heating.

5 Early cases of cervical cancer can be treated by vaporising the cancerous tissue which is usually close to the surface. Which type of laser would you choose for this procedure?

6 Some diabetes sufferers lose their vision as new blood vessels grow across the retina. Explain why argon-ion laser treatment is useful for treating this condition.

Key ideas

- Lasers light is monochromatic and coherent. Lasers produce a well-collimated beam of light, often of high intensity.

- Lasers are useful in surgery; they can make fine, controlled incisions and cauterise the wound.

- Short wavelength lasers (excimers) can break molecular bonds directly. Longer wavelength lasers (photo-thermal) rely on the heating effect of the absorbed energy.

- The wavelength of the laser determines how much energy different body tissues absorb.

13.4 Seeing with sound

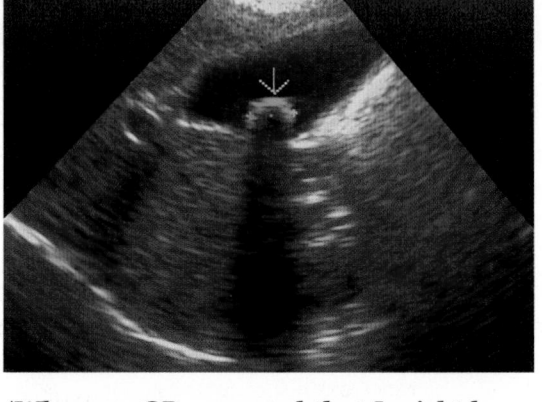

'When my GP suspected that I might be suffering from a gallstone, I was worried that I might need surgery. Fortunately doctors at the local hospital were able to use low-power ultrasound to locate the stone and then high-power ultrasound to break the stone up into tiny pieces. I didn't need an operation at all.'

Ultrasound can now be used to produce detailed images in real-time at a relatively low cost and with very little risk to the patient. Ultrasound is suitable for the diagnosis of a wide range of conditions, from heart valve disorders to diagnosis of bladder tumours.

Generating ultrasound

The term 'ultrasound' refers to sound waves of such high frequency that they cannot be detected by the human ear. According to this definition, ultrasound starts at around 20 kHz, but medical applications use much higher frequencies than that, typically between 1 MHz and 20 MHz.

Sound waves are pressure waves produced by a vibrating object. Producing ultrasound for medical use needs a source that can vibrate several millions times per second. Ultrasonic generators use

Fig. 9 The piezoelectric effect

a An a.c. signal is applied across a crystal of piezoelectric material.

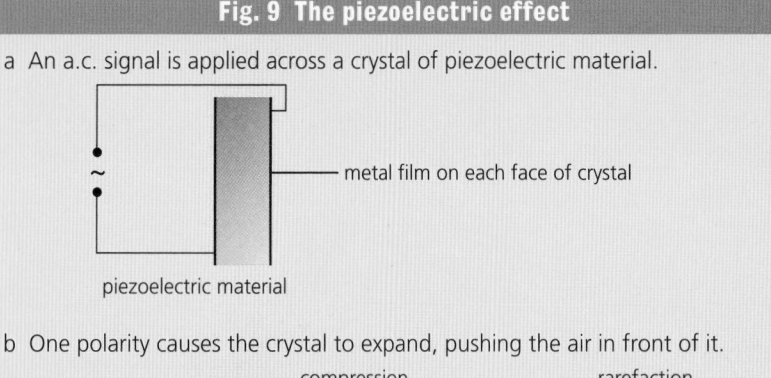

metal film on each face of crystal

piezoelectric material

b One polarity causes the crystal to expand, pushing the air in front of it.

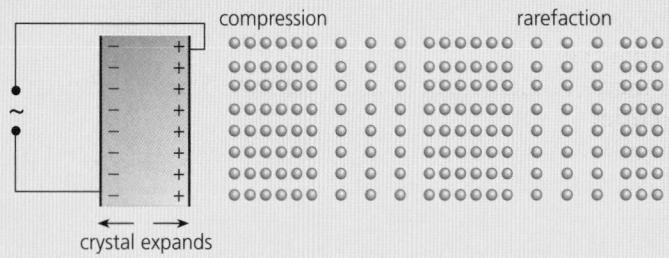

compression   rarefaction

crystal expands

c When the polarity reverses, the crystal contracts. This sequence is repeated millions of times each second, causing a pressure wave (ultrasound) to be transmitted.

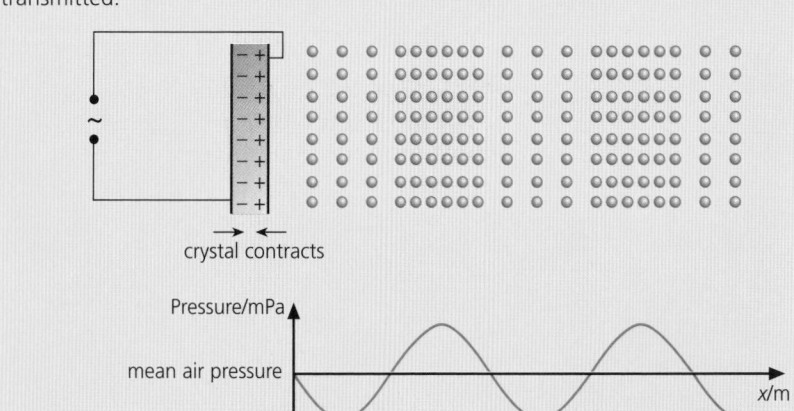

crystal contracts

Pressure/mPa

mean air pressure

x/m

Fig. 10 A piezoelectric transducer

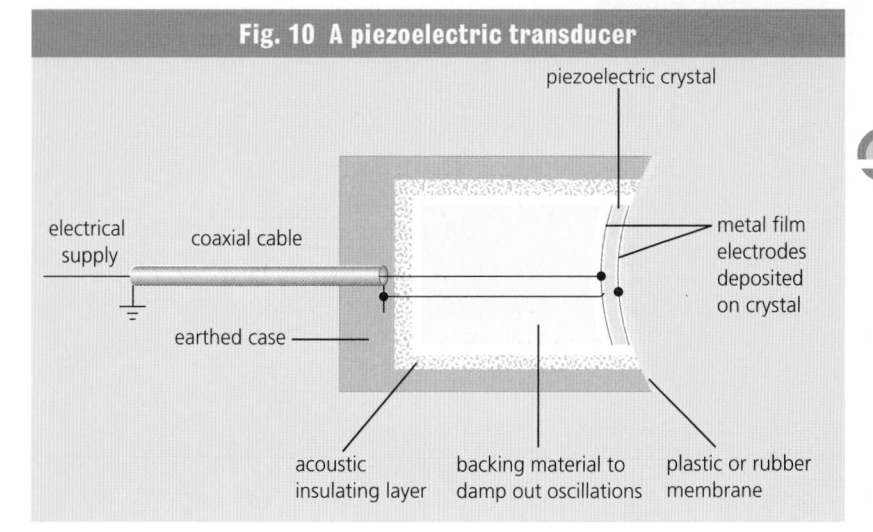

piezoelectric crystal

electrical supply

coaxial cable

metal film electrodes deposited on crystal

earthed case

acoustic insulating layer

backing material to damp out oscillations

plastic or rubber membrane

piezoelectric materials as **transducers** to convert electrical signals to pressure waves. Piezoelectric materials deform when a potential difference is applied across their faces (Fig. 9). As an alternating p.d. is applied across the material, it vibrates at the same frequency as the electrical signal. The piezoelectric element has a **natural frequency** that is determined by the material and by its physical dimensions. When the frequency of the a.c. signal matches its natural frequency, the element **resonates**. At resonance, the ultrasonic wave has its largest amplitude for a given input of electrical energy.

The piezoelectric effect also works in reverse. If a piezoelectric element is deformed, by an ultrasound wave, for example, a potential difference results across its faces. Such materials can therefore be used to detect, as well as generate, ultrasound (Fig. 10).

Ultrasound in the body

Ultrasound waves travel as **longitudinal** waves through the body, moving through different tissues at different speeds. The speed of sound, c, in a material depends approximately on the elasticity of the material and its density:

$$c = \sqrt{\frac{K}{\rho}}$$

where K is the bulk elastic modulus and ρ is the average density of the material. The frequency of the sound also has a slight effect on its speed. At the frequencies used in medical applications the velocity of sound is approximately 1540 m s^{-1} in soft tissue (Table 2 on p. 156).

7   **Olive oil has a density of 920 kg m^{-3} and its bulk elastic modulus is 1.60 GPa. Calculate the speed of sound in olive oil.**

The **intensity**, I, of an ultrasound wave is the energy that is transferred through a unit area per second. The unit of intensity is the watt per square metre, W m^{-2}. As sound travels through a material, its intensity is reduced because the medium

155

absorbs some of the wave's energy, transferring it to internal energy. This causes a heating effect in the body tissue. In addition, some of the wave's energy is scattered from its original path, which reduces its intensity.

The reduction of intensity as the wave travels through a material is known as **attenuation**. Equal thicknesses of the material attenuate the intensity of the wave by the same proportion, i.e. the first centimetre may reduce the wave's intensity by one half; the second centimetre will reduce that by half again, so that the intensity has dropped to one quarter of its original value. This is **exponential attenuation** (Fig. 11). The intensity at a distance x in the material, I_x, is given by:

$$I_x = I_0 \, e^{-\mu x}$$

where I_0 is the original intensity on entering the material and μ is the intensity attenuation coefficient for that material, measured in units of m^{-1}.

In practice, the intensity ratio I_x / I_0 is often expressed in decibels (see chapter 9).

$$\text{intensity ratio (dB)} = 10 \log_{10}\left(\frac{I_x}{I_0}\right)$$
$$= 10 \log_{10}(e^{-\mu x})$$
$$= -10\mu x \log_{10} e$$

But because $\log_{10} e = 0.4343$

$$\text{intensity ratio (dB)} = -4.343\mu x \ (\text{in } m^{-1})$$
$$= -\mu x \ (\text{in dB } m^{-1})$$
$$\mu \ (\text{dB } m^{-1}) = 4.343\mu \ (m^{-1})$$

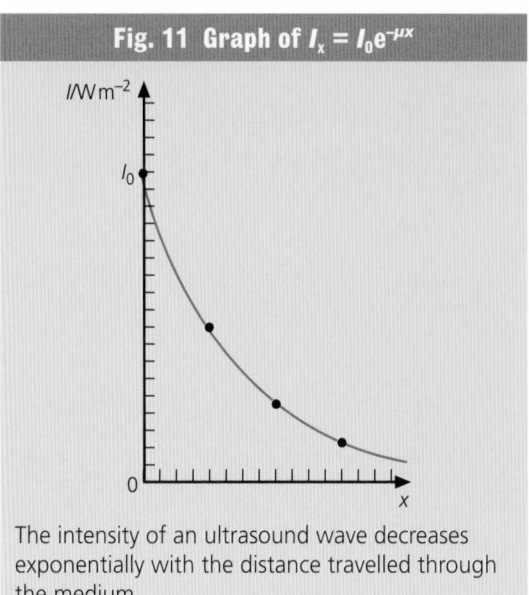

Fig. 11 Graph of $I_x = I_0 e^{-\mu x}$

The intensity of an ultrasound wave decreases exponentially with the distance travelled through the medium

For an ultrasound wave of frequency 1.0 MHz travelling in breast tissue, μ is about 100 dB m^{-1}. After travelling 5 cm, the ultrasound intensity drops to:

$$-100 \text{ dB } m^{-1} \times 0.05 \text{ m} = -5 \text{ dB}$$

only 0.32 of the original intensity.

For most soft tissue in the body, μ is almost proportional to frequency, so high-frequency ultrasound is attenuated more than low-frequency ultrasound. This is a problem because higher frequencies are diffracted less and would give higher resolution images. A solution is to make the transducers so small that they can be placed close to the tissue being studied, reducing attenuation.

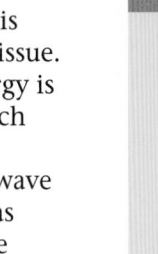 8 **Ultrasound is often used to diagnose breast cancer. For ultrasound at 10 MHz travelling in breast tissue, $\mu \approx 10$ dB cm^{-1}. By what factor will the intensity drop after travelling 2 cm in breast tissue? Express your answer both in dB and as a fraction.**

Table 2 Speed of Sound in different media			
Material	Speed of sound, $(m \, s^{-1})$	Average density, $\rho \ (10^3 \text{ kg } m^{-3})$	Specific acoustic impedance, $Z \ (\text{kg } m^{-2} \, s^{-1})$
bone	3500	1.85	6.48×10^3
dry air	340	0.0013	4.39×10^2
fat	1450	0.952	1.38×10^6
muscle	1580	1.08	1.70×10^6
water	1500	1.00	1.50×10^3
steel	5800	7.86	4.56×10^4
brain	1550	1.02	1.58×10^6

The measured value of the speed of sound in various media. The actual value depends on the exact density and elasticity of the material, as well as the frequency of the sound. (We will discuss specific acoustic impedance later in the chapter)

Key ideas

- Ultrasound waves are generated by resonant vibrations of piezoelectric transducers.

- The speed of sound in a material depends on its density, ρ, and its bulk elastic modulus, K.

- The intensity of a sound wave is the energy transferred per second through unit area.

- Ultrasound is attenuated exponentially as it passes a distance x through body tissue: $I_x = I_0 e^{-\mu x}$, where μ is the intensity attenuation coefficient.

13.5 Scanning techniques

Reflection at boundaries

As ultrasound travels through the body, some of its energy is reflected as the wave passes from one material to another (Fig. 12). These 'echoes' from the boundaries between different materials are used to build up an image of the internal structure of the body.

The amount of energy that is reflected at each interface depends on the **specific acoustic impedance** of the two materials. Specific acoustic impedance, Z, is defined as the product of density and the speed of sound:

$$Z = \rho c$$

When a plane wavefront strikes the boundary between two materials the proportion of the incident intensity, I_I, that is reflected, is given by:

$$\frac{I_R}{I_I} = \left(\frac{Z_2 - Z_1}{Z_2 + Z_1}\right)^2$$

Where I_R is the intensity of the reflected wave, and Z_1 and Z_2 are the specific acoustic impedances of the two media.

The ratio I_R / I_I is known as the **reflection coefficient**, α. It can also be expressed in decibels:

$$\frac{I_R}{I_I} = 10 \log_{10}\left(\frac{I_R}{I_I}\right)$$

The intensity of the transmitted wave, I_T, is the difference between the intensities of incident and reflected waves:

$$I_T = I_I - I_R$$

9 **Explain why ultrasound cannot be used to produce an image of a normal lung.**

10 **Calculate the reflection coefficient for an ultrasound wave as it strikes:**
   a **a bone–brain boundary;**
   b **a fat–muscle boundary.**
   (use the data in Table 2)

A-scans

Early applications of ultrasound used simple echoes to measure the position of body parts. This technique is known as an **amplitude-scan (A-scan)**. In fact, the first application of ultrasound was to measure the position of the mid-line of the brain.

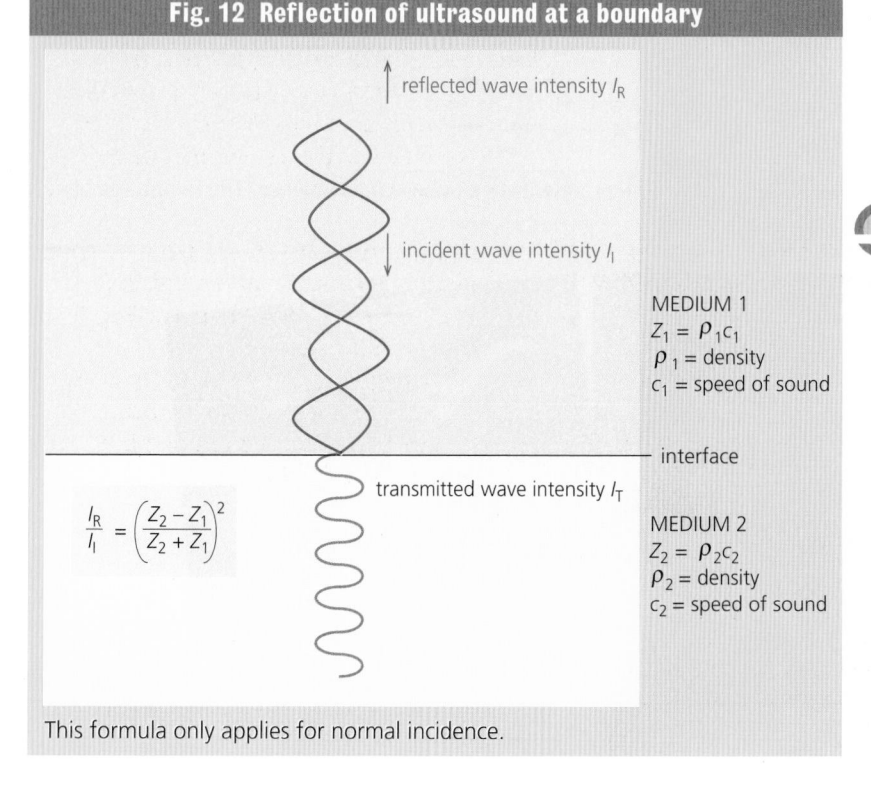

Fig. 12 Reflection of ultrasound at a boundary

reflected wave intensity I_R

incident wave intensity I_I

MEDIUM 1
$Z_1 = \rho_1 c_1$
$\rho_1 = $ density
$c_1 = $ speed of sound

interface

transmitted wave intensity I_T

MEDIUM 2
$Z_2 = \rho_2 c_2$
$\rho_2 = $ density
$c_2 = $ speed of sound

$$\frac{I_R}{I_I} = \left(\frac{Z_2 - Z_1}{Z_2 + Z_1}\right)^2$$

This formula only applies for normal incidence.

Fig. 13 Simplified A-scan apparatus and an output

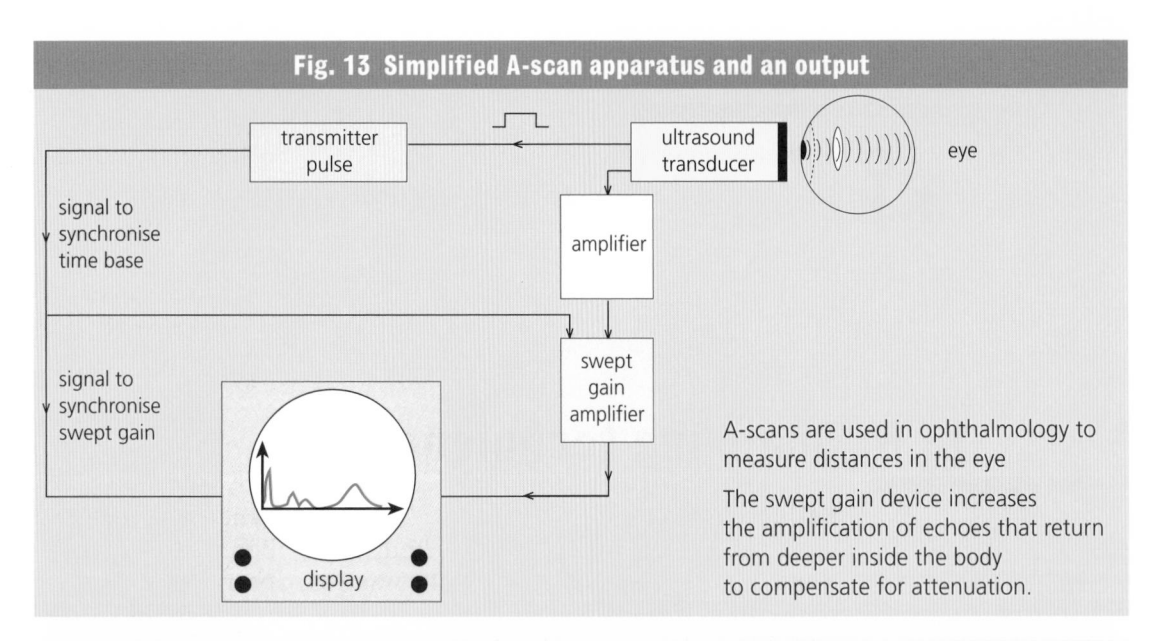

transmitter pulse

ultrasound transducer

eye

signal to synchronise time base

amplifier

signal to synchronise swept gain

swept gain amplifier

display

A-scans are used in ophthalmology to measure distances in the eye

The swept gain device increases the amplification of echoes that return from deeper inside the body to compensate for attenuation.

Fig. 14 The B-scan technique

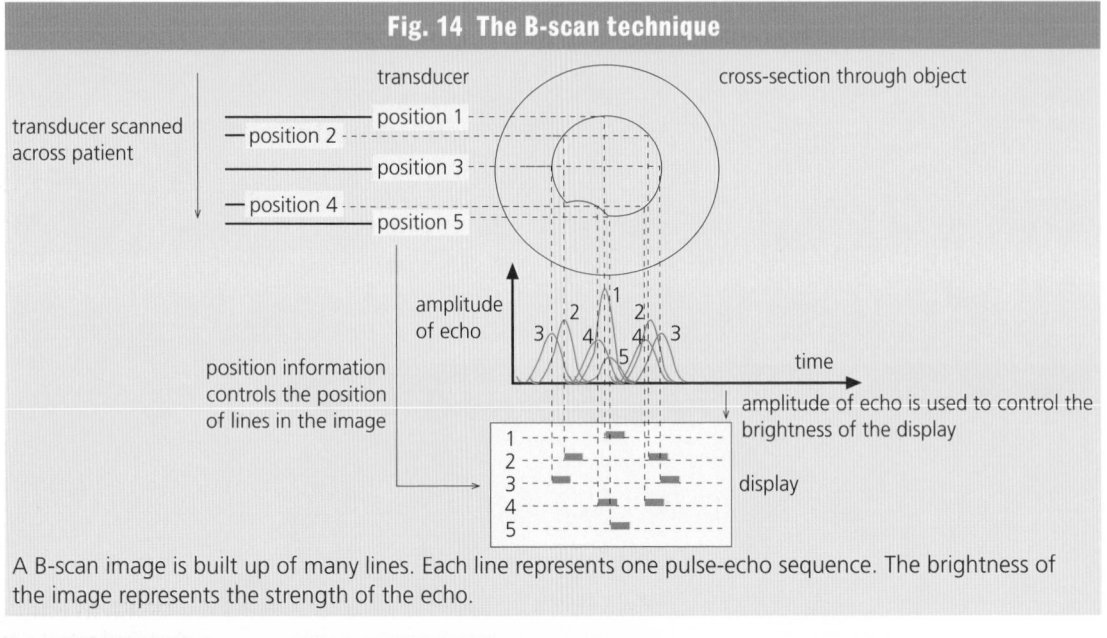

transducer

cross-section through object

transducer scanned across patient

position 1
position 2
position 3
position 4
position 5

amplitude of echo

position information controls the position of lines in the image

time

amplitude of echo is used to control the brightness of the display

display

A B-scan image is built up of many lines. Each line represents one pulse-echo sequence. The brightness of the image represents the strength of the echo.

A jelly is applied between the transducer and the patient's skin. The jelly has an acoustic impedance close to that of skin. The jelly excludes any air and prevents a large echo from the air–skin interface.

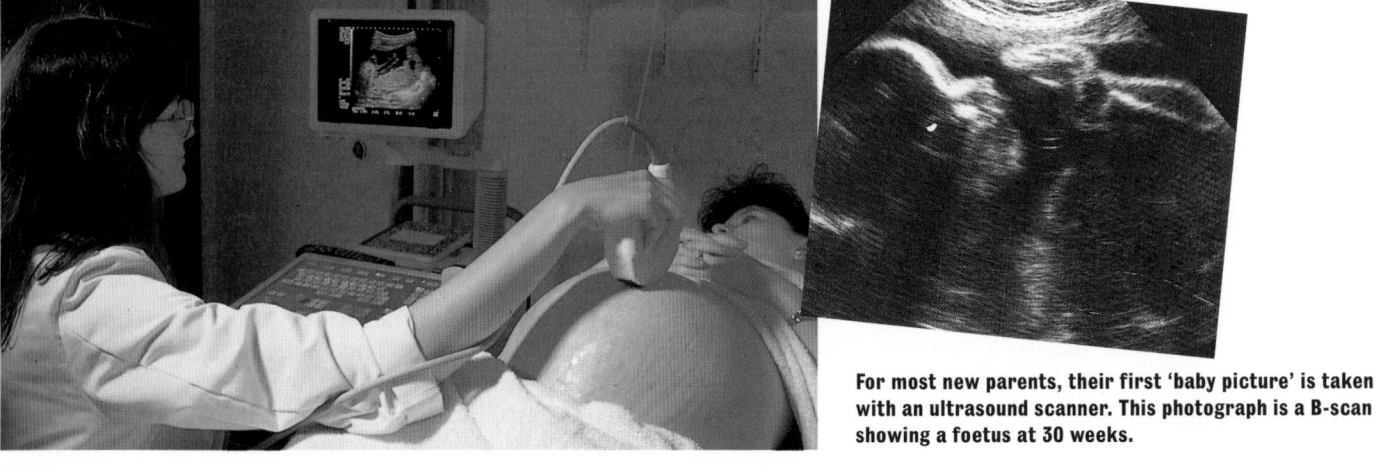

For most new parents, their first 'baby picture' is taken with an ultrasound scanner. This photograph is a B-scan showing a foetus at 30 weeks.

Fig. 15 Scanning techniques used in B-scan imaging

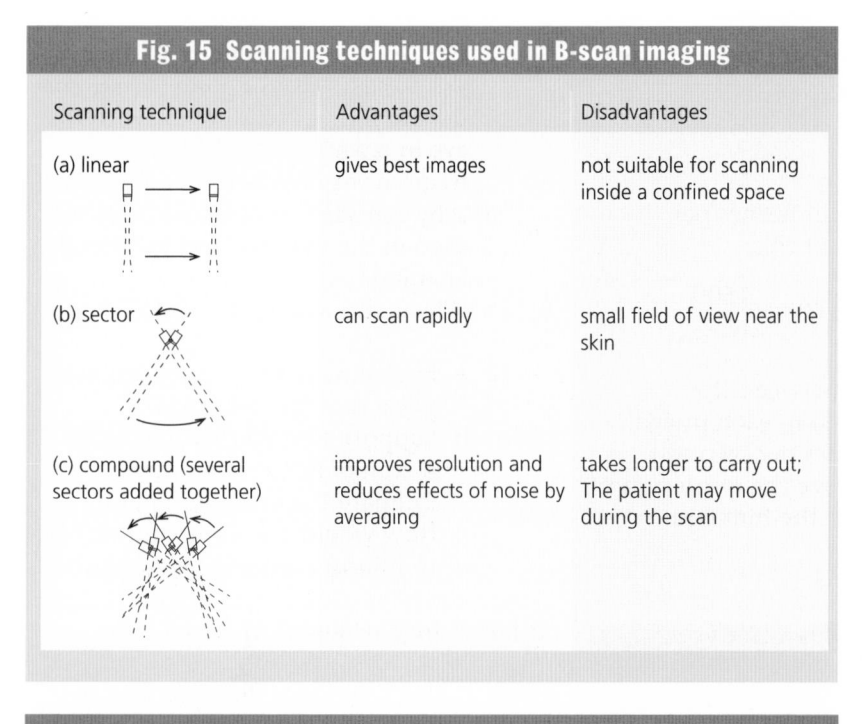

Scanning technique	Advantages	Disadvantages
(a) linear	gives best images	not suitable for scanning inside a confined space
(b) sector	can scan rapidly	small field of view near the skin
(c) compound (several sectors added together)	improves resolution and reduces effects of noise by averaging	takes longer to carry out; The patient may move during the scan

Fig. 16 Arrays of transducers

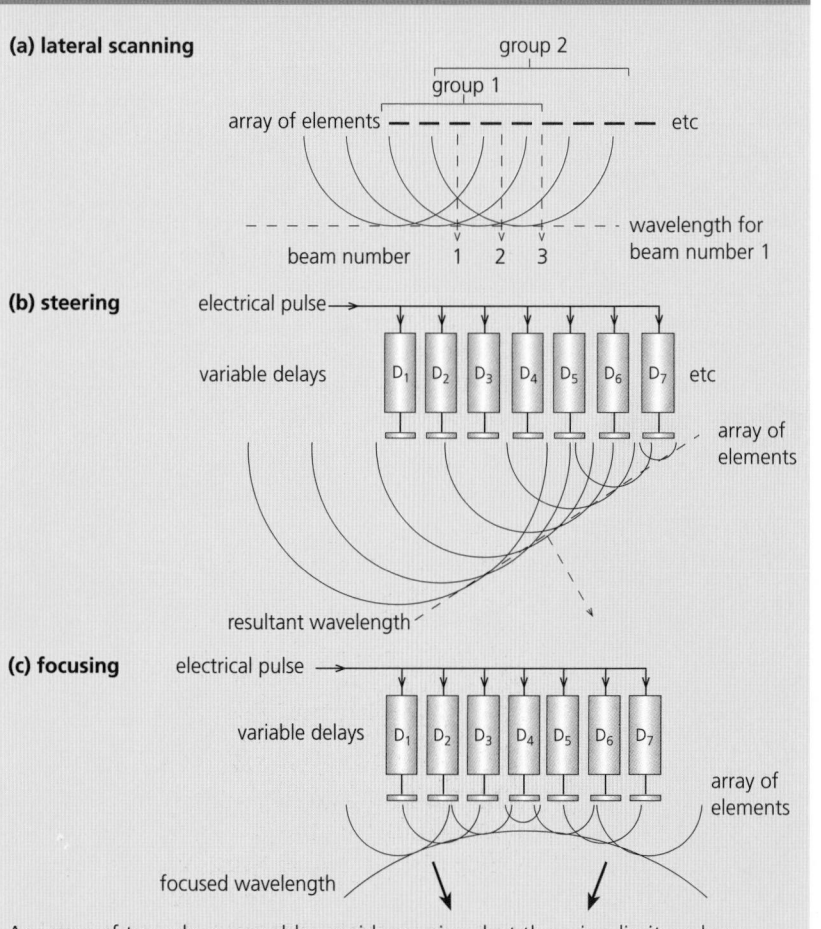

(a) lateral scanning

(b) steering

(c) focusing

An array of transducers enables rapid scanning, but there is a limit on how quickly a full image can be taken.

A transducer placed on the skin emits a single, short pulse. Echoes return from boundaries between different body tissues. The output is displayed as a graph on an oscilloscope, showing how the echo amplitude changes with time (Fig. 13). If you know the speed of sound in body tissue, it is possible to calculate the distance to any boundaries.

B-scans

Ultrasound scans of the developing foetus are now routinely used to determine gestational age and to detect multiple pregnancies or foetal abnormalities. These detailed pictures are carried out using the **brightness-scan (B-Scan)** technique (Fig. 14).

A B-scan image is generated by scanning the ultrasound beam over the patient. A rapid sequence of A-scans is carried out as the beam sweeps across. The strength of the echo signal is used to control the brightness of the picture, rather than the height of a trace on an oscilloscope. This is combined with information about the position of the transducer to create an image.

The ultrasound beam can be swept across the patient in a number of ways, depending on the clinical situation (Fig. 15). To be able to see moving structures, such as heart valves, in real-time the image must be refreshed around 100 times every second. This is done by using an array of transducers that can be triggered separately, with a slight delay between each one. This allows the beam to be steered across the patient (Fig. 16).

The number of complete images, or frames, that can be produced each second depends on how long it takes for the echoes from each pulse to return, and on how many pulses are used to create the full picture. The shortest possible time for one pulse, T_{min}, is given by:

$$T_{min} \text{ (s)} = \frac{\text{distance}}{\text{speed}} = \frac{2D_{max}}{c}$$

$$T_{min} \text{ (s)} = \frac{2D_{max}}{1500}$$

where D_{max} is the maximum depth that is imaged and c is the speed of sound in tissue (≈ 1500 m s^{-1}). If there are N lines in the image, N of these A-scans are required and the time for each frame is:

$$T_{frame} \text{ (s)} = \frac{2ND_{max}}{1500}$$

The maximum number of frames per second is the reciprocal of this:

$$\text{maximum frame rate (Hz)} = \frac{1500}{2ND_{max}}$$

There is a compromise between the number of A-scans (lines) in each image and the number of frames per second. More A-scans will improve the resolution of the image, but will limit the frame rate.

11 **Ultrasonic examinations of the eye are carried out using high-frequency ultrasound, up to 20 MHz, with the eye in a water bath. High frequencies give better resolution.**
  a Why can such high frequencies be used in the eye, and not for foetal imaging?
  b Why is the water bath used?

12 **a Explain why there is a maximum pulse rate for A-scans.**
  b Suppose that you wanted to do an A-scan of adult's abdomen. Estimate the maximum pulse rate.
  c How would this limit your ability to produce a real-time image?

Doppler measurement of blood flow

Ultrasound is also used to measure the speed at which blood is flowing. This is vital in monitoring heart function or in the diagnosis of arterial disease.

Any moving object, such as a red blood cell, reflects ultrasound back to the transducer just as a stationary object does. However, because the reflector is moving the reflected sound has a slightly different frequency to the original, transmitted wave. This is known as **Doppler shift** (Fig. 17). The Doppler effect occurs whenever the source and the detector of a wave are moving relative to each other.

The total change in the frequency, Δf, in an ultrasound wave of frequency, f, due to a blood cell moving at a velocity v, is:

$$\Delta f = \frac{2fv}{c}$$

where c is the velocity of ultrasound in tissue (Fig. 17). If the transmitted frequency is 3 MHz and the blood flows at around 0.2 m s^{-1}, the shift in the frequency is:

$$\Delta f = \frac{2 \times 3 \times 10^6 \times 0.2}{1500} = 800 \text{ Hz}$$

which is in the audible range.

The formula, $\Delta f = 2fv / c$, for the Doppler shift only applies for **normal incidence**. In general, blood cells will be moving at an angle to the sound wave (Fig. 18). In any artery or vein, the blood cells have a range of velocities, so the Doppler signal will be a

Fig. 17 The Doppler shift due to moving blood cells

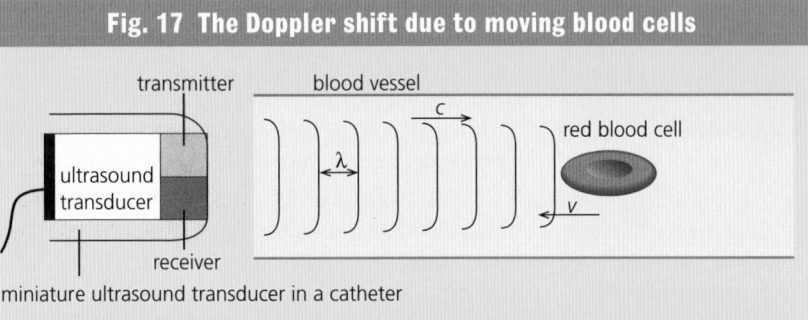

miniature ultrasound transducer in a catheter

Because the blood cell is moving towards the transmitter, it meets more waves per second than if it were stationary. This means that the frequency reaching the blood cell is greater than the transmitted frequency.

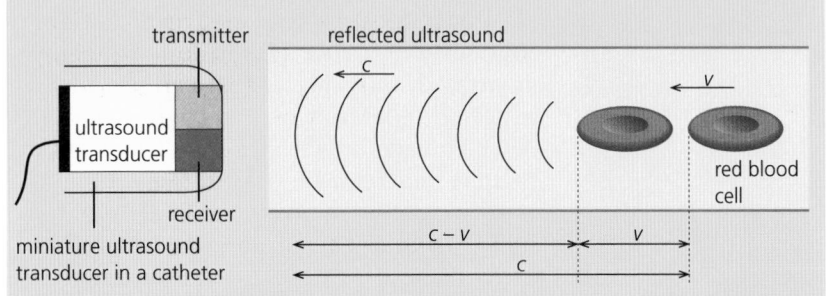

miniature ultrasound transducer in a catheter

The blood cell reflects some ultrasound back towards the receiver. Because the blood cell is moving, the reflected waves occupy a shorter distance than the transmitted waves. The reflected wavelength is shorter than that of the transmitted wave.

The frequency shift caused by the reflection from the moving blood cell is:

$\Delta f = 2vf / c$

where c is the speed of sound in blood and v is the velocity at which the blood cell travels towards the transmitter. (see chapter 3 for a full derivation of this equation)

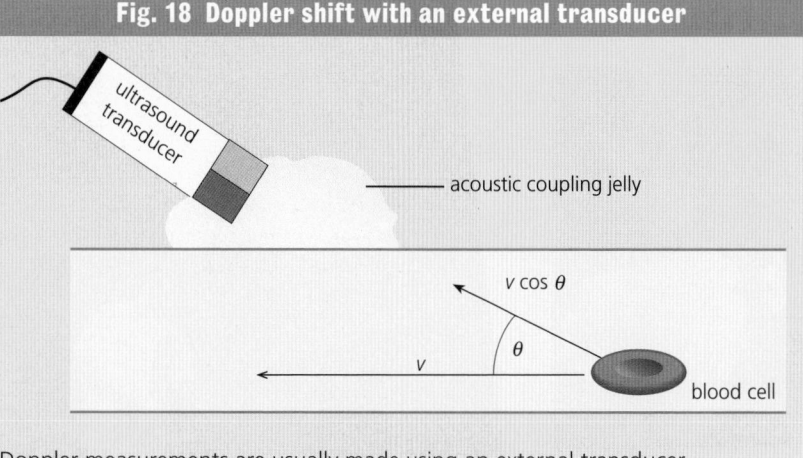

Fig. 18 Doppler shift with an external transducer

ultrasound transducer

acoustic coupling jelly

$v \cos \theta$

θ

v

blood cell

Doppler measurements are usually made using an external transducer. The angle between the ultrasound beam and the velocity of the red blood cell is now important. The Doppler shift becomes $\Delta f = 2fv \cos \theta / c$.

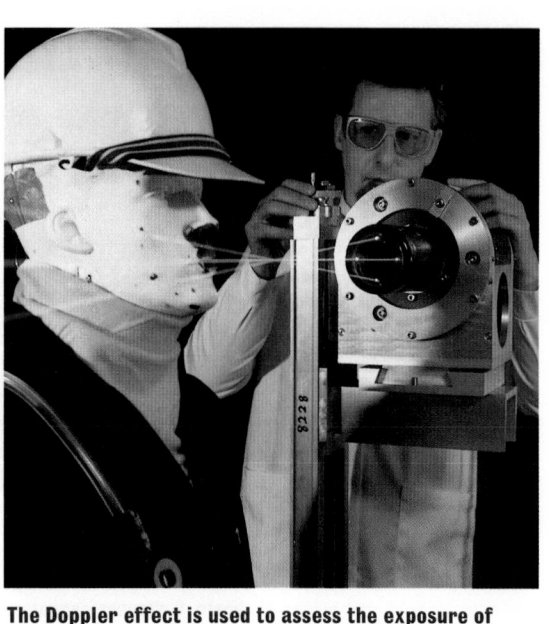

The Doppler effect is used to assess the exposure of workers to contaminants in the air. Lasers are directed at this breathing-simulation model to measure the velocity of air coming from the mouth.

range of frequencies, rather than a single tone. The range of frequencies changes with time as blood pulses through the arteries. Although the situation is complex, these changing Doppler spectra can yield useful clinical information.

Sonar therapy

Diagnostic ultrasound uses low power beams, typically less than 0.1 W m^{-2}. At these power levels there are no known risks, but at higher powers, ultrasound kills human cells due to an effect known as **cavitation**. When the amplitude of the ultrasound wave is large, the low pressure part of the wave, the rarefaction, allows a microscopic bubble of gas to expand rapidly. An instant later, the high pressure,

compressional part of the wave causes the bubble to collapse violently. The resulting high temperatures and pressures can rupture cell membranes and cause severe damage to tissues. The effect is used to break kidney stones into minute pieces that can be passed in urine, removing the need for surgery.

Ultrasound is also used to treat men who are suffering from enlarged prostate glands. In the future, focused sound may treat cancers, stem internal bleeding and even destroy blood clots that sometimes form in blood vessels.

Key ideas

- The specific acoustic impedance of a material, Z, is the product of its density, ρ, and the speed of sound in the material, c:

  $Z = \rho c$

- Ultrasound is reflected as it passes from one medium to another. The reflection coefficient, α, gives the proportion of the intensity that is reflected:

  $$\alpha = \frac{I_R}{I_I} = \left(\frac{Z_2 - Z_1}{Z_2 + Z_1} \right)^2$$

- An A-scan is a graph of echo amplitude against time. It can be used to measure distances inside the body. B-scans produce an image of part of the body.

- The Doppler shift caused by reflections from moving blood cells enables us to measure the speed of blood flow in the body.

14

Ronald Reagan began suffering from Alzheimer's disease while he was still President of the United States. Alzheimer's is so common that 1 in 10 of us will suffer from it by the time we are 65. Symptoms include memory loss. There is, as yet, no cure.

All in the mind

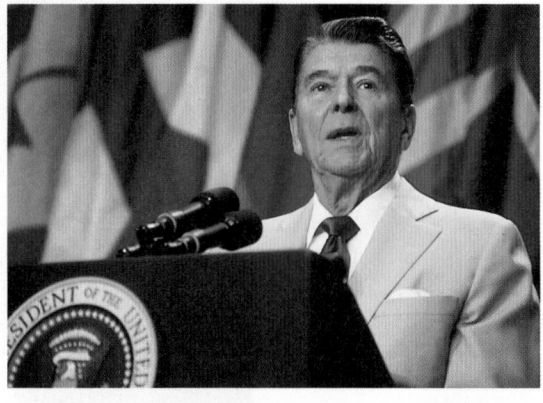

Muhammad Ali was perhaps the greatest heavyweight boxing champion of all time. In later life he was stricken with Parkinson's disease, a progressive illness of the brain. Sufferers cannot control their muscles and walking becomes difficult. The cause is poorly understood.

Ronald Reagan began suffering from Alzheimer's disease while he was still President of the United States. Alzheimer's is so common that 1 in 10 of us will suffer from it by the time we are 65. Symptoms include memory loss. There is, as yet, no cure.

Diseases of the brain have proved hard to understand, partly because it is so difficult to examine the brain. The skull is opaque to most parts of the electromagnetic spectrum and ultrasound is reflected by bone. Until the mid-1970s the only option was to open up the skull and have a look, often after the patient had died.

Now doctors use radiation from the extremes of the electromagnetic spectrum to produce images of the brain in action. Magnetic resonance imaging (MRI) relies on radio waves which can pass through the skull. At the other end of the spectrum, gamma rays are used in positron emission tomography (PET) to show brain activity, and X-rays are used in computer tomography to reveal details such as tumours within the skull.

14.1 Learning objectives

After working through this chapter, you should be able to:

- **explain** how X-rays are produced;

- **describe** the ways that X-rays interact with body tissue and **explain** how X-ray images are formed;

- **describe** the technique of magnetic resonance imaging, MRI;

- **give** an example of the preparation and use of radioisotopes in medicine;

- **discuss** the use of ionising radiation in treating disease.

14.2 X-ray vision

X-rays were discovered by Wilhelm Roentgen in 1895. Within a month of their discovery, doctors throughout Europe were using them to diagnose illness. However, scientists were unaware of the dangers of ionising radiation and many patients suffered from high X-ray doses. Modern techniques have made X-rays much safer.

The X-ray tube

When electrons accelerate or decelerate they emit electromagnetic radiation. The greater the change in velocity, the more energetic the radiation emitted. X-rays are high-energy photons associated with a short wavelength and are produced in the X-ray tube when high-speed electrons are stopped very quickly by colliding with a metal target.

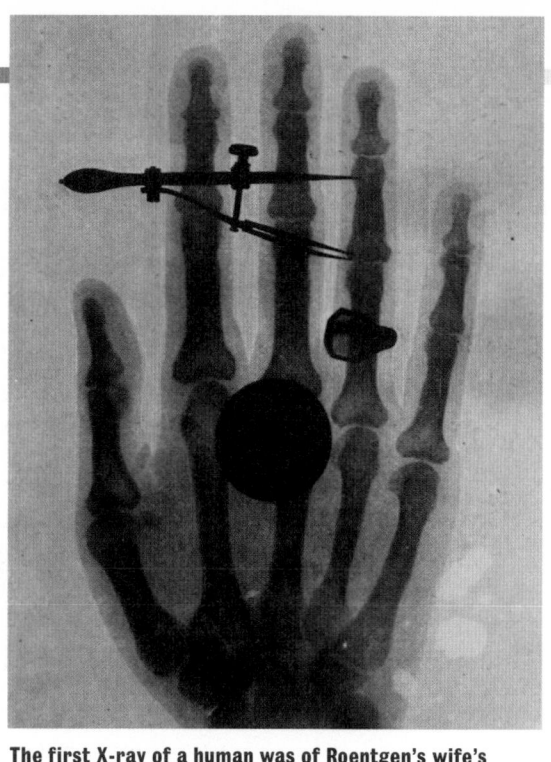

The first X-ray of a human was of Roentgen's wife's hand. The 15-minute exposure gave her an excessively high radiation dose.

In a modern X-ray tube (Fig. 2), the cathode is heated by an electric current. The cathode then emits electrons by **thermionic emission** and they are accelerated towards the anode by a potential difference of around 150 kV. When the electrons reach the target they interact with the target atoms. As the electrons slow down they emit a

---

Fig. 1 Roentgen's X-ray tube apparatus

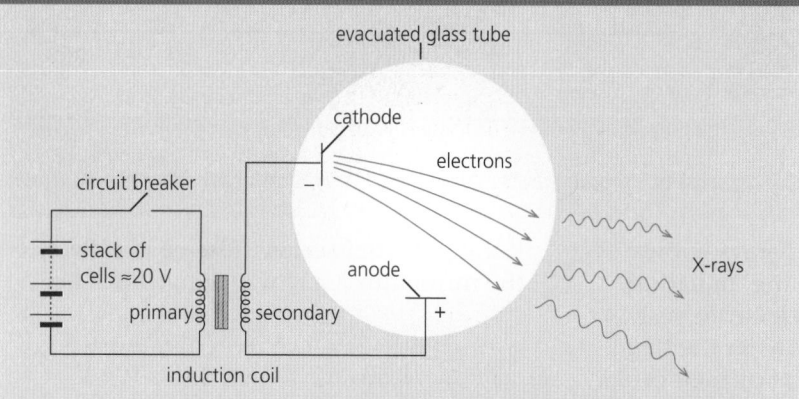

This is a simplified diagram of Roentgen's apparatus. An induction coil was used to supply a high potential difference, about 35 000 V, between the electrodes. Electrons were accelerated across the tube towards the anode. The electrons were not impeded by collisions with air molecules because of the very low air pressure in the tube, about one thousandth of atmospheric pressure.
When the electrons collided with the glass, their deceleration produced X-rays.

Fig. 2 A modern X-ray tube

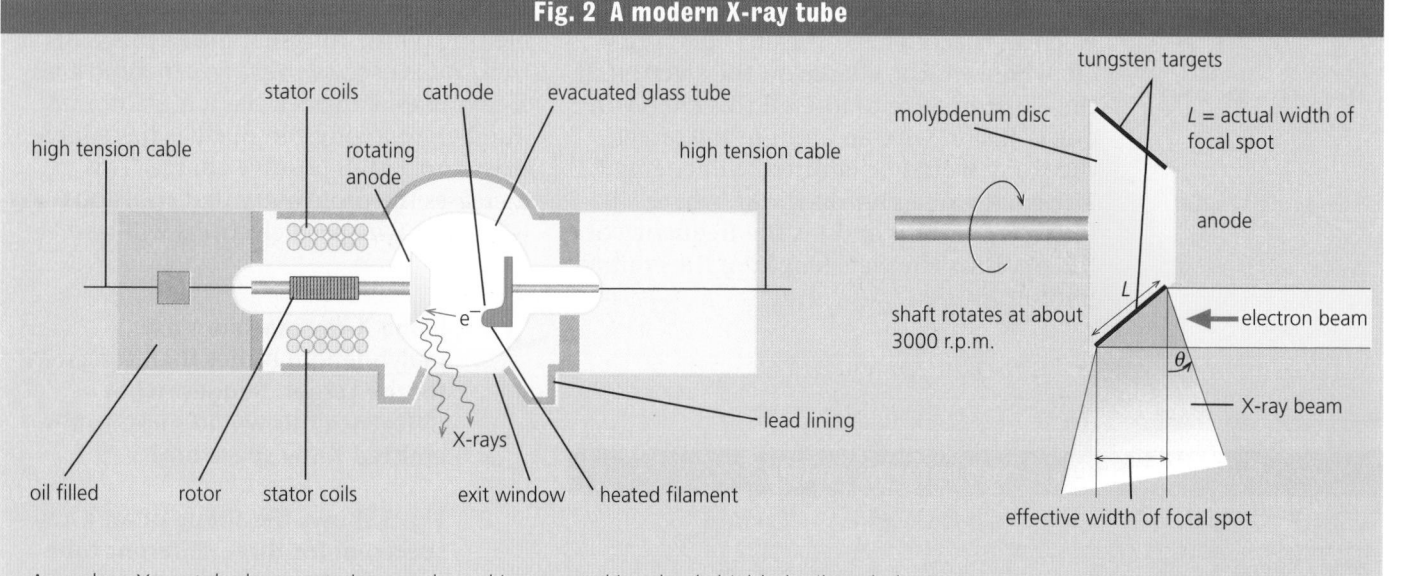

A modern X-ray tube has a rotating anode and is mounted in a lead-shielded, oil-cooled case.
The tungsten target is mounted on the anode. The cathode has a heated filament.
The anode has a bevelled edge to reduce the size of the focal-spot. The width of the target is L, but the width of the X-ray field at the target is $L \sin \theta$. For most applications θ is about 17°. The anode rotates to reduce local heating problems.

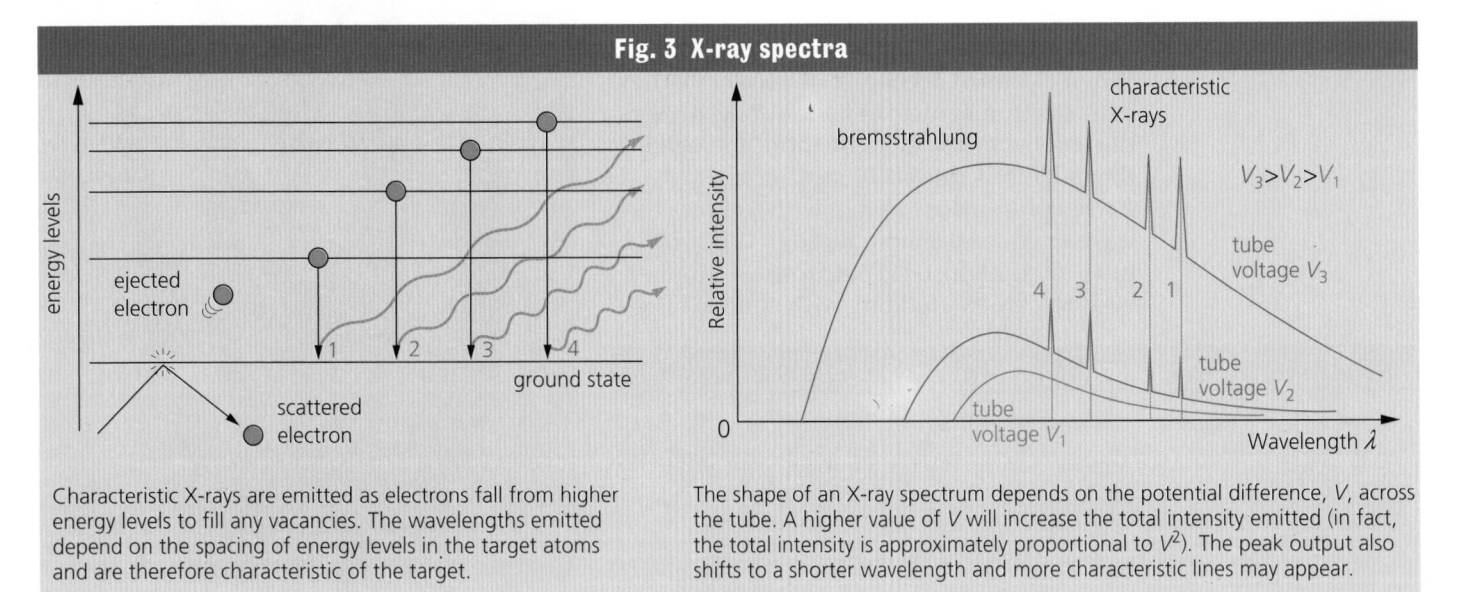

Fig. 3 X-ray spectra

Characteristic X-rays are emitted as electrons fall from higher energy levels to fill any vacancies. The wavelengths emitted depend on the spacing of energy levels in the target atoms and are therefore characteristic of the target.

The shape of an X-ray spectrum depends on the potential difference, V, across the tube. A higher value of V will increase the total intensity emitted (in fact, the total intensity is approximately proportional to V^2). The peak output also shifts to a shorter wavelength and more characteristic lines may appear.

continuous spectrum of X-rays known as **bremsstrahlung** or 'braking' radiation. Some of the high speed electrons will collide with inner electrons in the target atoms, knocking them out of their orbits and ionising the atom. **Characteristic** X-rays are then emitted as other electrons in the target atom drop from higher energy levels to fill the vacancy (Fig. 3). A line spectrum is consequently superimposed on the continuous bremsstrahlung.

The maximum possible energy of an X-ray photon depends on the potential difference, V, across the tube. As an electron is accelerated it gains energy, $E = eV$, where e is the charge on the electron. If the electron were to lose **all** this energy in one collision with an atom in the target, the X-ray would be emitted with energy E. The energy of a photon $E = hf$, where h is Planck's constant and f is the frequency of the photon. The wavelength of the emitted photon is:

$$\lambda = \frac{c}{f} = \frac{hc}{E} = \frac{hc}{eV}$$

If the potential across the tube is 150 kV, the minimum X-ray wavelength will be:

$$\lambda_{min} = \frac{6.63 \times 10^{-34}\ \text{J s} \times 3.00 \times 10^8\ \text{m s}^{-1}}{1.60 \times 10^{-19}\ \text{C} \times 150 \times 10^3\ \text{V}}$$
$$= 8.29 \times 10^{-12}\ \text{m}$$

In practice, less than 1 per cent of the energy in the electron beam is transferred to X-ray radiation. The rest is transferred to internal energy in the target, raising its temperature. The target has to be made of a metal with high values of thermal conductivity, specific heat capacity and melting point. Tungsten meets this criteria well and is used as the target in almost all X-ray tubes. Tungsten has a high atomic number, so a tungsten nucleus has a large mass and a high positive charge. This increases the probability that collisions with the high-speed electrons will lead to X-ray emission.

1 Some X-ray machines use molybdenum rather than tungsten for the target. Suggest what difference this would make to the emitted X-ray spectrum?

2 Fig. 3 shows the shape of an X-ray spectrum for three different tube voltages. Suggest why the characteristic don't lines appear on the lowest voltage curve?

Table 1 Properties of target metals		
	Molybdenum	Tungsten
Atomic number	42	74
Density (kg m^{-3})	10 200	19 300
Specific heat capacity (J kg^{-1} K^{-1})	250	125
Melting Point (°C)	2617	3410

3 X-ray tubes use an electric current to heat the cathode. Suggest what would happen to the X-ray output from the tube if this heater current was increased?

4 Some heavy duty X-ray machines use a tungsten target embedded in a molybdenum target. What is the advantage of this?

Key ideas

- X-rays are produced when high speed electrons strike a target.
- The maximum X-ray photon energy depends on the tube voltage, $E = hf = eV$.
- The minimum X-ray wavelength emitted by a tube is:

$$\lambda_{min} = \frac{hc}{eV}$$

- To reduce the temperature rise in the target, tungsten and molybdenum are used and the anode is rotated.

14.3 X-rays and matter

X-rays interact with matter in a number of ways. X-ray photons can be scattered by atomic electrons or totally absorbed.

A scattered X-ray photon is deflected from its path by an atomic electron. If the electron is very tightly bound to the atom, or the photon has very little energy, the electron will remain in the atom and the X-ray photon will not lose any energy. This is known as **elastic** or **coherent** scattering.

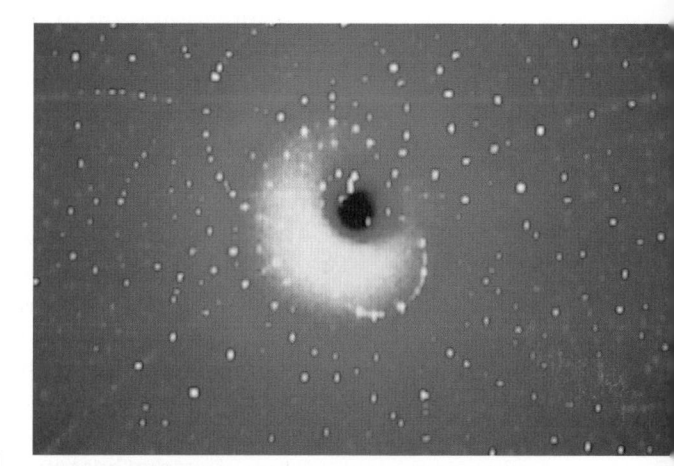

The X-ray diffraction pattern of lysozome. The patterns are due to the elastic scattering of X-rays and can help determine the structure of crystals or biological molecules.

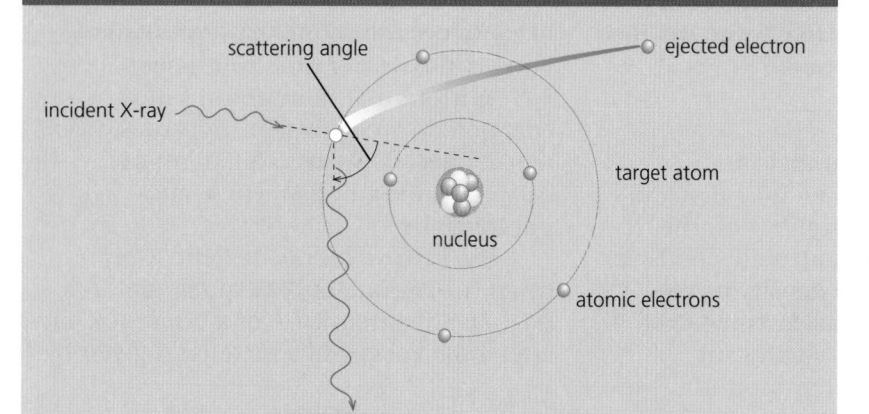

Fig. 4 Compton scattering

scattering angle
ejected electron
incident X-ray
target atom
nucleus
atomic electrons
scattered X-ray

When photon energy is greater than electron binding energy, the electron is ejected from the atom and the energy of the X-ray photon is reduced.

In medical X-rays, the photon energy is usually great enough to knock the electron out of its orbit, ionising the atom. In this case, the X-ray photon does lose energy. The larger the scattering angle, the more energy is lost. This is known as **Compton scattering** (Fig. 4). The probability that Compton scattering will take place is inversely proportional to the energy of the X-ray photon. Compton scattering also depends on the electron density in the target.

An X-ray photon can be totally absorbed

by an atom. In the **photoelectric effect** (see CAMS Physics Core, p.155) *all* of the photon's energy is transferred to an atomic electron, ejecting it from the atom. The difference between the photon's energy and the electron binding energy appears as kinetic energy of the ejected electron (Fig. 5). The probability of the photoelectric effect occurring is roughly proportional to:

$$\frac{Z^4}{E^3}$$

Z is the atomic number of material and E is the photon energy. The photoelectric effect is important in bone and soft tissue at low photon energies, less than 5 keV.

A third process which occurs at photon energies greater than 1.02 MeV is **pair production** (Fig. 6). The X-ray photon disappears and its energy is used to create an electron and a positron. These particles cause ionisation in the surrounding tissue. When the anti-matter positron meets an electron, the two particles are **annihilated**, causing two identical γ-rays, each of 0.51 MeV energy, to be emitted in opposite directions.

5 Lead is used to shield X-ray tubes. Radiographers often wear lead aprons or work from behind lead-lined screens. Why is lead a suitable material for shielding?

6 The X-ray tubes used in radiotherapy have higher tube voltages. What difference does that make to the way the X-rays interact with the human body?

X-ray attenuation

Compton scattering, photoelectric absorption and pair production all act to attenuate (reduce the intensity of) the X-ray beam. This **attenuation** depends on the atomic number and density of the target as well as the initial energy of the photons. Bone contains significant amounts of calcium and phosphorous, so its effective atomic number, $Z_{eff} = 14$, is higher than that of soft tissue, $Z_{eff} = 7$. The X-rays used in diagnostic radiology have a peak photon energy of around 50 keV. At this energy the photoelectric effect is more

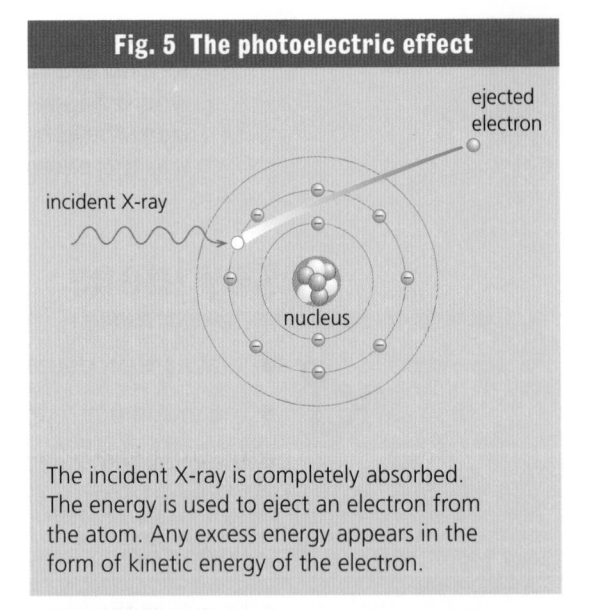

Fig. 5 The photoelectric effect

The incident X-ray is completely absorbed. The energy is used to eject an electron from the atom. Any excess energy appears in the form of kinetic energy of the electron.

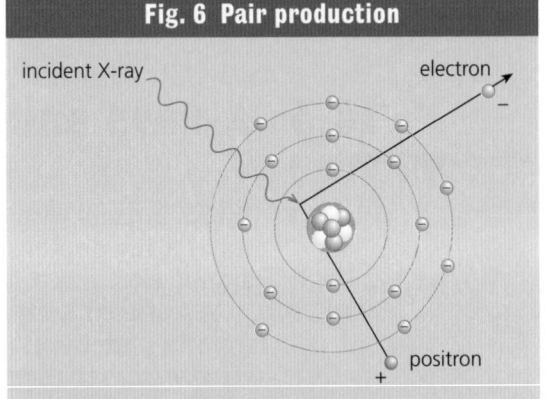

Fig. 6 Pair production

Pair production only occurs at photon energies above 1.02 MeV. This is the minimum energy required to create an electron–positron pair. Pair production is the dominant interaction between X-rays and matter at high photon energies.

likely to occur in bone than soft tissue. Bone is also denser than soft tissue. These factors mean that bone absorbs more X-ray energy than an equivalent thickness of soft tissue. This allows us to differentiate between bone and tissue in X-ray photographs.

For a narrow, monoenergetic X-ray beam the attenuation is exponential (Fig. 7). The intensity, I, of a beam of X-rays after a thickness x in a material is given by:

$$I = I_0 e^{-\mu x}$$

where I_0 is the original intensity of the X-ray beam and μ is the linear attenuation coefficient, measured in m^{-1}. A given thickness of material will reduce the X-ray intensity by half. This thickness is known as the **half-value layer**.

We can use the equation, $I = I_0 e^{-\mu x}$, to find the half-value thickness for bone.

$$I = I_0 e^{-\mu x}$$

$$\text{So } \frac{I}{I_0} = e^{-\mu x}$$

At the half-value thickness,

$$\frac{I}{I_0} = \tfrac{1}{2}$$

So, taking logs of each side of the equation gives:

$$\ln\left(\tfrac{1}{2}\right) = -\mu x_{\frac{1}{2}}$$

The linear attenuation coefficient for bone for monoenergetic, 150 keV X-ray photons, is about 0.6 cm^{-1} (Fig. 8).

For 150 keV X-rays in bone the half-value thickness (HVT) is:

$$x_{\frac{1}{2}} = \frac{\ln\left(\tfrac{1}{2}\right)}{0.6} = 1.1 \text{ cm}$$

7 Use the graph in Fig. 8 to explain why X-rays are so good at revealing broken bones.

8 It is possible to use X-rays to 'see' soft tissue behind bone using 150 keV X-rays, but not using 50 keV photons. Explain, with calculations, why this is so. (Take μ_{bone} at 50 keV to be 1 cm^{-1})

The density of a material, ρ, also affects its ability to absorb energy from X-rays, simply because the X-ray photon has more atoms, or more massive atoms, to interact with in the same volume. To take account of this, a **mass attenuation coefficient**, μ_{m}, is defined as:

$$\mu_{\text{m}} = \mu / \rho$$

This is now independent of density, so that the value of μ_{m} for water is the same whether the water is in liquid, solid or gaseous form.

Fig. 7 Exponential absorption

(a) For a narrow, monoenergetic X-ray beam the attenuation is exponential.

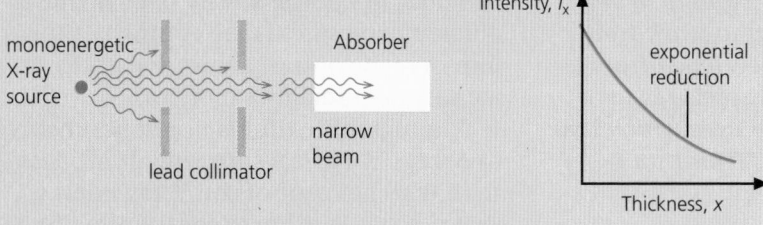

(b) A real X-ray beam will be wide, there will be more scattered radiation, so the intensity will be greater than for a narrow beam.

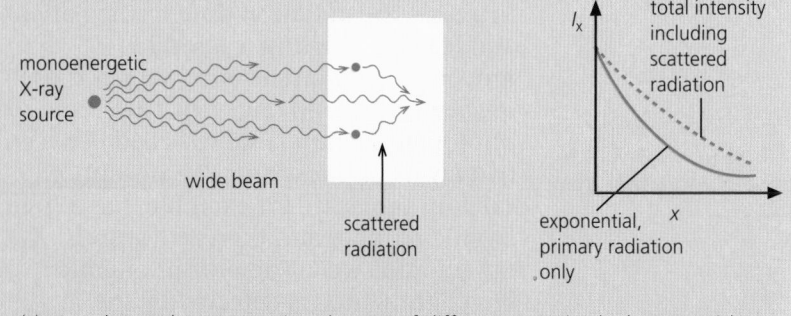

(c) A real X-ray beam contains photons of different energies (polyenergetic). The lower energy photons are absorbed first and the X-ray beam tends to get 'harder', i.e. the average energy of the photons increases, as it passes through the material.

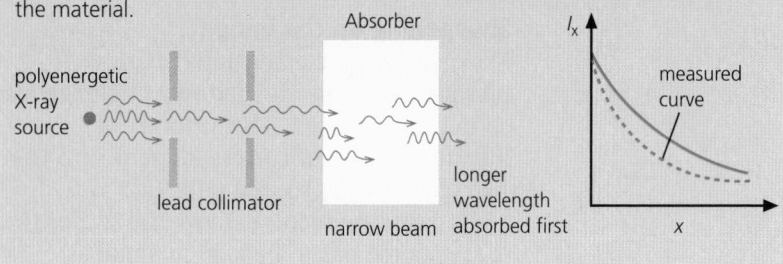

Fig 8 Graph of μ vs. energy for bone and tissue

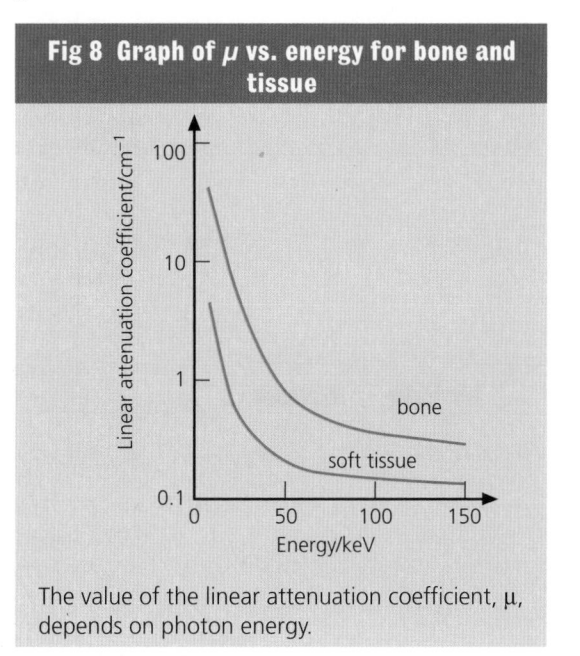

The value of the linear attenuation coefficient, μ, depends on photon energy.

Key ideas

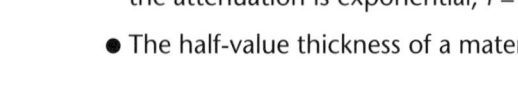

- X-rays interact with matter via the photoelectric effect, Compton scattering, and pair production.

- An X-ray beam is attenuated as it passes through matter. For a monoenergetic X-ray beam the attenuation is exponential, $I = I_0 e^{-\mu x}$.

- The half-value thickness of a material will reduce the X-ray intensity by a half.

14.4 Getting the picture

'In brain surgery there isn't much room for manoeuvre. Removing a brain tumour is a nightmare – if I take away too little tissue the tumour is likely to grow again, and if I remove too much I could rob the patient of some vital function. I need a detailed map of the patient's brain to work from. X-rays have developed from simple shadow pictures to detailed 3-d images which now give me the information I need.'

X-ray film

Traditional X-rays use photographic film to record an image. X-ray photons cause ionisation in silver halide grains in the film. When the film is developed those grains that have been exposed to X-rays turn black. The greater the exposure, the darker the film will be. The amount of variation in darkness, or optical density (Fig. 9), due to different exposures is the **contrast** of the film. A high contrast allows doctors to identify abnormalities more easily.

Photographic film is not very sensitive to X-rays. A typical film will absorb less than 0.10 per cent of the X-ray energy that reaches it. Consequently, a relatively long exposure time is needed to get a well-exposed image. But a prolonged exposure increases the radiation dose to the patient and leads to blurring, caused by movement. An intensifying screen is used to speed things up (Fig. 10). The photographic film is sandwiched between two layers of phosphor. The phosphor, calcium tungstate for example, has a high atomic number and therefore absorbs X-ray photons well. The phosphor emits blue light which is detected by the photographic film. The overall efficiency is much greater than for film alone.

Sharpening up the image

X-ray images are essentially shadow pictures and, like all shadows, the edges are sometimes blurred. The amount of blurring, or **unsharpness**, depends on the size of the X-ray source (Fig. 11).

To keep the picture sharp, the size of the X-ray source has to be kept as small as

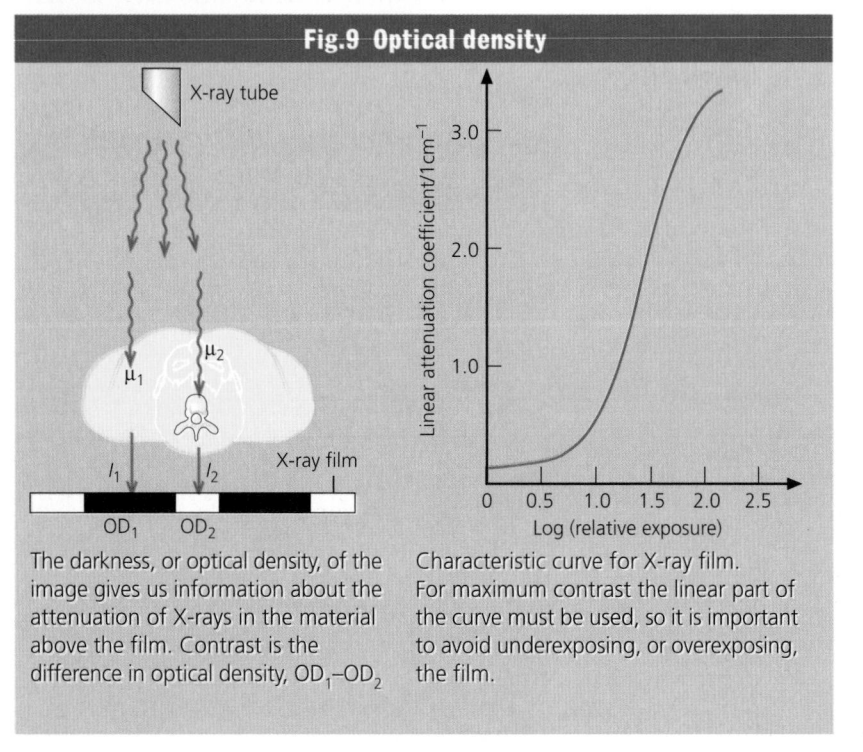

Fig.9 Optical density

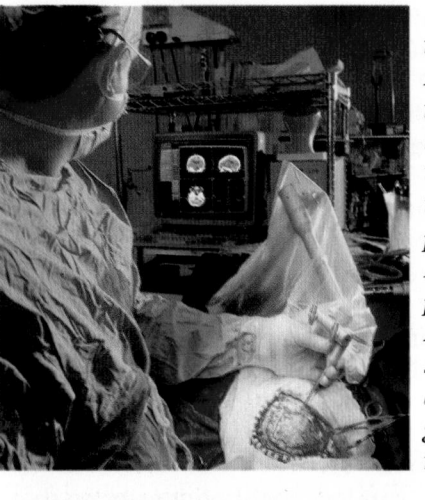

The darkness, or optical density, of the image gives us information about the attenuation of X-rays in the material above the film. Contrast is the difference in optical density, OD$_1$–OD$_2$

Characteristic curve for X-ray film. For maximum contrast the linear part of the curve must be used, so it is important to avoid underexposing, or overexposing, the film.

Fig. 10 Structure of an intensifying cassette

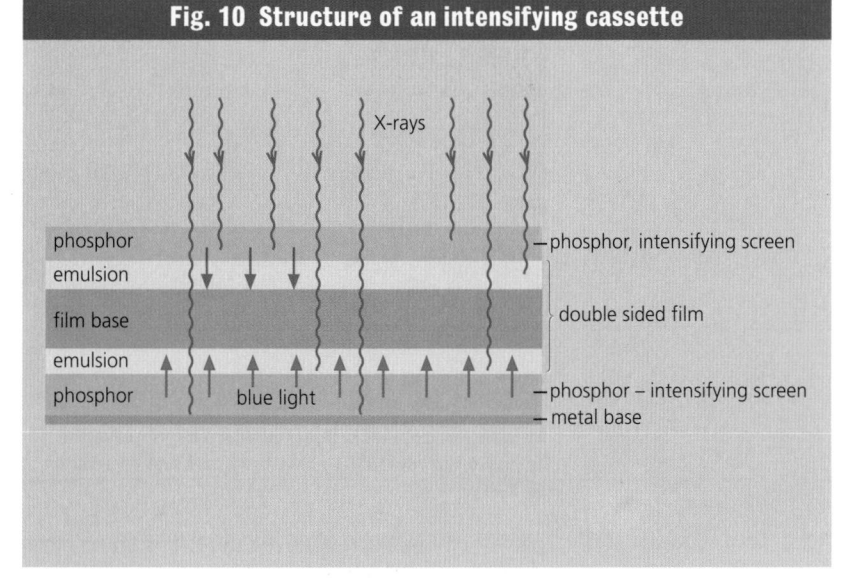

Fig. 11 The umbra/penumbra effect

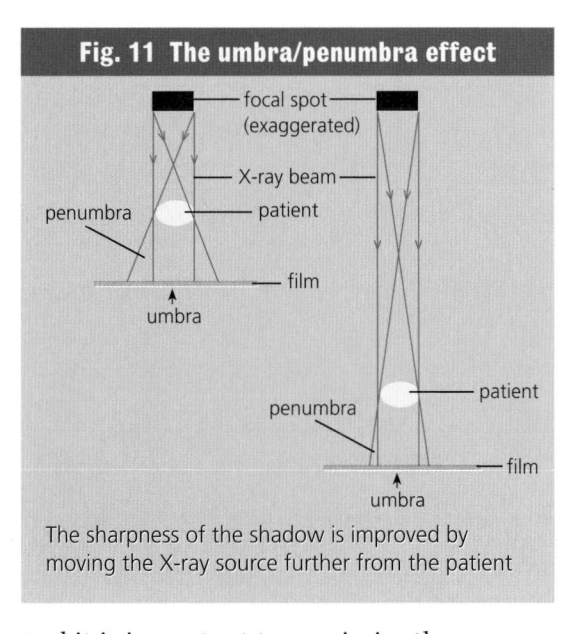

The sharpness of the shadow is improved by moving the X-ray source further from the patient

possible. This is done by focusing the electron beam and using a target inclined to the beam (Fig. 2). It is important to keep the film close to the patient. Unsharpness can be decreased by moving the X-ray source further from the patient, but the **inverse-square law** means that the intensity of X-radiation at the patient is also decreased.

The contrast of an X-ray photograph is reduced by scattered radiation. The amount of scattered radiation can be cut down by placing a grid, constructed of lead strips, between the patient and the film (Fig. 12). The grid allows most of the primary radiation to pass through but blocks some of the scattered radiation. The grid itself would be imaged on the film, but the grid can be moved during the exposure to blur out its shadow.

Imaging soft tissue

The contrast between images of different soft tissues, or between normal tissue and a tumour, is often very small. One way to visualise internal organs is by using a **contrast medium**. Patients who need an X-ray of their digestive tract often need to eat a 'barium meal', a thick suspension of barium sulphate.

In some applications, such as mammography, small differences in attenuation are crucial and could signify breast cancer. The difference in density and effective atomic number, Z_{eff}, between an abnormality and normal tissue are small

and it is important to maximise the contrast. Low tube voltages are used for this because low-energy X-ray photons are predominantly absorbed by the photoelectric effect. Absorption by the photoelectric effect is proportional to Z_{eff}^4, so small differences in Z_{eff} can be made apparent.

Doctors often need to see moving images to aid diagnosis, particularly of bowel or heart problems. **Fluoroscopy** uses a fluorescent screen rather than a film to produce a visible image in real time, so that moving parts can be seen.

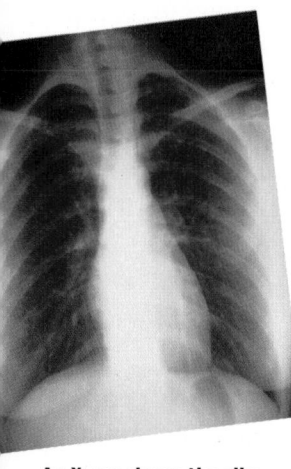

An X-ray shows the ribs clearly, but other organs, such as the intestines, are hard to see.

Fig. 12 Anti-scatter grids

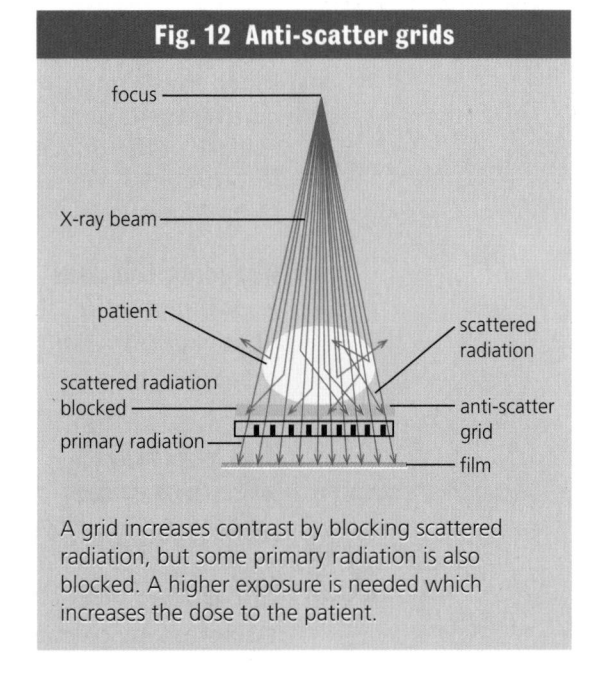

A grid increases contrast by blocking scattered radiation, but some primary radiation is also blocked. A higher exposure is needed which increases the dose to the patient.

Fig. 13 An image intensifier

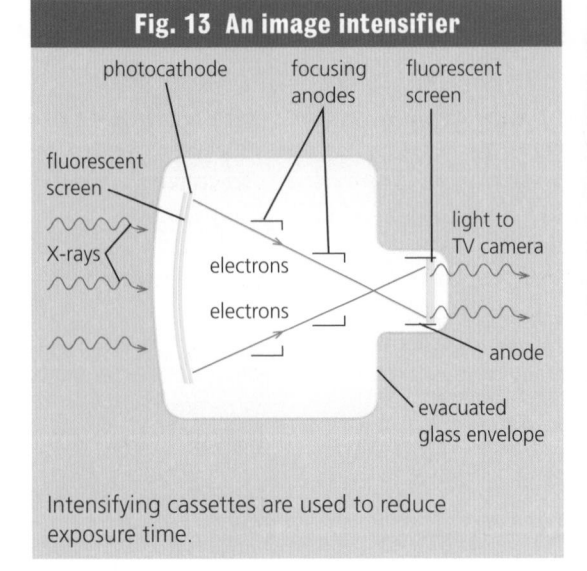

Intensifying cassettes are used to reduce exposure time.

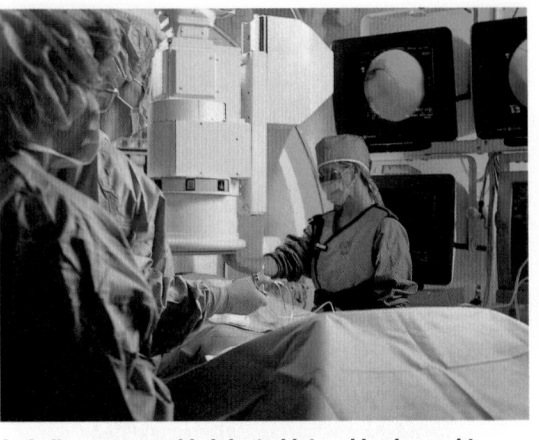

An iodine compound is injected into a blood vessel to increase the contrast so that the heart can be seen on an X-ray.

An **image intensifier** can be used to produce a real-time X-ray image of the patient (Fig. 13). X-rays strike a phosphor, often caesium iodide, which then emits light. The light photons strike a photocathode, releasing electrons which are focused by electrodes inside a vacuum tube. The electrons accelerate across the tube until they strike a fluorescent screen which provides a visible image, in the same way that a TV screen does. The output can be recorded via a video camera.

The output screen is smaller than the input screen. This reduction, and the acceleration of the electrons across the tube, makes an image up to 1000 times brighter than the original. This means that much lower intensity X-rays can be used, cutting the dose to the patient. Even with the use of the image intensifier, fluoroscopy gives a relatively high dose, often 15 times that of a conventional X-ray.

Reducing the dose
A malfunctioning X-ray tube could give a high exposure. Therefore, hospital physicists must regularly monitor the X-ray dose to patients and staff.

Diagnostic X-rays are responsible for most of our exposure to man-made radiation, so it is important to keep the dose as small as possible. An important way of reducing the dose is to filter out the low-energy component of the X-ray spectrum. Because low-energy photons are unlikely to reach the X-ray film, they cause a dose to the patient without giving any diagnostic information. A filter that absorbs photons principally by the photoelectric effect is ideal.

Moreover,

$$\text{probability of absorption} \propto \frac{1}{\text{photon energy}}$$

So low-energy photons will be absorbed preferentially. In practice, a filter made from a few millimetres of aluminium is used.

9 A filter for a diagnostic X-ray beam should use photoelectric absorption rather than the Compton effect. Give two reasons why this is true.

Key ideas

- The contrast of an X-ray picture is diminished by scatter. A grid is used to reduce scatter.

- Organs, such as the stomach, can be imaged by the use of a contrast medium.

- Fluoroscopy gives a real time image. The dose can be reduced by the use of an image intensifier or by the use of a filter.

14.5 X-ray slices

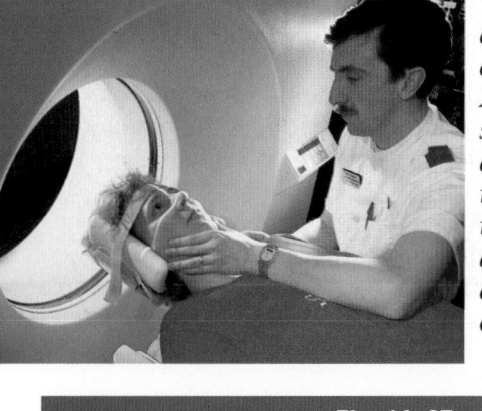

'Finding a brain tumour with a conventional X-ray is a difficult task. Conventional X-rays images are just shadow pictures – two-dimensional projections of a three-dimensional object – so they carry no information about depth. Another difficulty is the lack of contrast.'

X-ray computer tomography (CT) offers a solution to both of these problems. Modern CT scanners can produce high-contrast images of slices through the head or body.

Image contrast depends on different intensities of X-ray radiation reaching the film. This in turn relies on variations in the average linear attenuation coefficient in the path of the X-ray beam. The contrast has to vary by at least 2 per cent if we are to see the differences on X-ray film. We can calculate the intensity reaching the film using the equation $I_x = I_0 e^{-\mu x}$.

For a typical diagnostic X-ray beam, muscle has a linear attenuation coefficient, μ, of about 0.180 cm^{-1}. For 1 cm of muscle:

$$\frac{I_x}{I_0} = e^{-\mu x} = 0.835$$

Compare this with the results obtained for bone, blood and air (Table 2).

A 1 cm thickness of bone is easily detectable, but a blood vessel is not.

Modern X-ray CT scanners can reveal detail as fine as 1 mm with density differences of less than 1 per cent. The technique uses a pencil beam of X-rays which is scanned across the patient. A detector records the intensity at each position and the results are digitised and passed to a computer where the image is reconstructed (Fig. 14).

CT scanners are expensive and they give a significantly higher radiation dose to patients, but these disadvantages are outweighed by the detailed images that

Fig. 14 CT scanning

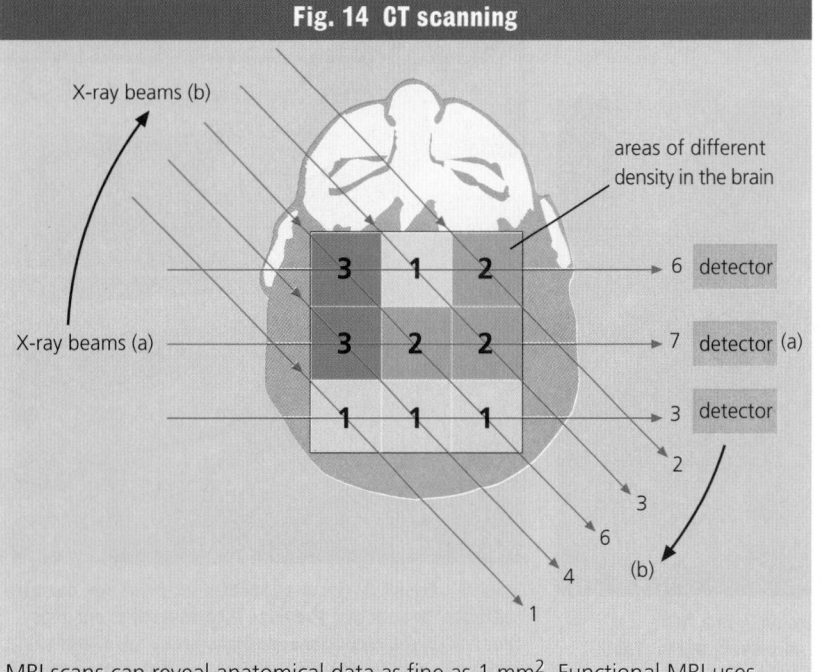

X-ray beams (b)

areas of different density in the brain

X-ray beams (a)

3	1	2	→ 6	detector
3	2	2	→ 7	detector (a)
1	1	1	→ 3	detector

2
3
6
4   (b)
1

MRI scans can reveal anatomical data as fine as 1 mm^2. Functional MRI uses magnetically labelled tracers to reveal activity in the brain.

Table 2 Linear attenuation coefficients				
Material	Linear attenuation coefficient, μ	$I_x/I_0 = e^{-\mu x}$ (based on 1 cm of absorber)	Transmission relative to muscle	Contrast compared to muscle percentage
Bone	0.48	0.619	$\dfrac{0.619}{0.835} = 0.74$	−26%
Air	0.0	1.0	$\dfrac{1}{0.835} = 1.20$	+20%
Blood	0.178	0.837	$\dfrac{0.837}{0.835} = 1.02$	+0.2%

they can provide. These images are vital to radiotherapists in treating cancer patients.

Radiotherapy

Radiotherapy uses ionising radiation to kill cancer cells. The radiation used is generally gamma rays or very hard (high proton energy) X-rays.

Cobalt–60 is often used as a source of gamma radiation in radiotherapy. It has a half-life of 5.3 years. Cobalt–60 emits gamma rays with an energy of 1.17 MeV and 1.33 MeV. Radiation at this energy is very penetrating; very little of the dose is delivered to the skin and surface tissues.

High-voltage X-ray machines are an alternative to gamma irradiation. Peak X-ray intensities of up to 5 MeV are used.

These X-rays are produced by electrons accelerated to high speeds in a linear accelerator. Superficial cancers, e.g. skin cancer, can be treated by low-energy X-rays with a peak voltage of around 20 keV.

10 **Using high-energy radiation for radiotherapy reduces the damage done to bone. Why?**

11 **X-rays from high-voltage tubes present a potential hazard for radiotherapy staff. Give two reasons why this is the case.**

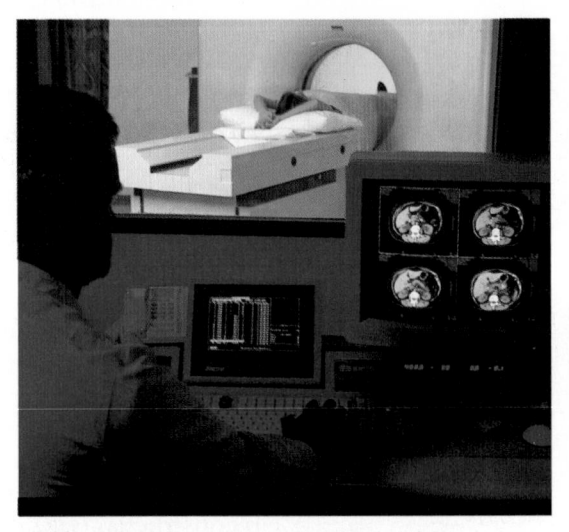

Modern CT scanners can acquire data in a few milliseconds. The scanner has no moving parts. The X-ray source is moved by rapidly deflecting a beam of electrons around a circular target.

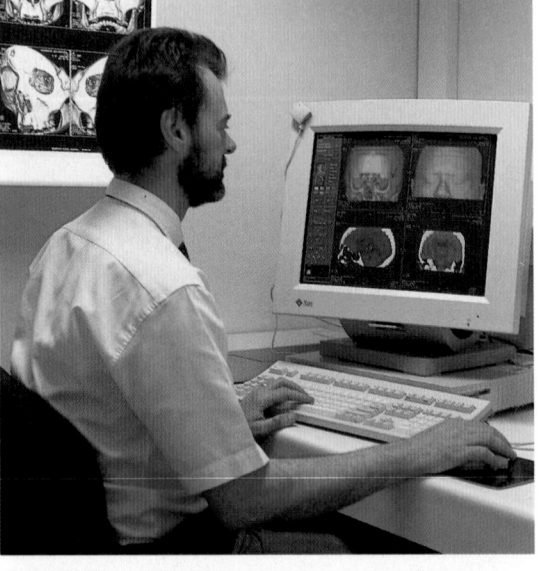

Medical physicists produce treatment plans for cancer patients. By splitting the dose into several exposures from different directions, doctors make sure that the cancer gets a high radiation dose, with the minimum of damage to surrounding tissue.

Key ideas

- An aluminium filter is used to remove low-energy photons from a diagnostic X-ray beam.

- As X-rays pass through a material the beam intensity is reduced. This attenuation depends on the linear attenuation coefficient, μ, of the material. μ depends on photon energy.

- Radiotherapy uses high energy X-ray or gamma ray photons to kill cancer cells.

14.6 Watching the brain work

The latest generation of radionuclide imagers are known as PET scanners. These use positron emitting isotopes to reveal activity in the brain. Detection occurs from the gamma ray produced when a positron is annihilated. This picture shows the lesions in the brain that are typical of an Alzheimer patient.

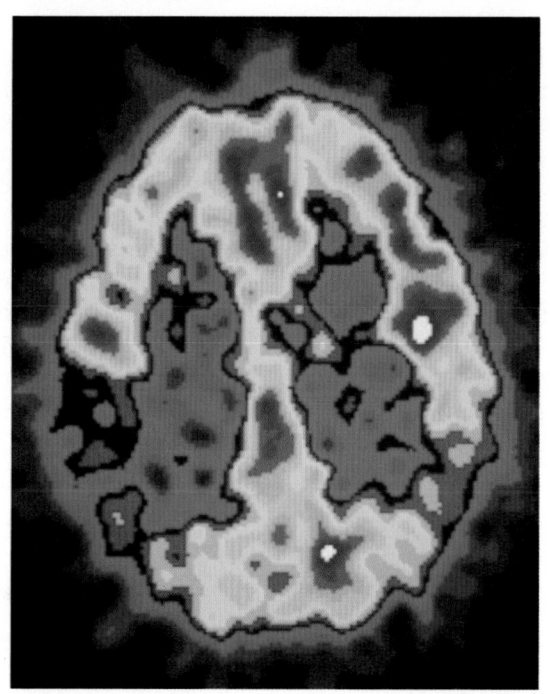

CT scans have given us anatomical maps of the brain, but they tell us nothing about function. New techniques such as radioactive isotope imaging and magnetic resonance imaging can show us which parts of the brains are active when we carry out different tasks.

Nuclear medicine

Though the brain is only about 2 % of our total body mass, it accounts for up to 25 % of the total oxygen demand and 15 % of the blood flow. Radioisotope scanning relies on the fact that when different parts of the brain are active, the blood flow to that area will increase. By attaching a radioactive isotope to blood, we can monitor the blood flow by detecting the radiation that is emitted. Technetium–99, ^{99}Tc, has proved to be an ideal isotope for this purpose. It has a half-life of 6 hours and can be produced on-site in a hospital from the decay of molybdenum–99, which has a half-life of 66 hours (See CAMS Physics Core, Fig. 9 p. 155). Technetium–99 emits a gamma ray of a single energy, 140 keV, which has a half-value thickness in tissue of 4.6 cm. There are no accompanying beta or alpha emissions, which would increase the dose to the patient.

Blood labelled with a compound containing trace amounts of technetium-99 will emit gamma rays. A gamma camera is used to detect these rays and to reconstruct an image of the brain (Fig. 15).

Fig. 15 Gamma camera

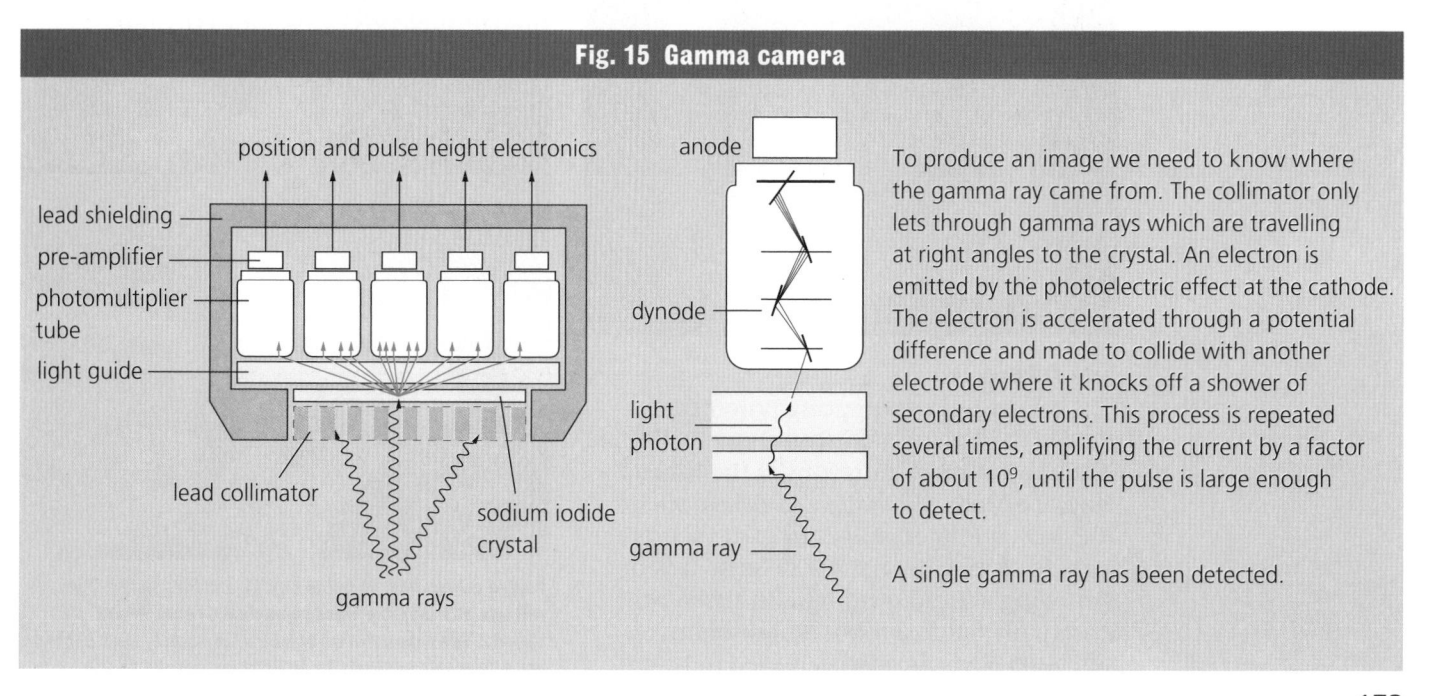

position and pulse height electronics

lead shielding
pre-amplifier
photomultiplier tube
light guide

lead collimator

gamma rays

sodium iodide crystal

anode

dynode

light photon

gamma ray

To produce an image we need to know where the gamma ray came from. The collimator only lets through gamma rays which are travelling at right angles to the crystal. An electron is emitted by the photoelectric effect at the cathode. The electron is accelerated through a potential difference and made to collide with another electrode where it knocks off a shower of secondary electrons. This process is repeated several times, amplifying the current by a factor of about 10^9, until the pulse is large enough to detect.

A single gamma ray has been detected.

Magnetic resonance imaging

Radioisotope imaging can produce pictures of the brain with a resolution of a few millimetres, showing the average activity over tens of seconds. This is a huge step forward, but we need quicker scans if we are to track the fleeting impressions of thoughts as they flash across the brain. Functional magnetic resonance imaging (MRI) promises to do just that.

At the heart of every hydrogen atom in our bodies is a proton. Protons spin, and because they are charged, they generate their own magnetic field. Normally these fields are randomly orientated. During an MRI scan, patients are placed in a strong magnetic field. The field is produced by large superconducting magnets which produce a flux density of between 1 and 2 tesla, about 10 000 times greater than the Earth's magnetic field. This strong field lines up the spinning protons so that their magnetic fields are all in the same direction. A pulse of radio waves is then directed at the patient. This disturbs the orientation of some of the protons. When the radio pulse stops, the protons return to their original states, emitting a radio frequency signal. The strength of the signal depends on the proton density, which is itself linked to the amount of water in the tissue. It is these signals which are used to reconstruct an image of a section through the patient's brain.

Key ideas

● Radioisotope imaging uses minute amounts of radioactive material to trace the passage of a compound through the body.

● Magnetic resonance imaging uses radio waves emitted from hydrogen atoms in our bodies.

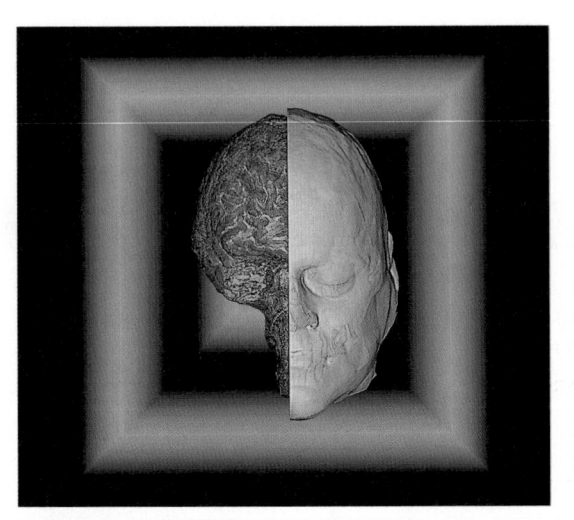

Computer-generated three-dimensional picture of the brain, based on successive MRI 'slices' through the brain.

The future

The advances in computing power that made CT, PET and MRI scanning possible are likely to continue. Surgeons at the Johns Hopkins Medical Institute in Baltimore now use 3-D computer images to plan their brain surgery. It may be that the delicate task of removing a tumour from brain tissue will eventually fall to a robot. Robot brain surgeons have already been used to help patients with Parkinson's disease and to take samples of brain tissue. A robot named Minerva, from Lausanne in Switzerland, has carried out operations to an accuracy of better than 0.3 mm. The very best that human surgeons can achieve is 1 mm.

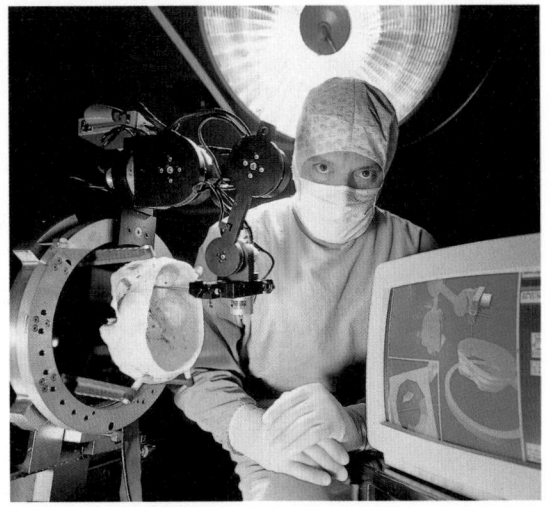

Future robots will be guided by CT and MRI scans. They will use ultrasonic probes to navigate round blood vessels. The robot will be armed with lasers, heat probes and ultrasonic scalpels to destroy cancerous tissue.

Answers to questions

Chapter 1

1 **a** image height = 80 mm, magnification = 2;
   b image height = 30 mm, magnification = 1;
   c image height = 33 mm, magnification = 0.67.
2 **a** image distance = 120 mm, magnification = 2;
   b image distance = 80 mm, magnification = 1;
   c image distance = 67 mm, magnification = 0.67.
3 If the object is further away from the lens than the focal point, the image is real. If the object is between the focal point and the lens, the image is virtual.

4

Object distance / cm	Focal length / cm	Substitute in formula	Rearranging terms	Image distance / cm	Is the image real or virtual?
50	20	$\dfrac{1}{50} + \dfrac{1}{v} = \dfrac{1}{20}$	$\dfrac{1}{v} = \dfrac{1}{20} - \dfrac{1}{50}$	33.3	real
36	20	$\dfrac{1}{36} + \dfrac{1}{v} = \dfrac{1}{20}$	$\dfrac{1}{v} = \dfrac{1}{20} - \dfrac{1}{36}$	45.0	real
20	30	$\dfrac{1}{20} + \dfrac{1}{v} = \dfrac{1}{30}$	$\dfrac{1}{v} = \dfrac{1}{30} - \dfrac{1}{20}$	−60.0	virtual
60	−50 (diverging lens)	$\dfrac{1}{60} + \dfrac{1}{v} = \dfrac{1}{-50}$	$\dfrac{1}{v} = \dfrac{1}{-50} - \dfrac{1}{60}$	−27.3	virtual

i.e. in the first example, a real image is formed 33.3 cm from the lens on the far side from the object;
in the last example, a virtual image is formed 27.3 cm from the lens and on the same side as the object.

5

Object distance / cm	Image distance / cm	Focal length / cm
20.0	60.2	15.01
30.0	30.0	15.00
40.0	23.9	14.96
50.0	21.4	14.99
60.0	20.0	15.00
70.0	19.2	15.07
	Average value:	15.01

6 (i) slight difficulty in focusing the image accurately;
(ii) slight difficulty in measuring the position of the lamp, lens and screen.
7 Focal length of lens = $\dfrac{1}{55}$ = 0.0182 m

The object is at infinity so the image will be formed at the focal point of the lens system. Therefore, the image distance = 0.0182 m = 18.2 mm. This is the depth of the eyeball.

Chapter 2

1 Red light. Using $\sin \theta = \dfrac{2}{d}$,

it can be seen that increasing the wavelength will increase the angle θ. This increases the width of the central maximum.

2 About 80 m.

Using $\tan \theta = \dfrac{\text{opposite}}{\text{adjacent}} = \dfrac{0.022}{80} = 2.75 \times 10^{-4}$

then θ = 0.0158°. This is about 57 seconds of arc. However, you might have difficulty seeing the coin further away than 40 m.

3 Ratio of areas = $\dfrac{\dfrac{\pi \times 76^2}{4}}{\dfrac{\pi \times 1^2}{4}} = 5776$

4 Ratio of areas = $\dfrac{\dfrac{\pi \times 800^2}{4}}{\dfrac{\pi \times 600^2}{4}} = 1.78$

5 Any equipment with a motor that has a commutator and brushes, e.g. a washing machine, food mixer, vacuum cleaner, hair drier, lawn mower or electric drill. Also, equipment with high-frequency electronic circuits, e.g a television or a personal computer.
6 You need to find the opposite side of a very long thin triangle; the adjacent side of the triangle is the distance to the Moon and the angle is 100 micro arc seconds.

100 micro arc seconds = $\dfrac{100 \times 10^{-6}}{60 \times 60}$ = 2.778×10^{-8} degrees

opposite = $\sin (2.778 \times 10^{-8}) \times 3.84 \times 10^8$ m = 0.186 m

Chapter 3

1 a The change in wavelength is:

$$\Delta\lambda = -\frac{v}{c} \times \lambda = \frac{50\,000 \text{ m s}^{-1}}{3 \times 10^8 \text{ m s}^{-1}} \times 600 \text{ nm} = 0.10 \text{ nm}$$

The new wavelength is the original wavelength plus this change, i.e. 600.10 nm.

Changes in wavelength are often this small.

b $(3999.84 - 4000) \times 3 \times 10^8 / 4000.00 = 12 \text{ km s}^{-1}$

2 a The Lyman alpha line emitted at a wavelength of 121.6 nm was observed at 700 nm. Use the Doppler formula to calculate the recession speed of the quasar:

$$\frac{\Delta\lambda}{\lambda} = v$$

Substitution gives:

$$v = \frac{700 \text{ nm} - 121.6 \text{ nm}}{121.6 \text{ nm}} \times 3 \times 10^8 \text{ m s}^{-1} = 1.43 \times 10^9 \text{ m s}^{-1}$$

b This is *clearly impossible* as the speed of the quasar cannot be greater than the speed of light! In fact, this formula only works for velocities up to about one tenth of the speed of light. At a red shift of 0.2, an error of 12% is introduced.

A better approximation can be made using the special relativity version of the formula.

3 The red shift calculated from the formula is 4.69.

Chapter 4

1 All stars hotter than the Sun look slightly blue. The slope of the right-hand side of the curve means that the blue emission is always slightly greater than the red.

2 If the light from the filament is yellow, its temperature will be less than the 5700 K of the Sun's surface but not so cool that it does not glow. Tungsten filaments are operated at temperatures between 2400 K and 3100 K.

3 If the light is white, it must comprise all the colours of the visual spectrum in equal proportions. The temperature of the gas in the flash tube will need to be several thousand degrees to achieve this result. It must be similar to the surface temperature of the Sun, or possibly a little hotter.

4

$$I = \frac{P}{4\pi D^2} \text{ so } D = \sqrt{\frac{P}{4\pi I}} = \sqrt{\frac{3.9 \times 10^{26} \text{ W}}{4\pi \times 1500 \text{ W m}^{-2}}} = 1.4 \times 10^{11} \text{ m}$$

This agrees quite well with the accepted value of 1.49×10^{11} m.

Chapter 6

1

Distance	Parsecs	Light travel time	m
1 parsec	1.00	3.26 yr	3.09×10^{16}
1 light-year	0.31	1 yr	9.47×10^{15}
Earth to Sun (1 AU)	0.00	8.31 min	1.50×10^{11}
Earth to Proxima Centauri (next star)	1.30	4.2 yr	$3.98 \times 10_{16}$
Earth to Sirius	2.64	8.6 yr	8.14×10^{16}
Across Milky Way	3.07×10^4	1×10^5 yr	$9.47 \times 10_{20}$
Earth to Andromeda (neighbouring spiral galaxy)	6.75×10^5	2.20×10^6 yr	2.08×10^{22}

2 Using $m - M = 5 \log \dfrac{d}{10}$

$$11 - 3 = \left(5 \log \frac{d}{10}\right)$$

$$\therefore \log \frac{d}{10} = \frac{11 - 3}{5} = \frac{8}{5}$$

$$\therefore d = 10 \log^{-1}\left(\frac{8}{5}\right) = 398 \text{ parsec}$$

3 a 251 parsec;
b 631 parsec.

4 The mean value of the Pole Star's apparent magnitude is 2.11. By reading from the magnitude/period graph (Fig. 7), the Pole Star, with a period of 4.0 days, can be seen to have an absolute magnitude of –3.0.

Using $m - M = 5 \log \dfrac{d}{10}$

$$2.11 - (-3.0) = \left(5 \log \frac{d}{10}\right)$$

$$\therefore \log \frac{d}{10} = \frac{2.11 + 3.0}{5} = 1.022$$

$$\therefore d = 10 \log^{-1}(1.022) = 105 \text{ parsec}$$

Recent parallax measurements by the Hipparcos satellite give a distance of 132 parsec.

5 The inverse-square law is used here. The galaxy is dimmer and hence further away.

Distance $= 0.75 \text{ Mpc} \times \sqrt{1000} = 23 \text{ Mpc}$

Chapter 7

1 Time = 200 Mpc × 3.26 ly = 652 million years. This light started out long before the dinosaurs roamed the Earth.

2 The speed of light, 3.0×10^8 m s^{-1}. Light from objects moving away faster than this would never reach us.

3 $d = \dfrac{v}{H} = \dfrac{3.0 \times 10^5 \text{ km s}^{-1}}{67 \text{ km s}^{-1} \text{ Mpc}^{-1}} = 4.5 \times 10^3$ Mpc

The speed of light must be given in km s^{-1} not m s^{-1}.

4 $g = \dfrac{GM}{r^2} = \dfrac{6.67 \times 10^{-11} \text{ N m}^2 \text{kg}^{-2} \times 1.4 \times 2.0 \times 10^{30} \text{ kg}}{(15000 \text{ m})^2}$

$= 8.3 \times 10^{11}$ m s^{-2}

This is over a billion times greater than the Earth's gravity.

5 Using the acceleration due to gravity from question 4:
work done = $mgh = 60 \times 8.3 \times 10^{11} \times 0.001 = 5.0 \times 10^{10}$ J

6 Time taken = $\dfrac{\text{work done}}{\text{power}} = \dfrac{5.0 \times 10^{10} \text{ J}}{200 \text{ W}} = 2.5 \times 10^8$ s

$= \dfrac{5.5 \times 10^8 \text{ s}}{60 \times 60 \times 24 \times 365{,}25} = 7.7$ years

7 $r = \dfrac{2GM}{c^2} = \dfrac{2 \times 6.67 \times 10^{-11} \text{N m}^2 \text{ kg}^{-2} \times 3 \times 2 \times 10^{30} \text{ kg}}{(3 \times 10^8 \text{ m s}^{-1})^2}$

$= 8.9 \times 10^3$ m = 8.9 km
(very small in astronomical terms).

Chapter 8

1 The ratio of the areas is:
$\dfrac{A_2}{A_1} = \dfrac{\pi r_1^2}{\pi r_2^2} = \dfrac{8^2}{1.5^2} = 28$

Only 28 times more light can pass into your eye. The vast majority of the increase in sensitivity is due to photochemical changes in the retina.

2 Without goggles there is very little change in the refractive index as light passes from water ($n = 1.5$) into your cornea ($n = 1.38$). Your lens is unable to refract light enough to form a focused image. When you wear goggles there is a layer of air in front of the cornea and refraction at the cornea is restored.

3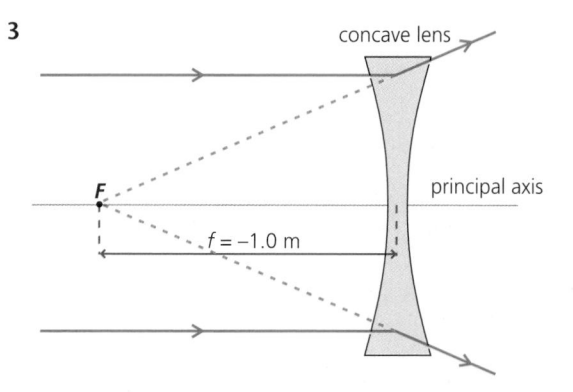

Parallel light is diverged, as if it had come from the focal point.

4 -5 D + 50 D = 45 D

5 The stiffening of the lens as you get older makes the process of accommodation slower and more difficult. Constant refocusing would be a particular problem.

6 a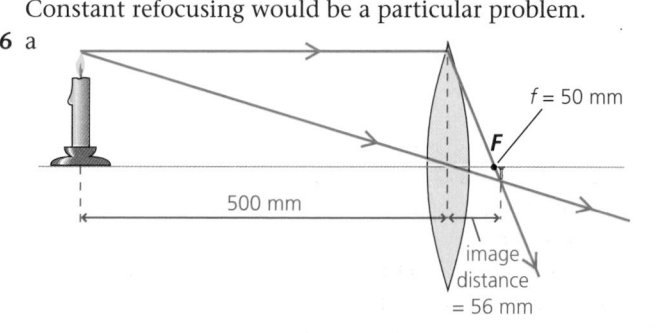

The image would be at 55.6 mm (to 3 s.f.).

b The image of an object at infinity is formed at the focal length, so lens would need to move from 50 mm from the film to 55.6 mm from the film, a total distance of 5.6 mm.

7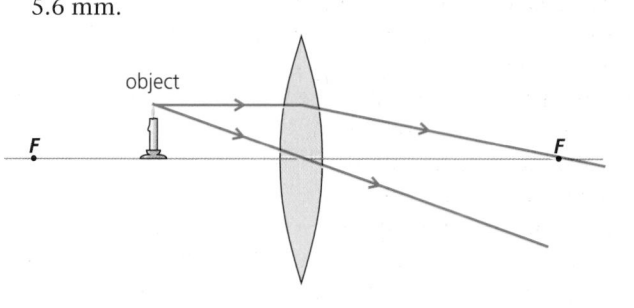

The rays of light continue to diverge even after they have passed through the lens; they will never meet to produce a real image.

8 To give you a reasonable depth of field.

9 The smallest resolvable angle is 0.6 minutes = 0.6/60 = 0.01° = 1.74×10^{-4} rad. Use $s = r\theta$ to find r.

$r = \dfrac{s}{\theta} = \dfrac{1.5 \times 10^{-2}}{1.74 \times 10^{-4}} = 86$ m

10 Use $\dfrac{1}{f} = \dfrac{1}{u} + \dfrac{1}{v}$ so $\dfrac{1}{v} = \dfrac{1}{f} - \dfrac{1}{u}$.

a $\dfrac{1}{v} = \dfrac{1}{0.2} - \dfrac{1}{0.4} = \dfrac{1}{0.4}$ so $v = 2.5$ m

b $\dfrac{1}{v} = \dfrac{1}{0.2} - \dfrac{1}{0.2} = 0$ so $v =$ infinite; no image can be formed.

c $\dfrac{1}{v} = \dfrac{1}{0.2} - \dfrac{1}{0.1} = 5 - 10 = -5$ so $v = -1/5$ or -20 cm. This is a virtual image.

11 Use lens power $= \dfrac{1}{f} = \dfrac{1}{u} - \dfrac{1}{v}$.

a $\dfrac{1}{f} = \dfrac{1}{u} + \dfrac{1}{v} = \dfrac{1}{1} + \dfrac{1}{0.025} = 1 + 40 = 41$ D

b $\dfrac{1}{f} = \dfrac{1}{u} + \dfrac{1}{v} = \dfrac{1}{0.25} + \dfrac{1}{0.02} = 4 + 40 = 44$ D.

Lens power has to be $44 - 41 = 3$ D

12 a $\dfrac{1}{v} = \dfrac{1}{0.20} - \dfrac{1}{1} = 4$ $v = 0.25$ m. $u = 1.0$ m,

so magnification $= \dfrac{v}{u} = \dfrac{0.25}{1} = 0.25$

b If the magnification $= 1$, $v = u$, so $\dfrac{1}{f} = \dfrac{2}{u}$, $u = 2f$.

In this case, 40 cm.

13 Low-light, or scotopic, vision depends only on rods because cones need higher levels of light to function. Rods all contain the same photopigment and cannot distinguish between different wavelengths.

14 The mixture of green and red light looks yellow to the human eye because it stimulates the different cone cells in exactly the same way that a single wavelength of 'yellow' light does. The eye cannot distinguish between:
a a combination of long wavelength (red) and shorter wavelength (green) light and
b a single intermediate wavelength (yellow)

15 If we look directly at an object, its image will fall on the fovea. There are no rods in that area of the retina and cones cannot respond to low-intensity light. By looking slightly away from the star we make sure that the image falls on rod cells.

16 In poor light we rely on rod cells for our vision. These take a relatively long time to signal the arrival of a photon of light, about 300 ms. In this time, a fast tennis serve will travel well over the length of the court.

17 Several rods are connected to the same nerve fibre. This increases the sensitivity by aggregating the signal from several rod cells so that they reach a detectable level, but it decreases the resolution of the image since the rod cells are acting as a single pixel.

Chapter 9

1 Loudness is subjective, it depends upon the listener and on the frequency of the sound.

2 1×10^{-12} W m^{-2} $\times 10^{14} = 100$ W m^{-2}

3 The inverse-square law applies. At one tenth of the distance, the intensity is $10^2 = 100$ times greater.

4 The ear has a logarithmic response, so doubling the power only produces $\log 2 = 0.3$ times the loudness.

5 Sound intensity level is 105 dB. $105 = 10 \log \dfrac{I}{I_0}$. $\dfrac{I}{I_0} = 10^{10.5}$.

So intensity $= 3.16 \times 10^{10} \times 1 \times 10^{-12} = 0.0316$ W m^{-2}.

Total power $=$ intensity $\times$ area, and the area of a 10 m radius sphere is $4\pi r^2 = 1.26 \times 10^3 = 1.26 \times 10^3$ m^2. So power $= 0.0316 \times 1.26 \times 10^3 = 40$ W (39.7 to 3 s.f.)

6 A sound intensity level of 90 dB is $1 \times 10^{-12} \times 10^9 = 0.001$ W m^{-2}.

If the power is 40 W then Area $= \dfrac{40}{0.001} = 40\,000$.

This gives a radius (distance from the speaker) of

$\sqrt{\dfrac{40000}{4\pi}} = 56$ m.

7 95 dB $= 1 \times 10^{-12} \times 10^{9.5} = 0.00316$ W m^{-2}. 80 dB $= 1 \times 10^{-12} \times 10^8 = 0.0001$ W m^{-2}. Total intensity is 0.00326 W m^{-2}, which is a sound intensity level of 95.14 dB. The shout doesn't make much difference!

8 a Sound intensity level $= 10 \log (8 \times 10^{-7} / 1 \times 10^{-12})$ $= 59$ dB.

b Because it is the same loudness as a 1 kHz sound of 60 dB, the 3 kHz sound has a loudness of 60 phons.

c The ear is slightly more responsive at 3 kHz; the slightly lower intensity sounds just as loud as the 1 kHz sound.

9 Sucking sweets promotes saliva and hence swallowing. Swallowing helps to open the Eustachian tube which keeps the pressure the same in the inner and outer ears.

10 Percussive sounds reach full volume very quickly. The protective muscles in the middle ear cannot react in time to reduce the amplitude of the vibrations.

12 The audiogram should show hearing loss centred at around 4 kHz.

Chapter 10

1 **a** About 70% of body mass is in the torso and head. For an average person this is 0.7×65 kg = 45.5 kg. Because we have two legs, the force on one thigh bone is $\frac{45.5 \times 9.8}{2} = 220$ N.

The diameter of a thigh bone is approximately 4 cm, so the cross-sectional area = $\pi(2 \times 10^{-2})^2 = 1.25 \times 10^{-3}$ m^2.

Stress = $\frac{F}{A} = \frac{220}{1.25 \times 10^{-3}} = 176$ kPa.

b Jumping to a height of 30 cm requires a force, F, applied over a distance, d. The work done in raising the centre of gravity by 0.30 m is $0.30 \times 650 = 195$ J = $F \times d$. Suppose that the jumper crouches for 0.25 m before jumping, therefore $d = 0.25$ and $F = 195/0.25 = 780$ N, if this is shared evenly between both legs, there will be a stress of 312 kPa.

When the person lands, the deceleration, a, is

$a = 0 - \frac{v}{0.1}$.

Falling from a height of 0.3 m gives $v = \sqrt{2 \times 9.8 \times 0.3} = 2.42$ m s^{-1}. So $a = 24.2$ m s^{-2}, and $F = 650 \times 24.2 = 15\ 700$ N. This is a stress of 6.28 MPa.

2 **a** The potential difference at rest is 70 mV. This gives $E = 70 \times 10^{-3} / 0.01 \times 10^{-6} = 7$ MV m^{-1}.

b When depolarised, the potential drops to 35 mV, $E = 3.5$ MV m^{-1}.

3 **a** The fulcrum is at the tip of the toe.

b Taking moments about the tip-toe, T is less than W, therefore the effort is less than the load, and the mechanical advantage is greater than one.

4 The stick will support some of the load, therefore reducing the overall force on the hip joint. Using a stick gives the person a wider base and allows the centre of gravity to shift away from the affected side, which again reduces the force on the damaged hip.

5 Carrying a suitcase shifts your centre of gravity further from the geometric centre of your body. When walking with a case, you have to lean further over to keep the centre of gravity over the foot that is in contact with the ground. This increases the shear forces acting on the hip.

6 The correct technique for weight lifting means that the back is kept as vertical as possible. This keeps the forces in the erector muscle as small as possible.

7 A is 3, atrial flutter; B is 1, sinus arrhythmia; C is 2, third degree heart block.

9 **a** Blood pressure is high in an artery, and changes rapidly. You need a transducer which can respond quickly.

b Venous pressure is much lower, so you need a transducer which does not block the flow of blood and which is sensitive.

Chapter 11

1 For 20-year-old woman, BMR = 150 kJ h^{-1} m^{-2}

$= \frac{150 \times 10^3}{60 \times 60} = 42$ W m^{-2}.

This is for 1.8 m^2 surface area, so total BMR = $42 \times 1.8 = 75$ W

2 **a** work = $12 \times 10 \times 1 = 120$ J: power = $\frac{120\ \text{J} \times 30\ \text{m}}{60\ \text{s}} = 60$ W

b Muscle is only about 25% efficient, so most energy will be transferred as heat; extra energy is also needed for metabolism.

c 1 kg of glucose releases 17×10^6 J of energy. To work at 500 W for 1 minute needs $500 \times 60 = 30\ 000$ J

So glucose needed = $\frac{30\ 000}{17 \times 10^6} = 0.002$ kg

3 **a** Running requires greater frictional force to provide a greater forward acceleration, but the coefficient of friction is too low.

b

To avoid slipping, $\mu \geq \tan\theta$. If is μ low then θ needs to be small.

If $\mu = \tan\theta = 0.3$, then $\theta = 16.7°$. For a leg of length 0.9 m, $\sin\theta = L / 0.90$. So $L = 0.26$ m. This value is only half the full stride length of 0.52 m.

4 $P = \varepsilon\sigma A (T^4 - T_0^4)$

a $(T^4 - T_0^4) = (308^4 - 308^4)$ so $P \approx 0$. Radiation emitted $\approx$ radiation absorbed.

b $P = 0.98 \times 5.7 \times 10^{-8} \times 1.44 \times (308^4 - 313^4) \approx -50$ W (energy absorbed from surroundings).

5 Say 10 litres/day = 10kg/day

$P = \frac{10 \times 2.425 \times 10^6}{60 \times 60 \times 24} = 280$ W

6 Humid air means less evaporation is taking place; we feel hotter and wetter.

7 Evaporation of liquid from the body is a source of heat loss. Wet clothes may be poorer insulation than dry clothes, so more energy is transferred to the air by conduction and convection.

8 (i) For a baby,

$$V = \frac{m}{\rho} = \frac{5 \text{ kg}}{1000 \text{ kg m}^{-3}} = 0.005 \text{ m}^3$$

$V = 4/3\pi r^3$ so $r = 0.106$ m

$A = 4\pi r^2 = 0.141 \text{ m}^2$

$A/V = 0.14/0.005 = 28$

For an adult, $r = 0.267$ m, $A = 0.898 \text{ m}^2$, $A/V = 11$

(ii) For a baby, $h = 0.5$ m, $r = 0.0564$ m, $V = \pi r^2 h$,

$A = 2\pi rh + 2\pi r^2$

$A/V = 39$

For an adult, $h = 1.9$ m, $A/V = 1.43/0.08 = 18$

9 It reduces the effective external surface area, so the penguins gain energy by absorbing radiation from other penguins.

Chapter 12

1 a Thick short tracks are made by heavily ionising, short-range alpha-particles.

  b The beta-particles undergo large deflections at the ends of tracks; beta particles are electrons and collisions with equal mass can lead to large deflections.

2 $E = hf$, and 1 MeV $= 1 \times 10^6 \times 1.6 \times 10^{-19} \text{ J} = 1.6 \times 10^{-13} \text{ J}$

So $f = \dfrac{1.6 \times 10^{-13}}{6.6 \times 10^{-34}} = 2.42 \times 10^{20} \text{ Hz}$

3 $T_{1/2} = \ln 2/9.9 \times 10^{-7} \text{ s}^{-1} = 8.1$ days

4 100×10^6 Ci $\times 3.7 \times 10^{10} = 3 \times 10^{11}$ Bq

5 $2 \times$ half-life $= 2 \times 8 = 16$ days

6 $\dfrac{1}{T} = \dfrac{1}{24} + \dfrac{1}{8}$ $T = 6$ days

7 a $2.58 \times 10^{-4} \times 34 = 8.8$ mGy

  b f-factor $\times$ dose $= 40 \times 2.58 \times 10^{-4} = 10$ mGy

8 Yes. Alpha-particles cause dense ionisation, lots of damage to cells in a short distance, which makes it hard for cell repair to take place.

9 All α-energy is deposited inside body. Much of the γ-energy will pass through body and end up elsewhere.

10 The body incorporates Sr– 90 into bone. β-rays can irradiate bone marrow (sensitive cells because new blood cells are being made).

11 Because children are growing, they have a large amount of dividing cells that are radiosensitive.

12 a It is easier for the body to repair damage caused by a fractional dose.

  b α-radiation damage is too difficult to repair.

13 (see glossary)

14 a a liquid scintillator

  b a gamma camera

  c a pocket ionisation chamber

15 a The dead time would cause the count rate to be underestimated.

  b It is relatively insensitive to alpha and gamma radiation.

16 The radiation was penetrating (probably gamma- or high-energy X-radiation).

17 The plastic had absorbed much of the radiation (which was probably alpha or low-energy beta-radiation).

Chapter 13

1 Cladding stops the core touching another material with a different refractive index, which could prevent total internal reflection. Total internal reflection only occurs when light is travelling from a medium with a higher refractive index into a medium with a lower refractive index.

2 a $\sin c = 1.45/1.55 = 0.935$, so $c = 69.3°$

  b numerical aperture $= (1.55^2 - 1.45^2)^{1/2} = 0.548$

  c The maximum angle is given by: $n_0 \sin i_{max} = 0.548$. So $i_{max} = 33°$.

3 Light will be absorbed and scattered out of the fibre by impurities; refracted out by irregularities at the core-cladding interface; and lost at places where the fibre bends excessively.

4 In a coherent bundle, each fibre carries information about one image point. The more image points, or pixels, there are, the more detailed the image will be. Fine fibres closely packed together will give a high resolution image. Incoherent bundles just carry light, not image information, and so the fibres can be much thicker.

5 Carbon dioxide lasers are absorbed by the water in cells and only penetrate about 0.2 mm into the body. This makes them ideal for treating surface tumours.

6 Argon-ion light is blue, it is transmitted by the eye, but strongly absorbed by blood; the blood is vapourised; no surgery is required.

7 $c = (K/\rho)^{1/2} = (1.60 \times 10^9 / 920)^{1/2} = 1318 \text{ m s}^{-1}$

8 In dB, intensity ratio $= -10 \times 2 = -20$ dB, which is $10^{-2.0} = 0.01$

Or $I_x = I_0 e^{-\mu x}$, so $I_x / I_0 = e^{-\mu x} = e^{-2.30 \times 2.0} = e^{-4.605} = 0.01$

9 Far too much energy is reflected at the first tissue–air boundary to be able to 'see' anything beyond that. The specific acoustic impedance of air is 4.40×10^2, that of tissue is approximately 1.5×10^6, so the reflection coefficient is $(1.49956 \times 10^6 / 1.50044 \times 10^6) = 0.9988$. Almost all the energy is reflected.

10

$$\frac{I_R}{I_I} = \left(\frac{Z_2 - Z_1}{Z_2 + Z_1}\right)^2$$

a $= (6.48 - 1.58)^2 / (6.48 + 1.58)^2 = 0.370$ (3 s.f.)

b $= 0.011$ (3 s.f.)

11 The eye only needs a depth of scan of 1 or 2 cm, but abdominal scanning needs more penetration. Higher frequencies would be attenuated too much. The water bath has almost the same acoustic impedance as the eye and minimises reflections from the outer surface of the eye.

12 a You cannot begin another pulse before all the echoes from the first pulse have returned. If you did, it would not be possible to distinguish between echoes from the two signals.

b Maximum pulse rate is about $1500 / 2 \times D_{max}$. If $D_{max} = 12$ cm, then max pulse rate = 6250 Hz.

c This limits either the number of frames per second or the number of lines in each image; for example with a frame rate of 100 Hz, there would only be time for 62 lines in each image.

Chapter 14

1 Molybdenum is less dense and has a lower atomic number. There are less charges for the target electrons to interact with and the total X-ray yield will be reduced. The characteristic lines will be at different wavelengths because of the different energy levels in tungsten and molybdenum atoms.

2 At low voltages, e.g. 50 keV, the tube electrons don't have sufficient energy to eject an atomic electron from its orbit.

3 A hotter cathode means greater thermionic emission and a higher tube current. This will increase the number of X-rays emitted but will not alter the shape of the energy spectrum.

4 Molybdenum has a higher specific heat capacity. The energy transferred to the anode will therefore cause a smaller increase in temperature.

5 Lead is a dense material with a high atomic number. The probability of photoelectric absorption is relatively high.

6 At higher voltages, X-rays of shorter wavelength are produced. These high-energy photons are unlikely to interact via the photoelectric effect, Compton scattering is dominant but pair production is becoming increasingly important.

7 At energies around 100 keV the linear attenuation coefficient for bone is 3 to 4 times that of bone.

8 At 50 keV, the linear attenuation coefficient is 1 cm⁻¹, so at the half-value thickness $I/I_0 = 0.5 = e^{-\mu x}$.

So $\ln(0.5) = -x$, $x = 0.69$ cm; this is much less than at 150 keV. These lower energy photons are absorbed more readily by bone and do not penetrate through to soft tissue beyond.

9 The Photoelectric effect absorbs photons, whereas the Compton effect merely reduces their energy and scatters them from their original path.

Photoelectric absorption is more effective at removing low-energy photons that would not pass through the patient and therefore do not help in making an image.

10 At these energies the major attenuation process is Compton scattering, photoelectric absorption is much less important, so there is no significant difference between materials of different atomic number. This means that bone does not receive a disproportionately higher dose than soft-tissue.

11 Less energy is absorbed by the photoelectric effect. More energy is scattered, and the scattered radiation is itself more penetrating.

Data section

Absolute zero   −273.15 °C

Avogadro's number 6.02×10^{23} mol^{-1}

Boltzmann's constant 1.38×10^{-23} J K^{-1}

Charge of electron -1.60×10^{-19} C

Gravitational constant 6.67×10^{-11} N m^2 kg^{-2}

Mass of electron 9.11×10^{-31} kg

Mass of proton 1.67×10^{-27} kg

Molar gas constant   8.31 J mol^{-1} K^{-1}

Molar volume at s.t.p. 2.24×10^{-2} m^3 mol^{-1}

Permeability of vacuum $4\pi \times 10^{-7}$ H m^{-1}

Permittivity of vacuum 8.85×10^{-12} F m^{-1}

Planck's constant 6.63×10^{-34} J s

Stefan's constant 5.67×10^{-8} W m^{-2} K^{-4}

Velocity of light 3.00×10^8 m s^{-1}

Wien's Law constant 2.90×10^{-3} m K

Sun

Equatorial radius	6.96×10^8 m
Mass	2.00×10^{30} kg
Mean density	1.42×10^3 kg m^{-3}
Sidereal rotational period (latitude 17°)	25.4 days
Luminosity	3.90×10^{26} W

Earth

Equatorial radius	6.37×10^6 m
Mass	5.97×10^{24} kg
Mean density	5.52×10^3 kg m^{-3}
g approximately	9.81 m s^{-2}
Mean distance to Sun (the astronomical unit)	1.495×10^{11} m
Solar constant	1.37×10^3 W m^{-2}
Mass of atmosphere	about 1×10^{-6} mass of Earth

Moon

Equatorial radius	1.74×10^6 m
Mass	7.33×10^{22} kg
g approximately	1.62 m s^{-2}
Mean distance to Earth	3.84×10^8 m

Mercury

Equatorial radius	2.44×10^6 m
Mass	3.30×10^{23} kg
g approximately	3.78 m s^{-2}
Mean distance to Sun	5.791×10^{10} m
Mean density	5.43×10^3 kg m^{-3}
Length of day	58.65 days
Length of year	87.97 days

Venus

Equatorial radius	6.05×10^6 m
Mass	4.87×10^{24} kg
g approximately	8.60 m s^{-2}
Mean distance to Sun	1.082×10^{11} m
Mean density	5.25×10^3 kg m^{-3}
Length of day	243.0 days
Length of year	224.7 days

Jupiter

Equatorial radius	7.15×10^7 m
Mass	1.90×10^{27} kg
g approximately	22.9 m s^{-2}
Mean distance to Sun	7.783×10^{11} m
Mean density	1.33×10^3 kg m^{-3}
Length of day	9.84 hours

Saturn

Equatorial radius	6.03×10^7 m
Mass	5.69×10^{26} kg
g approximately	9.05 m s^{-2}
Mean distance to Sun	1.427×10^{12} m
Mean density	0.69×10^3 kg m^{-3}
Length of day	10.2 hours

Light travel times

Earth to Sun	8.31 minutes
Sun to Pluto	5.46 hours
Sun to nearest star	4.2 years
Across our Galaxy	1.0×10^5 years
To Andromeda (M31)	2.2×10^6 years
To the edge of the observable Universe	1.5×10^{10} years

Glossary

absolute magnitude   the true brightness of a celestial object

absolute refractive index   the ratio of speed of light in the medium to the speed of light in a vacuum

absorbed dose   the energy absorbed per kilogram of irradiated material

absorption line   cool atoms in front of a hot object absorb particular narrow parts of the continuous spectrum

absorption spectrum   a spectrum that contains fine dark lines that correspond to colours absorbed by the atoms of various elements

accommodation   the ability of the eye to change its focal length by changing the shape of the lens

acoustic matching   ensuring that adjacent materials have a similar acoustic impedance, to reduce energy loss by reflection at the boundary

action potential   the pattern of changing potential difference that is transmitted down a nerve cell

activity of a radioisotope   the number of nuclei that decay per second

Airy disc   diffraction pattern caused by a circular aperture

amplitude-scan (A-scan)   a simple echo technique used in ultrasonic measurements; the size and timing of the reflected pulse gives the position of the change in the medium

angular magnification of a telescope   the increase in the angle between light rays from the top of an object's image and from the centre of the object's image when viewed through a telescope compared with viewing the object with the naked eye

antagonistic pair   two muscles, able to move a joint in opposite directions

aperture   the opening to a camera which admits light

apparent magnitude   the brightness of a celestial object as it appears to an observer on Earth

aqueous humor   watery fluid between the cornea and the lens in the human eye

astigmatism   a focusing problem in the eye caused by a cornea that curves more in some directions than others; can cause spheres to look egg-shaped

audiometer   a device used to test hearing by producing known sound intensity levels over a range of frequencies

background radiation   the average level of ionising radiation to which we are all exposed

basal metabolic rate   the rate of energy transfer required by an inactive human, just to keep alive

binary star system   two stars held together by gravity and which orbit their common centre of mass

biological half-life   the time taken for half the mass of a radioisotope to be excreted from the body

black dwarfs   a white dwarf after it has cooled

black hole   the result of the gravitational collapse of a massive object

blue shift   the increase in frequency of light emitted by an object as it moves towards an observer

bremsstrahlung   the continuous spectrum of X-rays given off by electrons as they are decelerated by a target

brightness-scan (B-Scan)   an ultrasonic technique where the strength of the echo is used to modulate the brightness of the output on a VDU

brown dwarf   the result of the gravitational collapse of an interstellar cloud of mass up to 80 times the mass of Jupiter

catheter   a narrow capillary tube inserted into the body to carry fluids, to introduce a contrast medium or to carry transducers to take readings of pressure, temperature, etc.

cavitation   rapidly expanding and contracting bubbles of gas caused by high power ultrasound; it can damage cells and cause local heating

characteristic X-rays   the line spectra of X-rays emitted from a target that is bombarded with electrons; the wavelength of the X-rays emitted depends on the target material

chromatic aberration   the converging of blue light to a point slightly closer to a lens than the convergence point of red light

cochlea part of the inner ear where sound vibrations are converted to electrical signals

coherent waves that have the same frequency, amplitude and a fixed phase relationship

coherent bundle an ordered collection of optical fibres that can carry images

collective effective dose the radiation dose delivered to a group of people, weighted to take account of the sensitivity of different parts of the body

collective effective dose commitment the collective effective dose due to a given source, that will be given to a future generation

coma the distortion of images from a parabolic mirror of objects off the optical axis

Compton scattering occurs when an X-ray collides with an atomic electron, ejecting the electron from the atom; the X-ray transfers energy and its wavelength is reduced

concentration gradient the rate at which the concentration of a given sunbstance changes with distance

conductive hearing loss hearing loss due to a failure of the outer or middle ear to transmit vibrations to the inner ear, e.g. due to a blockage in the ear canal

cones sensory cells in the retina which respond to a given range of wavelengths of light; responsible for colour vision

contrast the variation in darkness in an X-ray film due to different attenuation of X-rays in the patient

contrast medium a material of high density and/or atomic number introduced into the body to enable soft organs to be visualised

converging lens a lens that produces a real, inverted image

core temperature the temperature of the inner part of the body at which vital organs work best

cornea the outer covering of the front of the eye, where most of the refraction of light takes place

critical angle the angle of incidence, for a ray of light moving from an optically dense medium to a less dense medium, above which total internal reflection will occur

dark adaptation the process whereby an eye in low-light conditions gradually becomes more sensitive to light

dBA scale a logarithmic scale to measure intensity of sound, weighted to take account of the frequency response of the ear

dead time the time immediately after an ionising event when a G-M tube cannot detect further ionisations

decay constant the probability that a nucleus of a radioisotope will decay in a given time

diastolic blood pressure in the arteries during the relaxation of the left ventricle, i.e. minimum arterial pressure

diffraction the spreading out of waves from a barrier

diminished an image that is smaller than the original object

dioptres the unit used to measure the refractive power of a lens or surface

diverging a lens (concave) that makes parallel rays of light move apart

diverging lens a lens that produces a virtual image

Doppler effect the change in frequency of waves emitted by an object as it moves towards or away from an observer

Doppler shift the shift in frequency due to the movement of a transmitter and/or detector

dose equivalent radiation dose, weighted to take account of the biological effect of the type of ionising radiation

dynamic range (astronomy) the ability of a device to record very faint as well as very bright objects on the same image

dynamic range the difference between the largest and smallest sound levels that the ear can respond to

eclipsing binary a binary star system in which the orbital plane of the stars is edge-on to the observer so that the stars eclipse each other

effective half-life the time taken for the activity of a radioisotope in the body to drop by half; a combination of the physical and biological half lives

electrocardiogram a recording made of the electrical signals on the skin due to the action potential of the heart; used to diagnose heart disease

electron degeneracy pressure the pressure, due to partial collapse of the electron shells of atoms, that prevents a white dwarf from collapsing

emission line hot atoms emit radiation in particular narrow parts of the electromagnetic spectrum

emissivity a constant describing the ability of a surface to emit radiation

event horizon a sphere defined by the Schwarzschild radius of a black hole: inside this sphere nothing is visible and nothing escapes

excimer laser a laser which emits photons of sufficient energy to break inter-molecular bonds

exponential attenuation the reduction of the intensity, e.g. of sound or light, by a given fraction in a certain distance

exposure the amount of ionisation caused by X-radiation in a kilogram of dry air

far point the furthest distance at which the eye can focus

first magnitude stars the brightest stars seen by ancient Greek and Egyptian astronomers

flicker fusion the persistence of vision which causes the eye to see a succession of images as if they were continuous

fluoroscopy an X-ray technique used to produce real-time images

focal length of a lens the distance along the optical axis from the focal point to the centre of the lens

focal point rays of light which strike a convex lens, parallel to the principal axis, are converged to the focal point

fovea the region on the retina with a high concentration of cone cells

fulcrum pivot

galactic cluster a cluster of stars found in the thin disc of a spiral galaxy

galaxy a huge group of stars held together by their gravitational attraction

globular cluster a cluster of stars found in the spherical halo round the Milky Way

half-life the time taken for the activity of a radio-isotope to drop to half its original value

half-value layer the thickness of an absorber, e.g. lead, required to reduce the X-ray intensity to half its original value

Hertzsprung–Russell diagram a graph relating the absolute magnitude and the spectral class of stars

Hubble's law the proportionality of the recession velocity of a galaxy to its distance from Earth

hypermetropia long-sightedness

image intensifier a device in fluoroscopy to produce a visible image using a lower dose of X-rays

incoherent bundle a disordered collection of optical fibres used to carry light for an internal examination

intensity the power that passes through an area of 1 square metre, e.g. sound, X-rays, etc. measured in units of $W\ m^{-2}$

interferometer a group of radio telescopes that work together, though they are separated by great distances

interstellar dust clouds clouds of dust particles that occupy the space between the stars

inverse-square law doubling your distance from a point source of gamma-radiation cuts your radiation dose to one quarter; also applies to point sources of sound, light, etc.

ionising radiation radiation capable of ejecting electrons from any atoms with which it collides; emanates from the nuclei of radioactive atoms

iris a ring of smooth muscle which controls the size of the pupil in the eye

isotopes atoms of the same element which contain differing numbers of neutrons in their nuclei

lens formula links the object distance, u, and the image distance, v, to the focal length, f, of the lens: $1/f = 1/u + 1/v$

light adaptation the ability of the eye to become less sensitive in bright conditions

linear differential transformer a transformer with a moveable core used in direct blood pressure measurement

linear energy transfer the energy transferred by ionising radiation per unit length of its path

linearity of response the property of a CCD that the charge collected is directly proportional to the brightness of the source

Local Standard of Rest a reference frame, created by averaging all the proper motions of the local stars, from which to measure the motions of all stars

longitudinal waves which vibrate in the same direction that the wave travels, e.g. sound waves

magnification the ratio of image size to object size, also equal to v/u

man-sievert the unit of collective effective dose

mechanical advantage the amount by which levers, joints, etc. amplify; force = load/effort

moment the turning effect of a force, equal to force × perpendicular distance from pivot

monochromatic waves of a single wavelength

myopia short-sightedness

natural frequency the frequency at which an object will vibrate when displaced from equilibrium

neutron degeneracy pressure the pressure, provided by the neutrons attempting not to occupy identical states, that prevents gravitational collapse of a neutron star

neutron star the dense core, composed of neutrons, left behind after a supernova explosion

normal incidence striking a boundary between two materials at right angles

numerical aperture a quantity which defines the field of view of an optical fibre

open cluster *see* galactic cluster

optic nerve the nerve which carries electrical signals generated in the retina to the brain

optical axis the line that passes through the centre of a lens at a right angle to the lens

osteoclasts cells which break down bone

parallax the apparent movement of an object as the position of the observer changes

photo-thermal laser a laser which uses the heating effect of its light to cut through tissue, etc.

photoelectric effect a process where a photon of radiation is absorbed by material; the energy is transferred to an electron which is ejected from the atom

photopic bright conditions

physical half-life *see* half-life

piezoelectric transducer a device which generates a potential difference when it is compressed or expanded; it is used to generate and detect ultrasound

pixel the smallest element of a picture

pixel a tiny light-sensitive region in an array of silicon wafers

Planck radiation curve a graph showing the theoretical output of perfect radiation emitters at various temperatures

plane wave the shape of a wavefront arriving from a distant source

positive feedback a situation where an increase in the output causes a further increase in the input

power the rate of energy transferred measured in watts

power of a lens a measure of the refraction caused by a lens, measured in dioptres, D; power = $1/f$

presbyopia a defect of vision caused by stiffening of the lens which limits accommodation of the eye

principal axis a line drawn at right angles to the lens, passing through the optical centre, used in constructing ray diagrams

principal focus *see* focal point

proper motion the true, as opposed to apparent, motion of stars

pulsar a rapidly spinning star that emits synchrotron radiation in particular directions producing pulses of energy that are detectable on Earth

pupil the aperture of the eye

quality factor a weighting factor used in calculating the dose equivalent; accounts for the different biological effects of exposure to different kinds of ionising radiation

quantum efficiency of a detector the percentage of incoming photons that go to produce the image rather than being lost

radio resistant cells that can survive moderate doses of radiation

radioisotopes an isotope with an unstable nucleus which emits ionising radiation

radiosensitive cells that are particularly vulnerable to ionising radiation

ray diagram a scale drawing used to find out how a lens forms an image

Rayleigh scattering scattering of light by particles that are much smaller than the wavelength of the light

real image an image caused by the crossing of rays of light through a lens

red giant a star like our Sun that has left the main sequence: its outer layers expand to form a red-hot gas cloud

red shift the decrease in frequency of light emitted by an object as it moves away from an observer

reflecting telescope a telescope that uses mirrors

reflection coefficient a measure of the ultrasonic energy reflected from a boundary between two materials

refracting telescope a telescope that uses lenses

refractive index the ratio of the sine of the angle of incidence to the sine of the angle of refraction; also the ratio of the speed of light in a vacuum to the speed of light in the medium

relative biological effect the ability of ionising radiation to kill human cells compared to the effect of 250 keV X-rays

relativistic speed a velocity near to the speed of light

resonates large amplitude vibrations from an object subject to forced vibrations at its natural frequency

retina tissue of light-sensitive cells lining the back of the eye

rhodopsin a photopigment present in rod cells which dissociates when it absorbs a photon of light

rods light-sensitive cells in the retina which respond well in low light conditions

Schwarzschild radius the critical radius inside which light is trapped by gravitational forces near a singularity

scintillation the twinkling of telescopic images due to variations in the refractive index of the atmosphere caused by convection currents

scotopic low-light conditions

sensitivity the ability to detect fractional changes in intensity

sensorineural loss loss of hearing due to damage in the inner ear, auditory nerve or brain

singularity a point to which a star of mass greater than 2 solar masses collapses, and where the laws of physics break down

sixth magnitude stars the faintest stars seen by ancient Greek and Egyptian astronomers

solar mass the mass of the Sun

sound intensity the power in watts passing through an area of 1 square metre, perpendicular to direction of propagation

sound intensity level a logarithmic scale, measured in decibels, dB, which compares sound intensity to a reference level; the reference used is the threshold of hearing, 10^{-12} W m^{-2}

specific latent heat of vaporisation the energy needed to convert a kilogram of liquid to vapour, without any change in temperature

spectroscopic binary system a binary star system whose binary nature is only revealed when light gathered by a telescope is directed onto the slit of a spectroscope so that the Doppler shifts can be measured

spherical aberration the focusing of light rays from the edge and the centre of a lens or mirror to different points

standard candle a method of comparing the brightness of a local supernova with that of a distant one of the same type

superposition the process of adding waves together, often used to produce an interference pattern

synchrotron radiation the radiation emitted by high-energy particles moving at relativistic speeds in a strong magnetic field

systolic the blood pressure in the arteries when the left ventricle of the heart contracts, i.e. maximum arterial pressure

thermal capacity the energy needed to raise the temperature of an object by 1 °C

thermionic emission the ejection of electrons from a metal surface caused by heating

thermistor a semiconductor device for which resistance depends on its temperature

thermocouple a junction of two metals which generates an e.m.f. that depends on temperature

thermopile a device for detecting infra-red radiation which uses a number of thermocouples in series to detect temperature rises

threshold of hearing the lowest sound intensity that can be detected by a healthy human ear

transducer a device which produces a potential difference in response to a change in a physical quantity, e.g. pressure, temperature

ultrasonic sound waves with a frequency above 20 kHz

unresolved when two images overlap to such an extent that they cannot be distinguished

unsharpness the lack of quality of an X-ray image due to a region of partial shadow, or penumbra

virtual image an image caused by rays that can never cross and that cannot be formed on a screen

visual acuity the ability of the eye to resolve separate images

white dwarf a star that has finished generating heat from the fusion of helium from hydrogen, but is still very hot and dense

Wien's displacement law the relationship between the wavelength at the peak of the Planck radiation curve and the temperature of the black body

Index